D1265793

CONTRIBUTORS

BAYARD H. BRATTSTROM

J. L. CLOUDSLEY-THOMPSON

WILLIAM R. DAWSON

F. E. J. FRY

P. W. HOCHACHKA

JACK W. HUDSON

JAMES R. TEMPLETON

F. JOHN VERNBERG

WINONA B. VERNBERG

Comparative Physiology of Thermoregulation

Edited by G. CAUSEY WHITTOW

DEPARTMENT OF PHYSIOLOGY
UNIVERSITY OF HAWAII
SCHOOL OF MEDICINE
HONOLULU, HAWAII

Volume I

Invertebrates and Nonmammalian Vertebrates

 1970

ACADEMIC PRESS New York and London

ACADEMIC PRESS, INC.
111 Fifth Avenue, New York, New York 10003

United Kingdom Edition published by
ACADEMIC PRESS, INC. (LONDON) LTD.
Berkeley Square House, London W1X 6BA

LIBRARY OF CONGRESS CATALOG CARD NUMBER: 79-107580

PRINTED IN THE UNITED STATES OF AMERICA

CONTENTS

4. Amphibia

BAYARD H. BRATTSTROM

5. Reptiles

JAMES R. TEMPLETON

6. Birds

WILLIAM R. DAWSON AND JACK W. HUDSON

LIST OF CONTRIBUTORS

Numbers in parentheses indicate the pages on which the authors' contributions begin.

BAYARD H. BRATTSTROM (135), Department of Biology, California State College, Fullerton, California

J. L. CLOUDSLEY-THOMPSON (15), Department of Zoology, University of Khartoum, Sudan

WILLIAM R. DAWSON (223), Department of Zoology, University of Michigan, Ann Arbor, Michigan

F. E. J. FRY (79), Ramsay Wright Zoological Laboratories, University of Toronto, Toronto, Canada

P. W. HOCHACHKA (79), Department of Zoology, University of British Columbia, Vancouver, Canada

JACK W. HUDSON (223), Section of Ecology and Systematics, Division of Biological Sciences, Cornell University, Ithaca, New York.

JAMES R. TEMPLETON (167) Department of Zoology, University of Montana, Missoula, Montana

F. JOHN VERNBERG* (1), Duke University, Marine Laboratory, Beaufort, North Carolina

WINONA B. VERNBERG* (1), Duke University, Marine Laboratory, Beaufort, North Carolina

* Present address: Belle W. Baruch Institute for Estuarine and Littoral Science, University of South Carolina, Columbia, South Carolina

PREFACE

The purpose of this three-volume work is to present separate accounts of the means by which each of the major groups of animals regulates its body temperature, heat production, and heat loss. Readers who wish to obtain information about thermoregulatory processes in different species will, it is believed, welcome this as a convenient reference work. However, it is hoped that the treatise will have more than convenience value. The juxtaposition of chapters dealing with quite different animals might tempt the researcher to read about species other than the particular one in which he is immediately interested. In so doing he might well find that the specific problem with which he is concerned is better illuminated in another species. This of course is the essence of comparative physiology.

The composition of Volume I was dictated largely by the amount of information available on nonmammalian species. Because most experimental work on thermoregulation has been conducted on mammals, the second volume of this work will, accordingly, deal exclusively with mammals. Thus a hard and fast distinction between homeotherms and poikilotherms, ectotherms and endotherms, and regulators and nonregulators is avoided.

Although the arrangement of the first two volumes roughly follows taxonomic lines, this approach will be complemented in the third volume which will deal with special aspects of thermoregulation. In addition, in Volume III thermoregulation will be discussed from the standpoint of systems rather than species. It is hoped that this dual approach will lend to the work as a whole a measure of integration which could not be achieved by dealing with species or systems alone.

I am very grateful to Mrs. Jane Inouye, Miss Cecilia Tsunezumi, and Mrs. Ethel Moran for their great help in the preparation of this volume.

Chapter 1 AQUATIC INVERTEBRATES

F. John Vernberg and Winona B. Vernberg

I. Introduction

One major trend in the evolution of animals has been the development of progressively complex homeostatic mechanisms. As these mechanisms have evolved, organisms have become increasingly independent of fluctuations in their external environment. The development of various regulating mechanisms to control body temperature is an excellent example of one major approach utilized by animals to escape this tyranny of flux in environmental factors. Although some animals have finely perfected thermoregulatory abilities, others appear to have no mechanism for the control of body temperature. Between these extremes are organisms which exhibit varying degrees of thermoregulatory capability. These differences in thermoregulatory ability exist not only when widely separated groups of organisms are compared, but they may also be found within a species. Examples of intra-

1

specific differences in thermoregulatory control are found in different stages of development and in cyclic phenomena associated with any one stage of development, i.e., diurnal rhythms (Morrison, 1962). The purpose of this chapter is to discuss the thermoregulatory capabilities of aquatic invertebrates. Included in this arbitrary category of animals are all invertebrates, such as intertidal zone animals, which have strong affinities for an aquatic existence even if they are found in the regions between water and land.

Most aquatic invertebrates have no ability to regulate body temperature. The energy exchange of these animals is principally influenced by physical factors, such as the conduction and convection of heat, radiation, and evaporation of water. As a result of metabolic work, heat may be generated by the animal. In aquatic organisms, this heat may be lost by conduction to the surrounding water at a rate which greatly exceeds the heat loss from terrestrial animals to air, although the temperature of an active tissue located in the central core of the body may be higher than that of the surrounding environment. Evaporation could possibly play a role in heat dissipation only where aquatic organisms live in transition regions between water and land, i.e., the intertidal zone.

Rather than having mechanisms which regulate body temperature at a high constant level, as in most birds and mammals, many aquatic invertebrates compensate for changing temperatures by metabolic adaptation. Thus, within the genetic capability of any species, physiological compensation is the principal homeostatic device used in order to function in a habitat of fluctuating thermal conditions.

Acclimation to thermal changes by poikilothermic animals has received some attention, but there are few comprehensive studies dealing with aquatic invertebrates. Review papers by Bullock (1955), Prosser (1955, 1958, 1962, 1964), Precht (1958), Segal (1961), F. J. Vernberg (1962, 1963), Kinne (1963), and McWhinnie (1967) deal in detail with many aspects of thermal effects on aquatic invertebrates.

In general, two schemes of classifying the response of animals to changing thermal levels have been presented (Precht, 1958; Prosser, 1958). Precht describes five categories of response (Fig. 1). To characterize these responses, the rate function of some physiological parameter is determined at one acclimation temperature, then redetermined after the organism is placed at a new temperature. Type 1 is termed overcompensation. Here the rate of physiological function at a new high acclimation temperature is less than the rate at the original temperature, or, when the original low acclimation temperature is higher than the new acclimation temperature, the new rate is then higher. Type 2, in which the rates of activity are the same at both temperature levels, is referred to as complete compensation. In type 3, or incomplete compensation, the rate is between types

2 and 4. In type 4, there is no compensation, i.e., the rate conforms to a Q_{10} of 2–3, and type 5 is undercompensation. In this type the response is the reverse of type 1.

Prosser (1958) described five major patterns of acclimation which are based on the relative position and slope of R–T (rate–temperature) curves determined for a specific physiological function of cold- and warm-acclimated animals (Fig. 2). The system of Precht compares the response

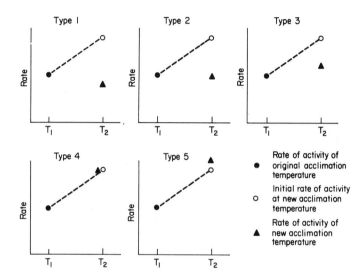

FIG. 1. Examples of the five types of capacity adaptation of Precht (1958). Type 1: supraoptimal, respiration of certain marine animals (Precht *et al.*, 1955). Type 2: ideal, cytochrome c oxidase activity of supraesophageal ganglion of fiddler crabs (F. J. Vernberg and Vernberg, 1967). Type 3: partial, proteolytic activity of gastric juice of snail (Mews, 1957). Type 4: missing, respiration of adult fiddler crab, *Uca rapax*, from Jamaica (F. J. Vernberg, 1959a). Type 5: inverse, respiration of supraesophageal ganglion (W. B. Vernberg and Vernberg, 1966). T_1 and T_2 refer to the initial and the new acclimation temperature, respectively.

at one temperature with the response at a second temperature, while Prosser's scheme compares responses of cold- and warm-acclimated animals over a wide range of temperatures.

These two schemes are of value to biologists, since they provide a basis for classifying and comparing the responses to temperature of organisms and their constituent parts. In addition, the type of response might give an indication of the functional mechanism involved, i.e., if the pattern was of a translation type, Prosser felt that this might be a reflection of a change in the activity of some enzyme system.

Research relative to these classification systems may be grouped into

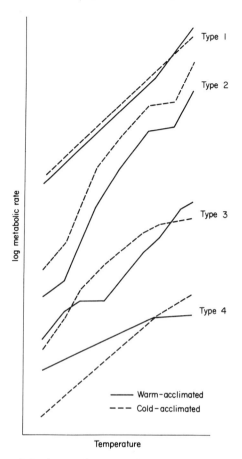

FIG. 2. Examples of the four main types of capacity adaptation of Prosser (1958). Type I: no acclimation, respiration of midgut gland of *Uca rapax* (F. J. Vernberg and Vernberg, 1964). Type II: translation, respiration of rediae of *Himsathla* (W. B. Vernberg and Vernberg, 1965). Type III: rotation, respiration of *Uca rapax* (W. B. Vernberg and Vernberg, 1966). Type IV: translation and rotation, respiration of heart of *Uca pugilator* (F. J. Vernberg and Vernberg, 1964).

two main categories. The first includes those studies which compare acclimation patterns of various physiological rate functions on an inter- and intraspecific basis, as well as a comparison of patterns for different ontogenetic stages. These comparisons have formed the necessary framework for evaluating physiological diversity in respect to differences in habitat temperatures. The second approach deals with cellular and biochemical mechanisms involved in temperature adaptation. This second line of investigation is particularly important in attempting to elucidate basic mechanisms which may be operative in various groups of organisms.

II. Acclimation Patterns

Two examples will serve to typify the first major line of research. The first deals with the metabolic response of latitudinally separated populations of fiddler crabs, while the second compares the metabolic response patterns of a parasite and its host.

Fiddler crabs, genus *Uca,* are found along the western Atlantic shore as far south in the southern hemisphere as Argentina and as far north

TABLE I

COMPARISONS OF TYPES OF ACCLIMATION IN *Uca* ACCORDING
TO PROSSER'S TERMINOLOGY

Species	Stage of life cycle or type of tissue	Type number	Comment
pugilator	Adults	II A	Populations from[a] Mass., Fla.
pugilator	Young adults	II A	Populations from[b] Mass., N.C., Fla.
rapax	Adult	I or III B	Animals from[a] Jamaica
rapax	Adult	III A	Animals from[a] Fla.
rapax	Adult	III A	Animals from[c] Santos, Brazil
rapax	Adult	Does not fit any described pattern	Animals from[c] Salvador, Brazil
pugnax	Adult	IV A	Animals from[a] N.C.
pugnax	Adult	II A	Populations from[a] N.Y., N.C.
rapax	Adult	II A	Populations from[a] Fla., Trinidad
pugilator	1st stage zoea	IV D	Populations from[b] Fla., N.C. (or Mass.)
pugilator	1st stage zoea	I	Populations from[b] N.C., Mass.
pugnax	1st stage zoea	IV A	Populations from[b] N.Y., N.C.
5 species of *Uca*	1st stage zoea	I	Three temperate zone species from N.C. and two tropical species
pugnax	Megalops	III B	Populations from[b] N.C., Mass.
pugilator	Megalops	Does not fit any described pattern	Populations from[b] Fla., N.C. (or Mass.)
pugnax	Gill	IV A	Populations from[a] N.C.
pugnax	Midgut gland	III A	Populations from[a] N.C.
rapax	Gill	III A	Populations from[a] Jamaica
rapax	Midgut gland	I	Populations from[a] Jamaica
rapax	"Brain"	IV B	Populations from[c] Santos, Brazil
pugilator	"Brain"	II B	Populations from[a] N.C.
pugilator	Muscle	III B	Populations from[a] N.C.
pugilator	Heart	IV C	Populations from[a] N.C.

[a] F. J. Vernberg and Vernberg (1964).
[b] F. J. Vernberg and Costlow (1966).
[c] F. J. Vernberg and Vernberg (1966).

in the northern hemisphere as Massachusetts. Some species have tropical zone affinities while others inhabit the temperate zone. Since the thermal regimes in these different zones vary significantly, distinctive patterns of temperature acclimation would be expected. Table I lists the patterns of acclimation, based on Prosser's classification, in various species of *Uca* determined at different stages of their life cycle, and it includes patterns for whole animals as well as tissues. Although in most cases, the metabolic response could be characterized as one of the patterns described by Prosser, some undescribed patterns were observed. In general, the acclimation pattern is not the same for the various stages in the life cycle. Not only may all the tissues respond differently, but no one tissue responds consistently

TABLE II

Types of Thermal Acclimation by Geographically Isolated Populations of *Uca* (after the Classification of Precht, 1958)

Species and location of population	Original acclimation temperature	
	High	Low
Uca rapax		
Santos	4	3
Salvador	4	3
Jamaica	4	4
Florida	3	5
Uca pugnax		
North Carolina	3	3
Uca uruguayensis		
Torres	3	4
Santos	5	3

in the same manner as the intact organism. Furthermore, a simple relationship between habitat temperatures, as reflected by a different latitudinal location, and the pattern of response is not apparent. However, these data are significant in demonstrating that inherent physiological differences have evolved in latitudinally separated populations of closely related animals, and that the mechanism at the tissue level is probably not the same in each population.

Classification of the type of temperature–metabolic response according to the scheme of Precht demonstrated marked differences in capacity adaptation among various populations. Also, if different patterns are an indication of the mechanisms involved, the compensatory mechanisms to low temperature appear to be unlike those for high temperatures (Table II).

Parasitic larval stages of two species of trematodes found in the same intermediate host, the snail *Nassarius obsoleta,* have patterns that are different from each other, and both are different from the host (Table III). Although these three species share a similar thermal environment, the close association between the host and its parasites has not resulted in the convergent evolution of their response to temperature (W.. B. Vernberg and Vernberg, 1965).

TABLE III

COMPARISON OF METABOLIC-TEMPERATURE ACCLIMATION
PATTERNS IN PARASITES AND THEIR HOST

Species	Precht's scheme	Prosser's scheme
Himasthla quissetensis	3	II
Zoogonus rubellus	4	IV A
Nassarius obsoleta	4	Does not fit any pattern

Examples and a discussion of the second major line of research are included in Section III.

III. Adaptations to Temperature Change

A. METABOLIC ADAPTATIONS

When the ambient temperature is decreased, the metabolic rate of an aquatic invertebrate characteristically decreases, as does its body temperature. The opposite response is noted when the environmental temperature is increased. If no homeostatic mechanism is operative, a Q_{10} of 2–3 is expected. However, there are numerous examples where the Q_{10} of the metabolic response is less than 2 or more than 3, indicating an independence from fluctuations in the environmental temperature, even though the body temperature probably tends to be the same as that of the external environment. Over the temperature range of 22°–28°C, a Q_{10} of 1.23 was found for the metabolic rate of *Uca rapax* from Jamaica, while over the range of 12°–15°C, the Q_{10} was 8.6. However, a Q_{10} value of 2.35 over the range of 17°–22°C indicated a nonadaptive response (F. J. Vernberg, 1959a). Respiratory compensation to one end of a temperature gradient may be found in one species, but no corresponding adaptive change at the other. Tropical fiddler crabs, *Uca rapax,* did not demonstrate metabolic compensation to temperature at 15°C, but a distinct acclimatory shift at higher temperatures was observed (F. J. Vernberg, 1959b). See reviews of Bullock (1955), Precht (1958, 1967), Prosser (1958, 1964), F. J. Vernberg (1962), and McWhinnie (1967) for more exhaustive discussions.

Tissues of some aquatic poikilotherms show adaptive changes to temperature. For example, the Q_{10} value for muscle respiration of a temperate zone fiddler crab, *Uca pugnax*, over the temperature range of $10°-15°C$, depends on the previous thermal history of the organism. This value for tissue from cold-acclimated animals is approximately 1.1, but it is 3.5 for warm-acclimated tissue (W. B. Vernberg and Vernberg, 1966). Muscle tissue from cold-acclimated animals is more temperature insensitive over this thermal range than tissue from warm-acclimated animals. Although these changes may be similar to those observed in the intact organism, not all tissues in one organism will react similarly to temperature (Precht, 1958; F. J. Vernberg and Vernberg, 1966; McWhinnie, 1967). The response of muscle tissue of cold- and warm-acclimated *Uca pugnax*, noted above, is different from that of the heart or supraesophageal ganglion over this same temperature range of $10°-15°C$. The Q_{10} values of heart from cold- and warm-acclimated animals are both approximately 1.5. Differences between tissues from a tropical species are even greater, i.e., the Q_{10} values of muscle tissue from cold- and warm-acclimated animals are about 2.0; for heart tissue from warm-acclimated animals, the Q_{10} is 2.0 and for cold-acclimated animals, it is 3.2, while for the supraesophageal ganglion from warm-acclimated animals the Q_{10} is 4.2, but it is only 1.3 for cold-acclimated tissue (W. B. Vernberg and Vernberg, 1966). Little is known of the mechanisms which regulate the responses of the separate tissues of the organism to give a coordinated response by the intact invertebrate organism. Recently, Das and Prosser (1967) have suggested that, at least in the lower vertebrates, there is neural control over the cellular responses.

At the biochemical level, even less is known of the mechanisms of temperature adaptation in most animal groups. This lack is especially evident in the aquatic invertebrates, although previous studies on tissues and the intact organism have demonstrated metabolic compensation. However, an ever increasing emphasis is being placed on this area of research, as evidenced by three recent review references (McWhinnie, 1967; Prosser, 1967; Troshin, 1967). Only a few recent different lines of study are presented here.

Exposure to low temperature results in an overall increase in the oxygen consumption of the crayfish, *Orconectes virilis*. Increased substrate utilization by homogenates of hepatopancreas indicated that both the Embden-Meyerhof and the hexose monophosphate routes were operative. These quantitative metabolic adjustments modified the ratio of oxidative routes employed for synthesis and thermogenesis (McWhinnie and O'Connor, 1967).

Cytochrome c oxidase activity in muscle was differentially influenced by temperature in species of tropical and temperate zone fiddler crabs. A higher level of enzymatic activity was found in cold-acclimated animals (*Uca pugnax*) from North Carolina and *Uca rapax* from Florida than in warm-acclimated animals. However, in the tropical population of *Uca rapax* from Puerto Rico, no statistical difference in activity was observed when comparing warm- and cold-acclimated animals. Hence, an intraspecific diversity was noted when comparing Florida and Puerto Rican populations. The cytochrome c activity of the supraesophageal ganglion from *U. pugnax* was higher in cold-acclimated animals, a response similar to that of muscles. Although the cytochrome activity of the supraesophageal ganglion of the Florida animals was unchanged with thermal acclimation, cold-acclimation decreased the activity of this enzyme in the Puerto Rican population (W. B. Vernberg and Vernberg, 1968). It is possible that this inhibitory effect may be significant in limiting the northward distribution of the tropical population.

During acclimation to cold, Rao (1963) demonstrated an increase in RNA in a mollusk, *Lamellidens marginalis,* which indicated an increased protein synthesis, including enzyme protein. The increase in RNA may be the result of increased capacity of the hexose monophosphate shunt to operate in cold-acclimated poikilotherms. Recently, Das and Prosser (1967) presented experimental evidence of the alteration of net protein synthesis in the tissues of goldfish. They proposed that this might result in the enzymatic and other biochemical compensatory mechanisms of thermal acclimation at the cellular level of the goldfish. Obviously, this work should be extended to include detailed studies on aquatic invertebrates.

B. Ability to Control Body Temperature

One method of determining if an organism is capable of some degree of thermoregulation is to compare the interior body temperature with the temperature of the surrounding environment. The available evidence indicates that at very low environment temperatures, body temperatures of aquatic invertebrates differ scarcely at all from the thermal environment. Kanwisher (1955) measured body temperatures of *Crassostrea virginicus, Mytilus edulis,* and *Modiolus modiolus* during freezing weather. He found that the interior body temperatures of the animals were all within a few tenths of a degree of the air temperature. As much as 75% of the water in these animals can be in the form of ice, with the remaining brine concentration approximately four times the normal value. Even at low temperatures, well above freezing (10°C), the interior body temperature of *Nassarius obsoleta* did not vary significantly from that of the thermal environment (W. B. Vernberg and Vernberg, 1965). From this evidence it would appear that at low temperatures, aquatic invertebrate organisms have adapted to cold temperatures other than by thermoregulation.

At higher temperatures, some semiaquatic organisms apparently can exercise a certain amount of thermoregulation by evaporative cooling. Gunn (1942) has pointed out that in truly aquatic organisms, it is impossible to lose water by evaporation. Therefore, aquatic invertebrates cannot have a body temperature lower than the temperature of the water. Work on intertidal zone animals, however, suggests that these animals are able to thermoregulate to a limited degree. Lewis (1963) worked with three species of tropical intertidal marine animals: a barnacle, *Tetracleta squamosa;* a limpet, *Fissurella barbadensis;* and a gastropod, *Nerita tesselata.* He found that none of these three animals absorbed radiation as do inanimate or blackbodies. Furthermore, all three had body temperatures lower than that of the surrounding environment: the tissue temperatures of the barnacles were 4.9°C lower than that of the blackbodies, limpet body temperatures were lower by 5.6°C, and the gastropod tissue temperatures were lower by 8.0°C. Lewis suggested that these lower body temperatures were accomplished through evaporative cooling. There seems to be a positive correlation between the ability to regulate body temperature and the habitat of the organism. The barnacle and limpet, which live at midtide level, do not regulate as effectively as does *Nerita,* which lives at the high tide level. Effective thermoregulatory ability has also been noted for the high tide level barnacle, *Tetraclita squamosa japonica* (Norio and Mori, 1963). Although these authors did not speculate on the mechanism, evaporative cooling would appear to be a likely possibility.

Thermoregulation by evaporative cooling has also been reported for fiddler crabs, genus *Uca* (Edney, 1961, 1962), and for the crab *Ocypode macrocera* (Pailey, 1961). Fiddler crabs have been reported in sand up to 50.2°C, but the body temperature was always lower. Edney (1962) attributes the lower body temperature of these crabs to transpiration and the convection of heat. In *O. macrocera,* body temperatures can be as much as 3°–4°C lower than the thermal environment of the crab. This evaporative heat loss, however, occurs only at low humidities (Pailey, 1961). Similar results were reported for the terrestrial mollusks *Arion ater* and *Helix pomatia* (Hogben and Kirk, 1945). In these animals, evaporative cooling kept the body temperature lower than the environmental temperature except at high humidities.

Typically, intertidal zone pelecypod mollusks close their valves during periods of stress when the tide recedes. Presumably this prevents excessive desiccation and loss of body fluids. Apparently they have become adapted to thermal stress by being more temperature resistant than subtidal species.

An indication of this evolutionary divergence is seen in the work of Schlieper *et al.* (1960). Ciliary activity of isolated pieces of gill tissue is stopped at lower temperatures for deep water forms than for shallow water species, which in turn are more sensitive than are intertidal species. For example, the cilia on the gill tissue of the subtidal species, *Aequipecten irradians*, stop beating after 38 minutes at 3.3°C, whereas the cilia of two intertidal species, *Modiolus demissus* and *Crassostrea virginica*, stop after 34.5 and 44.8 minutes, respectively, at 7.2°C (Vernberg *et al.*, 1963).

Unlike other bivalves, *Modiolus demissus* does not completely close its valves when out of water and it is appropriately classified as an airgaper. Lent (1968) studied the adaptive significance of this phenomenon by measuring the rate of water loss and the temperature of the pallial cavity. When the tide receded, the pallial cavity temperature was identical to the air temperature. The pallial cavity temperature dropped quickly, and within 30 minutes it was 2.1°C less than the air temperature. However, the ability to maintain this thermal differential was lost with time, i.e., after 2 hours the difference was only 1°C, after 14 hours about 0.5°C, and the pallial cavity was isothermal with the air after 21 hours. This thermal response appears to be somewhat related to the rate of water loss in that the greatest percentage water loss occurs within the first 20 hours. Lent proposed that this does not constitute active control of body temperature, but is a passive physical phenomenon, since dead animals showed similar rates of water loss. This ability to reduce the body temperature by evaporative cooling, as indicated by measurements of the pallial cavity temperature, appears to have slight survival value when the animals are exposed to elevated temperatures. The LT_{50} (temperature at which 50% of the exposed animals died) for a 10-hour exposure to a relative humidity of 80% is 37.8°C for airgaping animals, but it is only 36.4°C for those animals which are prevented from gaping by being clamped shut. These differences indicated a trend, but they were not statistically significant.

Ligia oceanica, an isopod which inhabits the intertidal and littoral zone, is able to maintain body temperatures below that of its environment (Edney, 1953). The internal body temperature is as much as 8°C lower than that of the ground temperature. This temperature depression is much greater than that for the more terrestrial isopods, i.e., for *Porcellio*, this value is only 2°–3°C. Differences in temperature depression values of animals from different habitats, ranging from moist to arid, is in the same order as rates of evaporation.

Apparently, not all intertidal zone animals can exercise even a limited degree of thermoregulation. Kenny (1958) did a series of experiments with the chiton, *Clavarizona hirtosa*. When the chitons were killed and placed next to live chitons on rocks for varying lengths of time, there was no difference between the body temperatures of the live and the dead mollusks. When the dead chitons were wetted, however, their body temperatures were lower than those of the live ones. Kenny concluded that these animals have no thermoregulatory control. He did find, however, that the chitons taken from the more exposed rocks had higher lethal temperatures (43°C) than did those taken from the reef rim (41°C).

C. INTEGUMENTARY MODIFICATIONS

In addition to thermoregulation by evaporative cooling, there have been some studies which indicate that pigmentation is involved in thermal control. Brown and Sandeen (1948) hypothesized that in fiddler crabs (genus *Uca*), blanching at high temperatures has a thermoregulatory role. Recently, Wilkens and Fingerman (1965) supported this hypothesis with studies on *Uca pugnax*. They found that in sunlight, the body temperature of dark crabs was higher than that of pale crabs.

D. BEHAVIORAL MECHANISMS

Another thermoregulatory mechanism is the diurnal phototactic rhythm reported for *Uca pugnax* by Palmer (1962). He found that these crabs had a daily rhythm, whereby, in the morning, they were attracted to light. Thus, some degree of thermoregulation is accomplished, since the crabs avoid light during the hottest part of the day.

Other behavioral patterns of invertebrates also tend to lend some thermoregulatory control. Both Edney (1962) and Wilkens and Fingerman (1965) observed that fiddler crabs (genus *Uca*) periodically return to their burrows. Since the burrows are several degrees cooler than at the surface, the crabs can lower their body temperature appreciably. In studies on the purple sea urchin, *Strongylocentrotus purpuratus*, Farmanfarmaian and Giese (1963) speculate that the distribution of this animal is a behavioral response to temperature. In central California this is an intertidal zone species. At the extreme southern range where the temperatures are higher, however, this species is found subtidally, where the temperatures are less stressful.

IV. Conclusions

Aquatic invertebrates respond to fluctuating temperatures in a number of ways, ranging from passive toleration to the utilization of well-developed homeostatic mechanisms. In contrast to the thermoregulatory ability of the higher vertebrates, metabolic compensation appears to be the more prevalent mechanism by which aquatic invertebrates have attempted to escape the tyranny of a fluctuating ambient temperature. However, some aquatic invertebrates do show limited thermoregulatory ability, which seems to have ecological significance. Based on the results of the few papers dealing with this subject, the principal thermoregulatory mechanisms of aquatic invertebrates, in addition to metabolic compensation, are evaporative cooling, integumentary modifications, and behavioral responses.

REFERENCES

Brown, F. A., Jr., and Sandeen, M. I. (1948). *Physiol. Zool.* **21,** 361.

Bullock, T. H. (1955). *Biol. Rev.* **30,** 311.

Das, A. B., and Prosser, C. L. (1967). *Comp. Biochem. Physiol.* **21,** 449.

Edney, E. B. (1953). *J. Exptl. Biol.* **30,** 311.

Edney, E. B. (1961). *Trans. Roy. Soc. S. Africa* **36,** 71.

Edney, E. B. (1962). *In* "Biometeorology," pp. 79–85. Pergamon Press, Oxford.

Farmanfarmaian, A., and Giese, A. C. (1963). *Physiol. Zool.* **36,** 237.

Gunn, D. L. (1942). *Biol. Rev.* **17,** 293.

Hogben, L., and Kirk, R. L. (1945). *Proc. Roy. Soc.* **B132,** 239.

Kanwisher, J. W. (1955). *Biol. Bull.* **109,** 56.

Kenny, R. (1958). *J. Roy. Soc. W. Australia* **41,** 93.

Kinne, O. (1963). *In* "Oceanography and Marine Biology, An Annual Review" (H. Barnes, ed.), Vol. I, pp. 301–340. Allen & Unwin, London.

Lent, C. M. (1968). *Biol. Bull.* **134,** 60.

Lewis, J. B. (1963). *Biol. Bull.* **124,** 277.

McWhinnie, M. A. (1967). *In* "Thermobiology" (A. H. Rose, ed.), pp. 353–374. Academic Press, New York.

McWhinnie, M. A., and O'Connor, J. D. (1967). *Comp. Biochem. Physiol.* **20,** 131.

Mews, H. (1957). *Z. Vergleich. Physiol.* **40,** 345.

Morrison, R. (1962). *In* "Comparative Physiology of Temperature Regulation" (J. P. Hannon and E. Viereck, eds.), pp. 389–414. Arctic Aeromed. Lab., Fort Wainwright, Alaska.

Norio, S., and Mori, S. (1963). *Japan J. Ecol.* **13,** 1.

Pailey, A. (1961). *J. Madras Univ.* **31,** 109.

Palmer, J. D. (1962). *Biol. Bull.* **123,** 290–294.

Precht, H. (1958). *In* "Physiological Adaptation" (C. L. Prosser, ed.), pp. 50–78. Am. Physiol. Soc., Washington, D.C.

Precht, H. (1967). *In* "The Cell and Environmental Temperature" (A. S. Troshin, ed.), pp. 307–321. Pergamon Press, Oxford.

Precht, H., Christophersen, J., and Hensel, H. (1955). "Temperatur und Leben." Springer, Berlin.

Prosser, C. L. (1955). *Biol. Rev.* **30,** 229.

Prosser, C. L. (1958). *In* "Physiological Adaptation" (C. L. Prosser, ed.), pp. 167–180. Am. Physiol. Soc., Washington, D.C.

Prosser, C. L. (1962). *In* "Comparative Physiology of Temperature Regulation" (J. P. Hannon and E. Viereck, eds.), pp. 1–44. Arctic Aeromed. Lab., Fort Wainwright, Alaska.

Prosser, C. L. (1964). *In* "Handbook of Physiology" (Am. Physiol. Soc., J. Field, ed.), Sec. 4, pp. 11–25. Williams & Wilkins, Baltimore, Maryland.

Prosser, C. L., ed. (1967). "Molecular Mechanisms of Temperature Adaptation," Publ. No. 84. Am. Assoc. Advance. Sci., Washington, D.C.

Rao, K. P. (1963). *Proc. Indian Acad. Sci.* B. **58,** 11.

Schlieper, C., Flügel, H., and Rudolf, J. (1960). *Experientia* **16,** 470.

Segal, E. (1961). *Am. Zoologist* **1,** 235.

Troshin, A. S., ed. (1967). "The Cell and Environmental Temperature." Pergamon Press, Oxford.

Vernberg, F. J. (1959a). *Biol. Bull.* **117,** 163.

Vernberg, F. J. (1959b). *Biol. Bull.* **117,** 582.

Vernberg, F. J. (1962). *Ann. Rev. Physiol.* **24,** 517.

Vernberg, F. J. (1963). *Temp. Meas. Control Sci. Ind.,* **3,** 135–141.

Vernberg, F. J., and Costlow, J. D. (1966). *Physiol. Zool.* **39,** 36.

Vernberg, F. J., and Vernberg, W. B. (1964). *Helgolaender Wiss. Meeresuntersuch.* **9,** 476.

Vernberg, F. J., and Vernberg, W. B. (1966). *Comp. Biochem. Physiol.* **19,** 489.

Vernberg, F. J., Schlieper, C., and Schneider, D. E. (1963). *Comp. Biochem. Physiol.* **8,** 271.

Vernberg, W. B., and Vernberg, F. J. (1965). *Comp. Biochem. Physiol.* **14,** 557.

Vernberg, W. B., and Vernberg, F. J. (1966). *Comp. Biochem. Physiol.* **17,** 363.

Vernberg, W. B., and Vernberg, F. J. (1968). *Comp. Biochem. Physiol.* **26,** 499.

Wilkens, J. L., and Fingerman, M. (1965). *Biol. Bull.* **128,** 133.

Chapter 2 TERRESTRIAL INVERTEBRATES

J. L. Cloudsley-Thompson

I. Introduction

The body temperature of invertebrate animals corresponds broadly with that of the environment. For this reason they are often called "poikilothermic," a term which, in itself, implies some absence of regulation. Thermal control is certainly by no means completely lacking, however, although it is often achieved by behavioral rather than by physiological mechanisms. For this reason, the term "ectothermal" (Cowles, 1962) is preferable to poikilothermic, for it indicates that most of the heat of the body is derived from the environment rather than from metabolic sources.

In addition, invertebrate animals combat the thermal demands made upon them by the environment through physiological means that enable them to survive temperature extremes. These mechanisms permit them to withstand heat or cold, rather than to regulate their body temperatures. For example, in diapause, an insect can often tolerate extremes of heat or cold that it could not survive in the active state. Such mechanisms are extremely important to invertebrates, and they are discussed in this chapter even though they are not, in a strict sense, thermoregulatory.

Although the effects of no environmental factor have been studied so extensively as have those of temperature, the multiple causes of heat and cold death are but little understood (Bělehrádek, 1935, 1957; Larsen, 1943; Prosser, 1961; Cloudsley-Thompson, 1962b). Vital limits vary greatly, and the distinction between regulators (homeotherms) and adjustors (poikilotherms) is not a sharp one, for there are various degrees of regulation (Prosser, 1955; Cloudsley-Thompson, 1968). It has often been assumed that in poikilotherms the rate of metabolism is related directly to body temperature. In fact, many species are able to tolerate a wide variation in body temperature (eurythermal) and show physiological compensation for such changes. Regardless of the latitude over which they are distributed or the seasonal temperature changes to which they are subjected, their physiological rates converge toward a mean value. Populations from colder regions often have higher metabolic and developmental rates than have populations from warmer habitats, when measured at the same temperature (Bullock, 1955). This again is not true thermoregulation, but it is an important form of temperature adaptation, and will be discussed in detail.

In the following pages, the Annelida, Mollusca, and Arthropoda will be considered. Other terrestrial invertebrates are so completely dependent upon moist conditions during their active life that they can be regarded as being virtually aquatic in habit, and little is known of their temperature adaptations (see Chapter 1).

II. Behavioral Mechanisms

A. Temperature Orientation

1. *Temperature Preference*

The most obvious way in which terrestrial invertebrates thermoregulate is by means of orientation mechanisms that direct them to regions of favorable ambient temperature. These mechanisms have been classified by G. S. Fraenkel and Gunn (1961). Probably all animals avoid dangerously high temperatures, and, in most invertebrates, this represents an extreme example of klinokinesis—the reflex turning away from a source of heat. A similar response, however, does not always occur to cold, by which animals are sometimes trapped and immobilized (Section II,B,2,b). As an insect's temperature rises, it passes through the stages of cold stupor, intermittent activity, normal activity, and excitement to heat stupor (Bodenheimer, 1934a). It is only in the middle ranges that it is able to show preference behavior; but then it is capable of distinguishing small differences in temperature (Heran, 1952; Herter, 1953).

Temperature preference experiments with terrestrial animals have often been confused by the fact that, whenever there is a gradient in temperature, there is also, inevitably, a gradient in the relative humidity of the air. Indeed, Wellington (1949) found that the larvae of the spruce budworm moth *Choristoneura fumiferana* in Canada, were not to any great extent influenced by temperature but by the evaporative power of the atmosphere. From an examination of the literature dealing with the experimental aspects of the subject, he concluded that, with few exceptions, the results attributed to temperature were, in fact, obtained without the influence of humidity being adequately eliminated. Although Wellington probably overstated the case, his point is a valid one. It has been further discussed by Palmén (1954).

Thomson (1938) overcame the difficulty when studying the reactions of *Culex fatigans* to temperature by carrying out experiments low down on the humidity scale, where the insects did not discriminate between comparatively large differences. In a study of the sensory physiology and behavior of millipedes *Oxidus (Paradesmus) gracilis* and *Blaniulus guttulatus,* which are extremely sensitive to desiccation, temperature choice chamber experiments were carried out over damp filter paper so that the animals were always exposed to saturated air (Cloudsley-Thompson, 1951a). Under these conditions, a klinokinetic preference was shown for temperatures of about 15°C. A klinokinetic orientation is one in which the frequency of turning, or the rate of change of the direction of movement, is dependent on the intensity of stimulation (G. S. Fraenkel and Gunn, 1961).

Larvae of the housefly *Musca domestica,* which select a temperature of 30° to 37°C while feeding, pupate in the ground at a temperature nearer 15°C. Larvae of dung flies, *Lyperosia, Stomoxys,* and *Haematobia* spp. also have preferred temperatures that correspond closely with their normal breeding place (Thomsen and Thomsen, 1937). The experiments from which these conclusions were drawn were also carried out in moist conditions. On the other hand, Hafez (1953) found that prepupating

larvae of *M. domestica* showed a temporary preferendum in the range of
8°–20°C. He suggested that the avoidance of higher temperatures was probably a larval safeguard against enforced pupation.

Many other variables also exist in behavior studies concerned with preferred temperatures. For example, even in a gradient apparatus designed
for observing small arthropods of 1.5 mm, 1 mm, or less, the air temperature
differs by more than 3°C from that on the floor. The air is cooler than
the floor in the warmer half and warmer than the floor in the cooler
half of the choice chamber (Madge, 1961). For this reason, many of the
experimental results described below are probably less accurate than was
thought when they were first carried out.

Nicholson (1934) estimated the thermal preference of sheep blowflies
in Australia by measuring their activity at different temperatures. He found
that *Calliphora stygia,* a cool-weather and southern species, showed a preference for a lower range of temperature (20° to 25°C) than did *Chrysomyia
rufifacies* (25°C), *Lucilia sericata* (25° to 30°C) or *Lucilia cuprina*
(30°C). Rising temperature affected the insects more than did constant
temperatures.

Deal (1941) tested the temperature preferences of 23 species of insects
over periods of three days in a linear gradient apparatus. He found that
preferences were shown for fairly wide temperature ranges. His work, in
particular, has been criticized by Wellington (1949) because he did not
pay sufficient attention to the effects of varying degrees of saturation deficiency in different parts of the apparatus. Wellington's criticisms certainly
explain some of the anomalous results that Deal obtained. Nevertheless,
his conclusion is valid that ranges of temperature, rather than absolute
temperatures, are often preferred.

The preferred temperature of the cockroach *Blatta orientalis* lies between
20° and 29°C and is not affected by changes of humidity (Gunn, 1934).
The upper limit of the preferred temperature ranges of *Periplaneta americana* and *Blatella germanica* is 33°C, while that of *B. orientalis* is 29°C
(Gunn, 1935). Wireworms, *Agriotes* spp., show a preference for 17°C as
against 11.5° and 21°C, or higher temperatures (Falconer, 1945). The
amount of locomotary activity shown by the spider beetle *Ptinus tectus*
depends upon the temperature and must, therefore, result in orthokinetic
orientation, that is, undirected orientation resulting from simple effects
on the rate of locomotion depending on the intensity of stimulation
(G. S. Fraenkel and Gunn, 1961). At a temperature of 20°C, about 25%
of the beetles are active if the temperature is rising fast or falling slowly
(Gunn and Hopf, 1942). Other examples of temperature preference orientation are cited by Carthy (1958).

The temperature sensitivity of honeybee workers may be very great, for they appear to detect temperature differences as small as 0.25°C. This figure was obtained when the bees were in a gradient at their preferred temperature range and the whole apparatus was allowed to cool. The bees were then observed to move to a new position as soon as the temperature in their immediate surroundings had dropped by this amount (Heran, 1952).

   a. Blood-sucking Arthropods. Orientation to warmth is an extremely important mechanism by which blood-sucking arthropods find their mammalian hosts and remain at a constant temperature. For example, Rivnay (1932) found that heat is the most important factor in stimulating bedbugs, *Cimex lectularius,* to obtain food. Light and humidity are far less important. The bug detects heat very slowly, however, and, at room temperature (23°C), 1.5 minutes are required before *C. lectularius* reacts to a source of heat at 4 cm distance, and, even then, a differential of at least 2°C is necessary. Similar conclusions were reached by Sioli (1937). In the case of *Rhodnius prolixus,* it is the air temperature and not radiant heat that is the source of stimulation (Wigglesworth and Gillett, 1934). *Rhodnius* is attracted equally by a test tube full of warm water and by a similar tube covered with aluminum foil, although the radiant heat emitted by the metal-covered tube is less than one-tenth of that from the plain glass tube.

   Again, the louse *Pediculus humanus corporis* shows a preference for temperatures of 29°–30°C, which helps to maintain it in its normal environment between the clothes and the skin. The response is always to air temperature, and there is no response to radiant heat from objects at 20° to 45°C (Wigglesworth, 1941). Lice appear to avoid high and low temperatures by klinokinesis, and they will follow a warm tube when it is moved (Homp, 1938). At unregulated humidity and in the absence of light, the preferred temperature of the chicken louse *Cuclutogaster heterographus* is 42.5°C, which is approximately the temperature of the head and neck of the host, where the parasite is usually found (Bair, 1950).

   A warm object is more attractive to the female yellow-fever mosquito *Aedes aegypti* than a cooler object, such that the numbers touching a ball warmed to 43.5°C are twice as great as those touching one at 32°C. This attractiveness is reduced when the temperature of the warmer ball reaches 50°C. The response is eliminated by the insertion of an airtight window of thallium bromide, despite the fact that this allows almost all the radiation to filter through. Heat convection must therefore be the factor which makes a warm object attractive to a mosquito (Peterson and Brown, 1951). This, it was suggested, explains why Parker (1948) failed to obtain a positive response of *Aedes* mosquitoes to a warm dry object from which only radiant heat reached the insects. In a later paper, Parker (1952) obtained results indicating that the response of female *A. aegypti* to a warm, dry surface and to a moist surface at room temperature is conditioned by the temperature and humidity of the air to which they are exposed at the time of the experiment and probably also by that to which they have been exposed prior to the experiment.

The sheep tick *Ixodes ricinus* follows a circular path around a source of heat at a distance from the center which depends upon the temperature there (Totze, 1933). Hungry ticks, in all stages of development, orient themselves to odorless glass tubes at 37°C. Temperatures higher than the surroundings are usually attractive unless they exceed 42°C (Lees, 1948). Temperature alone has little effect and a combination of temperature and odor stimuli is necessary to induce a marked response in the Australian cattle tick *Boophilus microplus,* according to Wilkinson (1953).

b. Field Observations. Field observations indicate that the small black spider *Lithyphantes albomaculatus,* which, in Denmark, makes its web between sparse plants of heather on stony ground climbs up its web to about 2 in. above ground level on hot days (Nørgaard, 1948). *Theridion saxatile,* which builds retreats of small pieces of stone suspended above the ground, has to leave its home on hot days, when the air temperature exceeds 30° to 35°C, and live in the open where the air is cooler; it dies if prevented from so doing (Nørgaard, 1956). Nørgaard (1951) has also related the distribution of the lycosid spiders *Pirata piraticus* and *Pardosa pullata* with the two microclimatic layers of the sphagnum bog in which they live. *P. pullata,* which inhabits the surface, has a preference for 28° to 36°C, while *P. piraticus* is found in the stalk layer and has a temperature preference of 18° to 24°C. When it is carrying its cocoon, however, the preferred temperature of *P. piraticus* rises to 26° to 32°C, which, presumably, is optimal for egg development. The thermal death point of *P. pullata* is 43°C and that of *P. piraticus,* 36°C. The literature on the responses of insects to temperature in the field is very extensive (Uvarov, 1931; Allee *et al.,* 1949; Andrewartha and Birch, 1954; Cloudsley-Thompson, 1962a; Clarke, 1967). It may affect many biological functions. For example, observations on *Cicada orni* among the pine forests of the Bay of Biscay indicate a minimum threshold for song of about 22°C (Cloudsley-Thompson, 1960). According to Heath (1967), periodical "seventeen-year" cicadas, *Magicicada cassini,* bask in sunlight but maintain body temperatures below 32°C by moving into shade when they become too warm. They are unable to fly below 20°C. The wings, although transparent, are used to shade the abdomen and may reduce the radiant heat load by some 5°C. The flight of the males, singing, and the synchronization of choruses are temperature-dependent, but other activities, such as the flight of females, copulation, and oviposition are more independent.

c. Interacting Factors. The preferred temperature is often to some extent influenced by the temperature of acclimation. Examples are afforded by locusts, beetles, bees, ants, ticks, and other arthropods (Prosser, 1961; Wigglesworth, 1965). Ants acclimated at 3° to 5°C cluster together (aggregate) at 23.5°C, while others acclimated at 25° to 27°C, selected 32°C (Herter, 1923, 1924). In contrast, the temperature preference of wireworms, *Agriotes* spp., was not influenced to any great extent by the previous temperature (Falconer, 1945).

The temperature preference of insects may be altered by both internal and external conditions. For example, the temperature preference of *Blatta orientalis* is much lower in insects that have been desiccated to 70% of their original weight (Gunn, 1934). In several species of insects, it has been shown that the environmental temperature may affect their light reactions (for references, *vide* Perttunen, 1959). A combination of the responses to these two factors results in the animals selecting optimum habitats. Thus, the bark beetle *Blastophagus piniperda* is clearly photopositive at 25°C, the photopositive response decreasing as the temperature is either raised or lowered from this value (Perttunen, 1958, 1959). There is also a difference between the light reactions of specimens observed in autumn and in spring at 20°C, the photopositive reaction being much more pronounced in the spring. In the spring, the range of the photopositive reaction is from 10° to 35°C, whereas in autumn, the same range is only from 20° to 30°C. The photopositive reaction reached its maximum intensity at 25°C in both groups (Perttunen, 1959). High temperatures did not, however, affect the negative response to light of the nocturnal desert tenebrionid beetles *Ocnera hispida* and *Pimelia grandis,* in Sudan, nor did it result in a reduction in the photopositive responses of *Adesmia antiqua.* Even at lethal temperatures, the only response shown was to dig into the sand (Cloudsley-Thompson, 1963b).

In a similar way, larvae and adults of *Tenebrio molitor* tend to be photonegative with a reduction in intensity of the reaction at higher temperatures. This may be related to the sheltered environment in which the beetles normally live (Perttunen and Paloheimo, 1963).

Reversal of the photopositive response of *B. piniperda* at low temperatures, however, is related to what is known about its behavior in its natural habitats, and must be an essential component among the other changes that take place when the hibernation period is about to begin. The beetles then leave the shoots of pine trees and descend to the ground (Perttunen, 1958).

2. *Sensory Physiology*

Warm-blooded animals have an absolute, nonadapting temperature-measuring device that controls their physiological homeostatic mechanisms. The body temperature of a man remains the same whether he has been living in the arctic or in the tropics. The same must be true of ectotherms, because, if they were to show much sensory adaptation, a steady drift in their preferred temperature would invalidate the entire principle of temperature regulation by behavioral means. The physiological basis of such nonadaptive receptors, however, is practically unknown, although the literature on the temperature preferences of invertebrate animals is considerable (G. S. Fraenkel and Gunn, 1961; Wigglesworth, 1965). The physiology of temperature reception in animals is discussed by Murray (1962), who points out that the threshold sensitivity may be as high in invertebrates as in mammals.

All animals appear to be sensitive to high temperatures, but it is doubtful whether there are any special sense organs responsible. In many terrestrial invertebrates, this sensitivity is distributed over the entire body; but it is usually most marked in the anterior regions. This is so in grasshoppers, for instance (Geist, 1928). The antennae of insects and other arthropods are usually especially sensitive to thermal stimuli. This is true in Collembola (Strebel, 1932), Phasmidae (Cappe de Baillon, 1936), Hemiptera (Herter, 1923, 1924), Diplopoda (Cloudsley-Thompson, 1951a), and others.

a. Antennae. Many blood-sucking insects detect the warmth emanating from their hosts by means of their antennae. Thus, the antennae and palps are the chief organs used by female mosquitoes, *Aedes aegypti,* in locating their hosts and sensing the stimuli which induce probing. The antennae function as direction distance thermoreceptors and the palps receive stimuli when the insect is near the skin of the host (Roth, 1951). The same is probably true of many other blood-sucking and ectoparasitic insects (Wigglesworth, 1965). Though the receptors on the antennae are probably the main heat receptors in the human louse, lice without antennae can still orient (Homp, 1938), and decapitated housefly larvae avoid high temperatures as strongly as do normal larvae (Hafez, 1950).

McIver and Harwood (1966) showed that trichoid sensillae on the basal segments of the antennae of the firebrat *Thermobia domestica* act as thermoreceptors. One week after antennectomy, however, some thermal discrimination is regained because the tarsi and maxillary palps also function as sites for thermoreception.

In crickets, while the antennae are sensitive to air temperature, the tarsi register that of the substrate (Herter, 1923, 1924). The same is true of the centipede *Lithobius forficatus,* which shows a preference for temperatures around 12°C, depending upon the relative humidity (Bauer, 1955). According to Kerkut and Taylor (1957), there is a temperature-sensitive band in the pad between the claws of the cockroach *Periplaneta americana* and in the first to fourth tarsal segments (the arolium and pulvilli). This is most active below 13°C and is sensitive to decreases of 1°C. It is stimulated by warming 5°C in the range of 0° to 28°C, but the activity is short-lived. Warming above 30°C, however, brings about prolonged electrical activity (Fig. 1).

b. Sensillae. The sense organs involved in temperature reception have not often been identified. In the beetles *Dorcus* spp., however, and the bugs *Pyrrhocoris* spp., temperature reception has been located in thin-walled trichoid sensillae (Gebhardt, 1953). G. R. M. Grant (1950) surveyed pub-

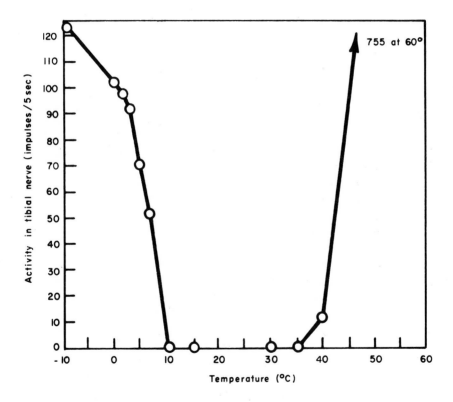

Fig. 1.   Effect of temperature on tarsal receptors in *Periplaneta americana*. The preparation was acclimated to 22°C and then subjected to various temperature changes. Impulses were recorded from the tibial nerve. From Kerkut and Taylor (1957).

lished accounts of the size, shape, and structure of the sensory pits in insects and concluded that these organs must be especially suitable for sensing infrared radiation. He suggested that pits of different sizes might be sensitive to bands of different wavelength, and that a combination of pits of varying sizes would enable an insect to determine, without making contact with it, whether a surface had a particular temperature.

Slifer (1951) suggested that certain paired, segmentally arranged specialized areas or fenestrae on the head, thorax, and abdomen of *Locusta migratoria* might serve as temperature receptors. J. Dunham (1962) measured infrared transmission in the fenestrae of *Melanoplus differentialis* and suggested that they might act like imperfect blackbodies, producing relatively highly heated surfaces for thermosensitive receptors, but Makings (1964) could not find any evidence that the fenestrae had a thermal function. In a later paper (1968), he showed that transpiration through "Slifer's patches" of *Schistocerca gregaria* and other acridids is extremely high (169 ± 52 mg/cm^2/hr). The patches show a transition effect at 40°C and can be explained as an adaptation for emergency cooling. They are normally protected by their position on the body, but the behavior of a heated locust, fluttering its wings, depressing its abdomen, and moving its prothoracic shield away from the prothorax, ventilates them. Stower and Griffiths (1966) studied the equilibrium body temperatures of hoppers of *S. gregaria* in the field and found that they were 3.2°C higher in the shade than the air temperature, when the latter was about 25°C or less, but lower than air temperature when this was above 31°C. It is doubtful, therefore, whether transpiration through Slifer's patches exerts a significant cooling effect on the body as a whole, but it may provide powerful local cooling where this is especially important.

Lacher (1964) showed by an electrophysiological investigation of the antenna of the honeybee that these insects possess sense organs which respond specifically to heat, and Loftus (1966) described a cold receptor on the antenna of *Periplaneta americana*. The efferent discharge rate is fairly steady below 25 impulses/sec at constant temperatures, but, when the temperature is rapidly lowered, the impulse frequency rises to a peak, the height of which depends on the extent of the cooling. During the next few seconds the frequency again falls below 25 impulses/sec. Rapid rewarming to the original temperature has the opposite effect. The impulse frequency drops sharply at first and then rises during the following seconds to the original level.

From time to time, insects of various orders have been reported swarming near sources of fire and smoke. Evans (1964) investigated the phenomenon, which occurs in all six species of the North American genus *Melanophila* (Buprestidae), and found in each a sensory pit contiguous with the lateral margins of both coxal cavities of the mesothoracic legs. These each contained between 70 and 100 sense organs sensitive to infrared irradiation of wavelength 0.8–2.7 μ. This was indicated by reflex twitching of the antenna on the side of the body stimulated by exposure to a source of radiation for a period as short as $\frac{1}{300}$ second. Evans suggested that these sense organs might operate often at considerable distance and that the antennae sense organs are used for orientation close to the source of stimulation. In a later paper (Evans, 1966a), he showed that in *M. acuminata,* a wax gland adjacent to each sense organ continuously secretes wax, which serves to protect the organs from dust particles. Evans (1966b) also calculated that a 50-acre fire in mountainous terrain could be detected by this insect from a distance 5 km.

Recently, infrared sensing has been described in sphingid and noctuid moths (Callahan, 1965a). From a histological study of the ommatidium of the corn earworm *Heliothis zea,* Callahan (1965b) concluded that the compound eye is a powerful absorber of infrared radiation, and of such a configuration that it can orient in total darkness to hot or warm spots of long-wave infrared radiation. The cornea has the configuration of an achromatic doublet, and the crystalline cone, which is coated in the night-adapted eye, of a field lens, with a quarter-wave, antireflection dialectric. All morphological units fit the theoretical configuration to be expected of a mosaic optic electromagnetic thermal radiometer. There is fast adaptation to ultraviolet daylight, and, when the moths are subjected to shortwave ultraviolet radiation, a lack of stimulated flight in an activity cage.

Temperature sensillae of the sheep tick *Ixodes ricinus* are short, thick-walled hairs borne on the dorsal and lateral aspects of the leg (Lees, 1948). The scorpion *Leiurus quinquestriatus* responds negatively to temperatures above 39°C; correlation between the distribution of short, thin hairs about 0.2 mm long and the sensitivity of parts of the body to heat suggests that these hairs may be thermal exteroceptors (Abushama, 1964). Apart from this, little appears to be known of temperature receptors in Arachnida.

From this account, it will be seen that comparatively little is known of the temperature stimulus—whether convection or radiation heat—to which invertebrates respond, or of the sense organs concerned. In most of the experiments described it is not possible even to tell to what kind of stimulus the animals were responding.

B. Avoidance of Heat and Cold

1. *Burrowing*

a. Annelida and Mollusca. The most important behavioral adaptation of invertebrate animals to hot, and especially to hot–dry, environments is the exploitation of burrowing habits. This is apparent mostly in annelids and arthropods, although many desert snails pass the summer estivating deep in cracks in the ground or in fissures of rocks. Some, such as *Leventina* spp. in Israel, excavate small cavities in limestone (Bodenheimer, 1935).

In wet-skinned, rapidly transpiring animals, such as slugs and snails, as in earthworms, it is not always possible to separate the effects of heat and of desiccation, as the two are closely interrelated in the field. However, even when body temperatures are effectively lowered by evaporation, very high ambient air temperatures are generally avoided. Also, evaporative cooling may not always be possible in humid microhabitats.

A. C. Smith (1902) found that the earthworm *Eisenia foetida,* an inhabitant of rotting vegetation and manure, where the environmental temperature may reach 20°C as a result of organic decomposition, showed no response to a rise in temperature from 20° to 30°C. At higher temperatures, however, the animals moved away from the source of heat and death occurred around 36°–40°C. It seems unlikely from these observations that environmental temperatures play much part in governing the activity of the species, since worms always burrow deep into the cooler depths of the soil during intense summer heat and thereby maintain themselves in the optimal conditions. In a similar way, the frozen upper layers of the soil are avoided during winter (Laverack, 1963). *Pheretima* sp. displays greatest burrowing activity at 20°C and shows a preference for this temperature in a gradient (W. C. Grant, 1953).

Animals naturally avoid dangerously high temperatures, and Dainton (1943, 1954) has shown that in slugs, *Agriolimax reticulatus,* activity is induced by rising temperatures above 21°C; the preferred temperature is 17°–18°C. Even more significant, however, is the stimulus afforded by falling temperatures (Section II,B,2,b.).

b. Arthropoda. The desert wood louse *Hemilepistus reaumuri,* which occurs in stony, clay deserts of North Africa and the Middle East, digs holes of 5-mm diameter vertically downwards for tens of centimeters. These holes are the result of cooperative efforts, and two animals can sometimes be seen head to head, thereby giving purchase to their rapidly moving legs. According to Verrier (1932), the digging reaction is released by a temperature of 35°C, if the soil is dry, and of 45°C, if it is wet, but this observation was not confirmed in the laboratory (Cloudsley-Thompson, 1956). Other desert species, such as *Porcellio albinus* and *P. angustulus,* do not dig holes, but live under stones and rocks in shallow wadis (Edney, 1958).

Millipedes are not found in arid regions, but the centipede fauna of hot deserts consists of typically burrowing forms such as *Orya* and *Scolopendra* spp. The burrowing habit is also widely developed amongst insects and arachnids and has been reviewed recently (Cloudsley-Thompson and Chadwick, 1964). Examples are afforded by Thysanura, Orthoptera, Hemiptera, Dermaptera, Neuroptera, Hymenoptera, Coleoptera, scorpions, Solifugae, and spiders (Pierre, 1958).

Not only excessive heat, but extremes of cold may be countered by burrowing, and many invertebrates spend their diapause periods deeply buried in the soil. For example, nearly all Colorado potato beetles, *Leptinotarsa decemlineata,* are killed by temperatures below —12°C and less than half of a population can survive —7°C for more than a few hours. From experiments and field observations, it has been found that the depth to which the beetles burrow in the soil at the onset of winter depends upon the texture of the soil. In loose, sandy soils, for instance, the majority of beetles hibernate at a depth of 14 to 24 in., but, in harder soils, which are better insulators, they aggregate in the top 8 in. (Mail, 1930, 1932; Mail and Salt, 1933). The thermal properties of soil microhabitats have recently been reviewed by Macfadyen (1967).

2. *Other Behavioral Mechanisms*

a. Heat. As long ago as 1932, Mellanby pointed out that experiments determining the thermal death points of insects indicate that there must be great differences between meterological conditions and the temperatures to which tropical insects are actually subjected. He emphasized the importance of evaporation in reducing temperatures in small spaces. The significance of microclimates on the distribution of terrestrial Arthropoda has recently been reviewed (Cloudsley-Thompson, 1962a); behavioral reactions which take animals to favorable microclimates have an extremely important thermoregulatory function.

Many insects aggregate for warmth in cold weather, and the converse occurs in hot weather. For example, bands of desert locusts, *Schistocerca gregaria,* have been found by Ellis and Ashall (1957) to disperse at high temperatures when the hoppers are virtually incapable of aggregating socially. This may result in some degree of temperature regulation.

Apart from selecting suitable environmental temperatures, poikilotherms often achieve thermoregulation by orienting their bodies to the rays of the sun (G. Fraenkel, 1929, 1930; Pepper and Hastings, 1952). Stower and Griffiths (1966) found that differences in orientation to the sun affected the equilibrium body temperature of hoppers of *S. gregaria* by as much as 6°C. During clear, warm, sunny days in North America, the larvae of ant lions, *Myrmeleon immaculatus,* orient themselves within their pits so that their bodies are in the coolest regions available to them. During the morning, the majority of larvae are found on the south and east sides of their pits (Green, 1955). Tropical termites protect themselves from excessive insolation by extending their nests in a north–south direction so that a comparatively small area is exposed to the noonday sun (Hesse *et al.*, 1951).

When the body temperature approaches 40°C, the air temperature under the elytra of the South African tenebrionid beetle, *Onymacris bicolor,* shows great fluctuations due to strong ventilation of the subelytral cavity, which brings in cooler air from outside. The related species, *O. multistriata,* does not ventilate its subelytral cavity to the same extent, and the temperature in the cavity closely follows that of the body. In addition, both species expose the genital apparatus at high temperatures. These diurnal beetles are thereby adapted to tolerate high temperatures for short periods and maintain a body temperature of 40°C for long enough to make it possible for them to run over exposed sand from one place of shelter to another (Bolwig, 1957). In most cases, however, the subelytral cavity of desert Tenebrionidae confers no thermal advantage, but reduces water loss by transpiration because the spiracles open into it (Cloudsley-Thompson, 1964b). Like the air sacs between the flight muscles and the body wall (Church, 1960b), they may, however, act as thermal insulators (Buxton, 1924b; Franz, 1930).

Whereas most scorpions are nocturnal in habit (Cloudsley-Thompson, 1956, 1958, 1963a), the South African *Opisthophthalmus latimanus* often comes to the mouth of its burrow during the day. In this species, characteristic "stilting" movements, in which the abdomen is elevated, occur as an adaptation to temperature stress. If cooling by stilting is not adequate, a photopositive scorpion becomes photonegative (Alexander and Ewer, 1958).

Social insects. Not only do bees conserve metabolic heat in their hives during cold weather (see below), but, when the hive gets too hot, they cool it by bringing water which is deposited on the upper parts of the combs. Then they fan vigorously with their wings and drive the air, cooled by evaporation, through the brood comb (Steiner, 1930a; W. Dunham, 1931). Fanning can be evoked experimentally by heating the hive, and it can change a normal upward circulation of 0.1 to 0.2 liters/sec to a downward air current of 0.5 to 1.0 liters/sec (Hazelhoff, 1954). At an outside temperature of 50°C, bees can keep the temperature inside their hive down to 38°C (Wohlgemuth, 1957). Similar results have been obtained with social wasps. In *Polistes gallica,* for example, temperature regulation is taken over principally by the queen. One insect, in an hour, at her best performance of 90 flights with a crop volume of 30 to 35 mm^3, can carry a total of more than 3 ml, which represents a heat of evaporation of 1831 cal (Steiner, 1930b). According to Lensky (1964a), the activity of the ventilating bees at the entrance to the hive, and the consequent velocity of the air currents they produce, are influenced by the temperature within the brood chamber, as is the activity of water carriers. On the other hand, the activity of bees carrying sucrose is dependent upon the external air temperature. The early literature on temperature regulation has been summarized by Himmer (1932).

Wood ants, *Formica rufa,* carry their larvae about the nest, placing them in whatever chamber may be at the most favorable temperature for development. When the sun's heat is greatest, the entrances to the nest are closed, which prevents the entry of warm air, and as the temperature drops, they are reopened (Raignier, 1948). *Acantholepis frauenfeldi* of the Sahara desert brings water to its nest from the salty damp sand of water-bearing strata, and this may have a thermoregulatory function (F. Bernard, 1951).

b. Cold. Many invertebrates are stimulated into activity by falling temperatures (Cloudsley-Thompson, 1961b). This is true of wood lice, millipedes (Cloudsley-Thompson, 1951a,b), insects, and other arthropods (Kerkut and Taylor, 1956, 1957, 1958; J. Bernard *et al.,* 1965). The shape of the steady rate curve of nervous activity at various temperatures suggests that *Lumbricus terrestis* may be most active in the field when the soil temperatures range between 13° and 19°C, and that, beyond these limits, activity falls (Laverack, 1961). Slugs are extremely sensitive to falling temperatures between 4° and 20°C (Dainton, 1943, 1954): temperature changes as slight as 0.1°C/hr are perceived. This accounts for their normal nocturnal activity except when daytime mists and showers superimpose minor temperature fluctuations and result in daytime activity.

No doubt extremes of cold are avoided, but, apart from the orthokinetic stimulation caused by falling temperatures just mentioned, and which may result in aggregation at a preferred temperature (Kerkut and Taylor, 1958), gradual cooling produces few negative behavior reactions among invertebrates. The animals merely slow down and become trapped at the cool end of a temperature gradient apparatus (Lees, 1948; Dainton, 1954).

A potent factor in the adaptation of terrestrial invertebrates to the arctic environment is the selection of suitable microhabitats (Scholander *et al.,* 1953b). Insects there warm themselves by basking in the sunshine, or take advantage of the higher temperatures that develop on the surface of the soil. Favored localities are evidently of the greatest importance and support a large proportion of the fauna (Downes, 1964, 1965).

Solar and nocturnal radiation exert decided effects upon the immediate habitats of insects that feed upon or within the parts of plants. Under winter conditions, when the sun is at low elevation in northern Canada, heating is still sufficient at latitude 46° 30′ N to raise coniferous foliage more than 2°C above the surrounding air. Snow-covered foliage remains above the air temperature on clear, calm nights, and below it on sunny days. This damping of daily fluctuations means that insects overwintering on branches beneath snow cover may experience about 8°C less total change per day than insects on exposed branches. Spruce budworm larvae, *Choristoneura fumiferana,* in their natural webs, experience temperatures of up to 8°C above ambient conditions in midsummer, and the silken tents of colonial species such as *Malacosoma pluviale* and *Hyphantria textor* trap air that frequently ranges from 8° to 13°C above outside air in full sunlight (Wellington, 1950). The increase in body temperature of *C. fumiferana* varies directly with radiation intensity (Shepherd, 1958).

Absorption of radiant heat from the sun is a common way of raising the body temperature of terrestrial poikilotherms in all parts of the world. Desert locusts, *Schistocerca gregaria,* orient their bodies perpendicularly to the sun's rays in the morning and evening when the air is cold, but, when they reach a temperature about 40°C, they turn parallel to the sun's rays, thus receiving minimal radiation. This orientation is in respect to heat and not to light rays, and occurs in blinded insects, although unilaterally blinded insects turn the unblinded side to the sun (G. Fraenkel, 1929, 1930). Similar results have been obtained by Pepper and Hastings (1952) in the grasshoppers *Melanoplus bivittatus* and *M. mexicanus.* The behavior of desert locusts in the field in relation to temperature and other environmental factors have been analyzed in detail by Kennedy (1939). The effectiveness of solar radiation is shown from the fact that, when a third instar migratory locust, *Locusta migratoria,* was exposed to sunlight, at an air temperature of 28°C, its internal temperature rose from 27.9° to 42.7°C within a period of 10 minutes (Strel'nikov, 1936).

Field studies on the alfalfa butterfly, *Colias philodice,* have also shown that solar radiation is the most important factor affecting body temperature in these insects, but its effective is modified by air temperature and evaporative cooling. Under sufficiently high radiation, and when the air temperature is not too low, *C. philodice* increases its body temperature by orienting itself perpendicular to the sun. When, however, body temperature reaches a critically high level, the insect regulates its temperature by decreased flight and by resting in the shade or on moist soil (Leigh and Smith, 1959).

The temperature excess of flies exposed to radiant heat depends, *inter alia,* on their size and also on the wind velocity (Fig. 2).

Thus, by choice of habitat or by behavioral responses, arthropods everywhere exploit, more or less directly, the incoming solar radiation. Sun basking is especially important to arctic and subarctic insects. Mosquito larvae, *Aedes communis,* in partly shaded pools, aggregate in the warmest sector and travel around the pool, clockwise, as conditions change during the day (Haufe, 1957). Other examples are cited by Downes (1965).

Indeed, terrestrial arthropods may often be as warm, or warmer than homeotherms, particularly on the ground where conditions change rapidly

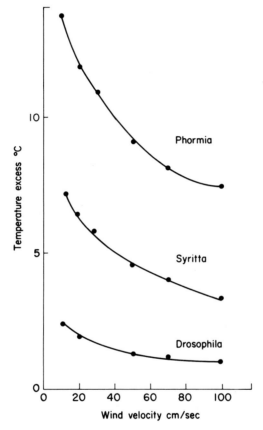

FIG. 2.   The effect of wind velocity on the temperature excess of large (*Phormia*), medium (*Syritta*), and small (*Drosophila*) flies exposed to a radiation of 1.5 cal/cm^2/min. Redrawn from Bursell (1964).

over small distances. Consequently, behavior, resulting in changes of orientation, has a profound influence (Parry, 1951).

C. CIRCADIAN RHYTHMS OF ACTIVITY

The burrowing habits, discussed above, are closely associated with circadian activity rhythms. In hot climates, many animals escape from the heat and drought of the daylight hours in their cool, dark retreats, from which they emerge during the night: in cold climates, poikilothermic animals tend to be day-active (Cloudsley-Thompson, 1961a,b). In the case of worms, wood lice, centipedes, and other rapidly transpiring animals, nocturnal habits are no doubt closely related to the need for water conservation. Physical factors of the environment are probably of greatest significance, in this respect, to animals living in hot, dry regions, where the climatic changes between day and night are most extreme (Cloudsley-Thompson and Chadwick, 1964; Cloudsley-Thompson, 1965). Many desert arthropods confine their activities to the hours of darkness when the temperature is low.

In a study of the ecology of sand dunes in Minnesota, L. N. Chapman *et al.* (1926) noticed that the population on the sand at night was entirely different from that of the daytime. Insects left the surface when its temperature neared 50°C to enter their burrows and daytime retreats. This type of ecological observation is extremely common and is a reflection of the importance of diurnal rhythms in temperature adaptive behavior (Cloudsley-Thompson, 1961a,b, 1962a).

The time of emergence of adult insects from their pupae may also be adjusted to the thermal demands of the environment, many temperature-sensitive insects emerging at dusk when conditions are most favorable. The subject has been investigated in some detail (for references, *vide* Cloudsley-Thompson, 1961b). Since the timing of such periodicity is usually controlled by changes in light intensity, it is not discussed here, except to point out that it may confer a number of ecological benefits, including thermal ones.

D. SEASONAL RHYTHMS OF ACTIVITY

Seasonal rhythms of activity are related to a great number of ecological factors and again are only partly thermoregulatory. The summer heat of the tropical desert and the winter cold nearer the poles is often passed in a state of diapause, discussed below (Section III,D).

Buxton (1924a) has remarked that some tenebrionid beetles, which are active in bright sunshine in Israel during the spring, shun the heat during the summer months and become crepuscular in habit. This observation has been extended by Bodenheimer (1934b, 1935). In most species which live as adults during the greater part of the year, there is a concentration of activity at noon in winter and at dawn and dusk in summer. Thus, the activity pattern of the ant, *Messor semirufus,* is modified by the seasonal environmental complex, especially temperature changes. In winter, activity is stopped by cool weather and in summer, by warmer temperatures. Although some individuals are active at all times of day, the peaks of activity fall during noon hours in winter, during the evening in spring, and during the entire night in summer (Bodenheimer and Klein, 1930).

According to Bodenheimer (1934b), the seasonal activity of nocturnal beetles is very different from that of day-active species. Of the latter, two-thirds of the individuals appear in Israel in spring with a minimum in summer. The nocturnal species, on the other hand, have their peak in summer with a minimum in December. Seasonal cycles in Hymenoptera, Diptera, Hemiptera, and Orthoptera have also been described by Bodenheimer (1935).

The autumnal migration to the South of the monarch butterfly, *Danaus plexippus,* and its northward movements in spring result in avoidance of the winter cold (Williams, 1930, 1938; Beall, 1941).

Seasonal rhythms of activity of the type mentioned above are generally less important in the ecology of invertebrate animals than are the seasonal reproductive cycles and seasonal quiescence or diapause discussed below (Section III,D).

III. Physiological Mechanisms

A. Temperature Regulation by Transpiration

1. *Annelida and Mollusca*

The body temperature of the earthworm, *Lumbricus terrestris,* after relatively short exposure to dry air, diverges increasingly from the wet-bulb thermometer reading. This is due to rapid desiccation of the surface of the body. Since the upper thermal death point of *L. terrestris* is relatively low (Table I), this means that earthworms are not adapted to long survival at ground level in sunlight, a fact which agrees well with observations on their behavior. Indeed, worms are not equipped to emerge from their burrows except when the soil surface is exceptionally cool and moist, and it is probable that the immediate ancestors of the Oligochaeta were already burrowing animals when they penetrated inland from the littoral zone, from the banks of estuaries, or from riparian swamps (Hogben and Kirk, 1944).

The water-binding power of molluskan slime is not an effective check to loss of water by evaporation. Consequently, the slug, *Arion ater,* at all times, and the snail, *Helix pomatia,* when fully extended, maintain a body temperature well below the dry-bulb temperature of the surrounding air (except when it is fully saturated) and slightly, if at all, above that of the wet-bulb thermometer. By withdrawing into its shell, however, the snail can appreciably reduce water loss by evaporation, and, in such circum-

TABLE I
THE UPPER LETHAL TEMPERATURES OF SOME TERRESTRIAL INVERTEBRATES

Species	Temperature (°C)	Duration of exposure	Authority
		Annelida	
Allolobophora terrestris	25.7	48 hr	Miles (1966)
Eisenia foetida	33.5	48 hr	Miles (1966)
Lumbricus terrestris	29.0	12 hr	Hogben and Kirk (1944)
		Mollusca	
Arion ater	31.0	1 hr	Hogben and Kirk (1944)
Helix pomatia	43.0	1 hr	Hogben and Kirk (1944)
		Isopoda	
Ligia oceanica	29.0	24 hr	Edney (1951a)
Oniscus asellus	31.5	24 hr	Edney (1951a)
Armadillidium vulgare	37.5	24 hr	Edney (1951a)
Armadillidium vulgare	41.6	30 min	Edney (1964a)
		Diplopoda	
Glomeris marginata	38.0	24 hr	Edney (1951a)
		Insecta	
Blatta orientalis	36.0	24 hr	Gunn and Notley (1936)
Periplaneta americana	37.0	24 hr	Cloudsley-Thompson (1962b)
Gryllulus domesticus	40.0	24 hr	Cloudsley-Thompson (1962b)
Labidura riparia	38.0	24 hr	Cloudsley-Thompson (1962b)
Pediculus humanus	38.0	24 hr	Mellanby (1934)
Pediculus humanus	46.5	1 hr	Mellanby (1934)
Culex fatigans	42.0	1 hr	Mellanby (1933)
Anopheles maculipennis	42.0	1 hr	Mellanby (1933)
Anopheles quadrimaculatus	41.0	13 min	Platt *et al.* (1957)
Auchmeromyia luteola (larvae)	43.5	1 hr	Garrett-Jones (1951)
Agriotes spp. (larvae)	36.0	indefinitely	Falconer (1945)
Tenebrio molitor (larvae)	42.0	24 hr	Mellanby (1958)
Tenebrio molitor (adults)	42.5	190 min	Bowler (1967)
Ocnera hispida	45.0	24 hr	Cloudsley-Thompson (1962b)
Xenopsylla cheopis (larvae)	37.0	24 hr	Mellanby (1932)
		Arachnida	
Buthotus minax	45.0	24 hr	Cloudsley-Thompson (1963a)
Leiurus quinquestriatus	47.0	24 hr	Cloudsley-Thompson (1962b)
Galeodes granti	50.0	24 hr	Cloudsley-Thompson (1962b)

stances, its body temperature approaches that of the surrounding air. It becomes identical with, and varies according to, the outside atmosphere, after formation of the epiphragm (Hogben and Kirk, 1944).

2. *Arthropoda*

Transpiration through the cuticle of terrestrial arthropods has been the subject of considerable attention (Edney, 1957). In species that possess an epicuticular layer of wax, which is relatively impermeable to water loss, evaporation is an insignificant factor, as compared with radiation and convection, in determining the equilibrium temperature in direct sunlight (Parry, 1951). Wood lice (Edney, 1951a,b), centipedes (Cloudsley-Thompson, 1956, 1959), millipedes (Cloudsley-Thompson, 1950; Edney, 1951a), and certain arachnids and insects, however, transpire water more rapidly. During short exposures, therefore, they can tolerate a higher temperature when the air is dry than when it is saturated. The upper lethal temperature of British wood lice in saturated air for 24 hours ranges from 37.5°C in *Armadillidium vulgare,* 36°C in *Porcellio scaber,* 31.5°C in *Oniscus asellus,* and 30.5°C in *Philoscia muscorum* to 29°C in *Ligia oceanica,* according to Edney (1951a). In air at 50% relative humidity, the lethal temperature is increased by 4.5° to 5.5°C for 15-minute exposures, but, during longer periods, the animals die from desiccation.

This helps to explain the fact that wood lice, although normally nocturnal, are sometimes to be seen in the open in direct sunlight. Edney (1952, 1953) measured temperature and relative humidity in the natural habitats of *P. scaber* and *L. oceanica* and concluded that the animals are compelled to come out into the open during the day when a combination of high temperature and high humidity causes their body temperatures to reach a dangerous level. Although the ambient air temperature may be even greater in the open, rapid transpiration causes a reduction in body temperature, after which the animals must retire to a moist microhabitat, where their water balance can be replenished. No differences in temperature depression between living and dead wood lice were found, indicating that no physiological control of evaporative water loss occurs (Edney, 1951b). Any increase in evaporation through movement of the living animals must therefore be negligible. On the other hand, Warburg (1965) found that the body temperature of *A. vulgare* decreases 2°-3°C each time the legs are moved.

Solomon (1937) found that although some adult earth mites, *Halotydeus destructor,* could survive at 38°C for as long as 2.5 minutes when exposed to this temperature for only 30 seconds and then removed to cooler surroundings (17°C), they nevertheless died within a few minutes. It is probable that irreversible damage had been done during the first 30 seconds of the longer exposure, but that the mites took 2.5 minutes to die. Nevertheless, survival was appreciably longer in dry than in saturated air, suggesting that some evaporative cooling took place.

Necheles (1924) found that, below 10°C, the temperature in the thorax of *Blatta orientalis* was maintained a little above the ambient air temperature by the heat of metabolism. Up to about 23°C, body temperature was effectively equal to the air temperature, and above 25°C, it depended upon the humidity of the air. In moist conditions, it was slightly above and in dry air, below the temperature of the air. At 30°C, the difference in dry air was about 3°C, and at 40°C it was about 5°C. Since the extremes of the environmental temperature range were thus moderated within the body—at any rate in dry air—Necheles concluded that the cockroach shows rudimentary thermoregulation. Some years later, Mellanby (1932) showed that a cockroach weighing 1 gm would have a surface area of 8 cm². If it kept its body temperature 5°C below an ambient air temperature of 45°C, it would absorb about 40 cal, which would evaporate 80 mg water, or 8% of its body weight. This figure is well within the 13% of body weight which Necheles found these insects capable of losing in 1 hour.

Bodenheimer (1929) obtained similar results with the desert locust *Schistocerca gregaria*. The body temperature of this insect at about 40°C was 3° or 4°C lower in dry air than in moist. Comparable results were also obtained by Koidsumi (1935) with the grasshopper, *Gastrimargus transversus*, at 30°C. As Gunn (1942) points out, it is worth noticing that in Koidsumi's data, the cuticle temperature is always lower than the internal body temperature. This must always be so in the steady state if heat exchange takes place mainly at the surface and not in the trachea. Presumably, therefore, 30°C was about the critical temperature at which the epicuticular lipoid layer of this insect becomes permeable (Wigglesworth, 1965), especially as the *Gastrimargus* cooled slightly more when dead than when alive. This was presumably due to the reduction of metabolic heat production in the dead grasshopper, but, of course, after death, cooling by tracheal ventilation would also have ceased. In any case, it seems questionable whether passive evaporation such as this constitutes thermoregulation in a biological sense. It is not really comparable with the active secretion of sweat and the dilatation of peripheral blood vessels which occur in mammals. Moreover, the lowering of body temperature is of only limited value to the insects. Desiccation probably kills more often than heat, and the locomotary behavior of insects is a far more efficient protection against high temperature than any lowering of body temperature by evaporation (G. S. Fraenkel and Gunn, 1961).

In some insects and arachnids, heat death is in no way related to desiccation. Indeed, excess moisture often adversely affects survival (Cloudsley-Thompson, 1962b). Mellanby (1932) found that in small insects such as fleas *Xenopsylla cheopis,* lice *Pediculus humanus,* and blowflies *Lucilia sericata,* the humidity of the air makes no difference to the lethal temperature when the duration of exposure does not exceed 1 hour. In larvae of *Tenebrio molitor,* humidity again has no influence in the case of small individuals—these die just below 42°C at all humidities. But larvae weighing over 100 mg can resist 43°C in dry air, since they are able to some extent to cool themselves by evaporation. As an insect becomes smaller, the ratio of volume to surface area becomes less, and, below a certain size, it can only appreciably lower its body temperature by evaporating a greater volume of water than it could afford to loose. Furthermore, the rate at which heat is taken up by the body is proportional to its surface area.

In experiments of longer duration, the greater saturation deficiency of dry air may result in some insect species dying from desiccation. For example, the cockroach, *Blatta orientalis,* withstands 37° to 39°C for 24 hours in moist air and only 34° to 36°C in dry air. Moist air is therefore more favorable than dry for long exposures, because, in dry air, death may result from desiccation even when the temperature itself is not fatal. Dry air is more favorable than moist in shorter exposures, since evaporation lowers the body temperature (Gunn and Notley, 1936).

In chinch bugs, Lygaeidae, survival at temperatures below about 50°C is favored by high humidity. At higher temperatures, survival is better at low humidity. Apparently, death below 48° to 50°C is due to desiccation and at higher temperatures to the effect of heat (Guthrie and Decker, 1954).

The survival of individual bees at high temperatures also depends on the duration of exposure and the relative humidity. At higher temperatures, bees survive short periods only and do best at low relative humidities because they can cool themselves more by evaporation. At somewhat lower temperatures, they can survive longer at high relative humidities, because desiccation is the limiting factor (Free and Spencer-Booth, 1962). In contrast, the temperature lethal to larvae of the Congo floor maggot, *Auchmeromyia luteola,* having completed the second molt, is defined within about 1°C (42.5° to 43.5°C) and does not appear to vary according to the relative humidity (Garrett-Jones, 1951). In desert beetles such as *Ocnera hispida* and *Pimelia grandis,* body water is retained so efficiently that the effect of humidity on the lethal temperature is not apparent (Cloudsley-Thompson, 1962b).

Evaporation dissipates relatively little of the heat generated by the wing muscles during flight in the desert locust *Schistocerca gregaria.* In dry air at 30°C, the temperature of the pterothorax above air temperature is reduced by less than 10%, or 0.5°C, by evaporation. Even at 40°C, the depression is only 20%, or 1.2°C, in dry air as compared with the temperature excess in moist air when no evaporation takes place. This is the highest temperature compatible with flight, and evaporation through the wax layers of the cuticle occurs only at temperatures well above this (Church, 1960a).

On the other hand, at high temperatures, the tenebrionid beetles, *Onymacris bicolor* and *O. multistriata,* ventilate the tracheae systems by rhythmic retractions and protractions of the head (Bolwig, 1957). This presumably results in some evaporative cooling. Again, the thoracic spiracles of the tsetse fly, *Glossina morsitans,* open synchronously in response to carbon dioxide or high temperature (Edney and Barrass, 1962). In slowly rising air temperatures, opening and closing of the spiracles commences at about 30°C, and full opening sets in between 39° and 41°C. As a result, there is a body temperature depression rising to 1.66°C at 45°C in dry air, which does not occur in moist air or when the spiracles are blocked. The lethal temperature for *G. morsitans* is 45°C for 5 minutes and 40°C for 1 hour (Jack, 1939), so the mechanism may have survival value in this instance. Some beetles ventilate the subelytral cavity, thereby increasing evaporative heat loss (see Section II,B,2,a). Rapid tongue folding and unfolding by honeybees not only concentrates the nectar, but also assists in evaporative cooling (Lindauer, 1955).

The adaptations of terrestrial arthropods to humid heat have been reviewed by Flemister (1964) and to dry heat by Cloudsley-Thompson (1964a). In general, evaporative cooling is of but slight importance to forms that possess an impervious integument.

B. Metabolic Heat Gain in Insects

1. *Solitary Insects*

Metabolic heat may be considerable in poikilotherms, especially in the flight muscles during activity. Some insects show warming-up movements, and flutter their wings before flight. For example, the butterfly, *Vanessa* sp., warmed up for more than 6 minutes at 11°C, 1.5 minutes at 23°C, 18 seconds at 34°C, and not at all at 37°C (Dotterweich, 1928). The muscle temperature of this butterfly is 35°C at takeoff and 37°C during flight. Sotavolta (1954) found that thoracic body temperatures more than 20°C above ambient air temperature occur in Lepidoptera, Hymenoptera, and Coleoptera. Heat produced by the saturniid moth, *Samia cecropia,* is proportional to muscular activity and is greater when the wings are vibrated than when they are fluttered. The ability to produce metabolic heat is greater in male than in female moths, and decreases with age (Oosthuizen, 1939).

As already mentioned, evaporation dissipates relatively little heat generated by the wing muscles during flight in *Schistocerca gregaria* (Church, 1960a), and the coats of hair on bumblebees, hawk moths, and noctuid moths are excellent insulators against convective heat loss. At normal flying speeds, they increase the temperature excess by 50 to 100%, or more and in a large hawk moth, probably by at least 8° or 9°C (Church, 1960b). The reason why Digby (1955) did not obtain any difference between pubescent and hairless insects in this respect is probably due to the fact that he worked only at low wind speeds (50 cm/sec).

Krogh and Zeuthen (1941) investigated the mechanism of flight preparation in various insects and showed that in *Vanessa atlanta,* moths, and bumblebees, the temperature of the wing muscles is usually above 30°C. A good flier, such as *V. atlanta,* can take to flight when the thoracic body temperature is as low as 20°C, but a high rate of flight is only achieved when this temperature exceeds 35°C. Poor fliers, such as the beetle *Geotrupes stercorarius,* on the other hand, are incapable of flight unless the temperature of their wing muscles exceeds 32°C.

More recently, Adams and Heath (1964) showed that the sphinx moth *Celeria lineata* maintains a mean thoracic temperature of 38°C when the ambient air temperature is 16° to 27°C. This insect does not take off voluntarily when its body temperature is below 32°C, although it is capable of strong flight at thoracic temperatures as low as 25°C. The preflight warm-up is therefore not strictly necessary, but ensures that the moth sets off at the peak of efficiency. The maximal body temperature tolerated voluntarily is 37.7°C. The ability to begin and cease flight activity fairly abruptly results in the economy of energy and compensates in part for small size and an unfavorable surface-to-volume ratio of the moth. That is to say, it requires far less energy than would be necessary to maintain a constant high thoracic temperature. Yet, in flight, the thermal efficiency of the moth is comparable with that of a bird. The cost of heat production to maintain a relatively constant thoracic temperature is high in large moths, but it is only a fraction of the cost of flight. Heath and Adams (1967) found that *Celerio lineata* warms up at a rate of 4.06°C/min and *Rothschildia jacobae* at 2.5°C/min, but abdominal temperatures rise only 2°–3°C during activity. The oxygen consumption of torpid sphinx moths increases by a factor of 2.27 when the ambient temperature is raised from 26° to 36°C. When thoracic temperature is being regulated, oxygen consumption increases from a mean of about 400 μl/gm min at 31°C to about 650 μl/gm min at 26°C. The giant silk moth *R. jacobae* regulates its thoracic temperature during activity to about 32°–36°C at ambient temperatures of 17°–29°C. Heat loss from large moths is offset by increased metabolism during periods of activity, at which time these insects are endothermal like birds and mammals. They differ, however, in two fundamental features: in the duration of the period of regulation and in the range of variation in body temperature that is tolerated.

The difference between these results and those of Church (1960a), who found that *Locusta migratoria* generates a body temperature excess of 6°C over an 11°C range of ambient temperature during flight, may be related to the biology of the species. Nocturnal moths have no radiant heat sources and must rely entirely on metabolic heat to produce the high body temperature required for activity, while diurnal locusts can also regulate their body temperatures by means of behavioral responses to radiant heat sources (Heath and Adams, 1965).

2. *Social Insects*

Metabolic heat is a much more important factor in temperature regulation in social than in solitary insects (Uvarov, 1931; Himmer, 1932; Allee *et al.,* 1949). In winter, most colonial Hymenoptera cluster together and the temperature of the colony is thereby kept well above the outside air temperature. If this falls to 8°–10°C, bees show great uneasiness. The outer bees are more active than those inside the cluster and frequently change places with them. Heat is conserved by the insulation of the hive and sometimes by closing its entrance (Lindauer, 1954). W. Dunham (1931) found a difference of only 0.7°C between maximal and minimal temperatures in the brood area of a honeybee hive throughout a 24-hour period, during which the temperature outside the hive varied through a range of 17°C.

The number of bees in a group is important to survival: a large number conserves heat and survives better below 25°C; a smaller number, well dispersed, survives better above 40°C. Such groups can maintain a 4°C positive differential at lower temperatures, but the difference decreases with a rise in ambient temperature. At the same time, the amount of food consumed per bee decreases with increasing temperature, and water consumption increases (Free and Spencer-Booth, 1958).

To a lesser extent, bumblebees are also able to control microclimatic conditions within their nests. Nielsen (1938) compared the temperature in an empty nesting box with that in a nearby box in which bees had made their nest, and with the open air. In July, when the nest was fully occupied, the bumblebees produced about 10°C excess temperature and, in the evening, as much as 13°C. This excess gradually diminished toward the end of August as the bees died off, and, when there were none left, it fell to less than 1°C.

Temperature regulation occurs, too, in the nests of social wasps (Himmer, 1932; Weyrauch, 1936), but the temperature of the brood and adults is too low to influence nest temperature in *Polistes gallica,* according to Steiner (1930b). In general, the temperature of wasp nests is less uniform than that of the nests of bees; and ants' nests show considerable temperature fluctuation (Himmer, 1932). The temperature within a termite mound may be 18° to 20°C higher in an occupied, than in an unoccupied region (Prosser, 1961). Although temperatures in the mounds of the Australian *Eutermes exitcosus* are not constant, the nursery temperature exhibits less variation than that of other portions and is continuously higher than that of the air, soil, and other parts of the mound (Holdaway and Gray, 1948).

The temperature within the bivouac or temporary nests of army ants, *Eciton* spp., is higher than that of the surrounding air (Schneirla *et al.,* 1954). These nests are formed wholly by the ants' own bodies clustered together and generally hang to the ground from an overhead support, such as a fallen branch or log. Control of intrabivouac temperature, through the conservation or release of excess heat, buffers the brood against external temperature fluctuations and is affected to a marked extent by the activity of the workers in the bivouac interior and in its wall. In the case of *Eciton hamatum,* both nomadic and stationary bivouacs, though following ambient temperature patterns, remain at least 1° to 2°C above environmental temperatures and exhibit reduced fluctuation (Jackson, 1957). Microclimatic control occurs to an even greater extent in the nest of nonnomadic ants. *Formica rufa* and allied species are known to generate heat physiologically (Raignier, 1948), and more or less precise microclimatic control is known for other species with permanent nests (Steiner, 1926, 1929; Kato, 1939; Stahel and Geijskes, 1940).

In his study of the thermal economy of the wood ant, *Formica rufa,* Raignier (1948) found that a relatively consistent temperature of 23° to 30°C was maintained by means of physiological heat and insolation. The nest temperature on dry, cool nights often showed a rise of 0.5° to 5.7°C on account of the return to the nest of large numbers of ants. During the night, and after showers, condensation in the form of mist formed a screen which stopped the loss of heat by radiation.

Heusner and Stussi (1964) measured the oxygen consumption of individual bees by means of a microrespirator, the oxygen supply of which was produced by the electrolysis of a saturated solution of copper sulfate. Reduction in the volume of oxygen in the respiratory chamber broke an electrical contact which connected through a relay to the electrolysis chamber. The amount of oxygen required to remake the contact was therefore proportional to the amount of electricity consumed. In this way, it was found that, during the day, even individual bees showed thermoregulatory metabolic heat production at temperatures below that of the hive (35°C). The insects also exhibited a diurnal rhythm, however, and at night they were truly poikilothermic and showed no compensation for environmental temperature changes (Fig. 3). Allowing for differences in weight and temperature, the metabolism of a bee at 35°C is of the same order as that of the basal metabolism of homeotherms.

Finally, mention should be made of the interesting suggestion of Luscher (1951) that the "fungus gardens," cultivated by *Macrotermes bellicosus* and other termite species, may have the primary function, not of providing

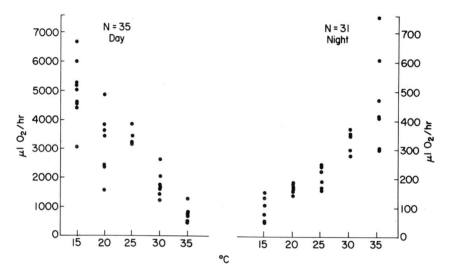

Fig. 3. Relation between oxygen consumption and ambient temperature in individual honeybees (*Apis mellifera*) during the day and at night. Each point represents the value for a single bee. N = number of bees. Redrawn from Heusner and Stussi (1964).

a source of food, as was previously thought to be the case, but, through bacterial fermentation, of maintaining a high constant temperature of about 30°C in the nest cavity.

C. Ability to Withstand High Temperatures

In general, soft-skinned, rapidly transpiring animals cannot withstand high body temperatures and die from desiccation before the effects of heat become apparent (see Section III,A,2). Their lethal temperatures under hot, moist conditions are usually low (Table I). On the other hand, insects and arachnids that inhabit warm environments are normally adapted to develop at higher temperatures than those from colder regions (Bertram,

1935). At the same time, the ability to survive exposure to extreme temperatures is related to the environment of the species (Andrewartha and Birch,
1954).

For example, nymphs of the firebrat, *Thermobia domestica,* which normally inhabit hot places like the hobs of bakers' ovens, may live indefinitely
at temperatures as high as 40°C (Sweetman, 1938), whereas those of
the related silverfish, *Lepisma saccharina,* which live in a cooler environment, are unable to withstand temperature above 36°C (Sweetman, 1939).
The distribution of the dipterous fauna of marine sand dunes in Sweden
has been shown to depend on the thermal relations of the species (Ardo,
1957). The wasp, *Bembex* sp., succumbs rapidly to temperatures above
42°C, but its wingless parasite, *Dasymutilla bioculata,* which must spend
much time on the hot sand, can withstand more than 10°C higher (L. N.
Chapman *et al.,* 1926). The hygrophilous grasshopper, *Aiolopus thalaninus,* of Egypt is able to resist rising temperatures, up to 45°C, without
any apparent effect on its activity, and *Sphingonotus carinatus* can withstand temperatures up to 41°C (Hafez and Ibrahim, 1964).

Ability to withstand high temperatures is characteristic of the invertebrate
inhabitants of hot deserts (Cloudsley-Thompson, 1964a, 1965; Cloudsley-
Thompson and Chadwick, 1964; Edney, 1967). For example, the lethal
temperature of the scorpion, *Leiurus quinquestriatus,* for a 24-hour exposure
at a relative humidity of less than 10%, has been estimated at 47°C
(Cloudsley-Thompson, 1962b). That of *Buthotus minax,* under similar conditions is 45°C, and it is much more sharply defined. In these animals,
lethal temperatures, like water relations, appear to be correlated with habitat and distribution (Cloudsley-Thompson, 1963a).

The lethal effects of heat on honeybees, *Apis mellifera,* are to some
extent influenced by diet. Thus, survival at 32°C after 12-hour exposure
was 100% for bees fed on a 30% solution of honey, 81% for bees given
only water, and 48% for controls that had neither food nor water (Lensky,
1964b). In contrast, the water content of the hemolymph of insects does
not appear to affect their thermal death point, provided, of course, that
death does not occur from desiccation. Mellanby (1958) found that *Tenebrio molitor* larvae, having approximately 42% of water from a culture
of bran, had the same lethal temperature as mealworms provided with
water and having only 25% dry matter and 75% water in their bodies.
Both acclimatized equally rapidly to higher or lower temperatures. Bowler
(1967), however, observed a dramatic fall in the ability of young beetles,
Tenebrio molitor, to tolerate exposure to 42.5°C in dry air. Mean survival
times fell from 190 minutes on the day of eclosion to 120 minutes after
five days. He suggested that this decline might represent a loss of high
pupal tolerance which is carried over into the imago, and that it may

be a feature of all holometabolous insects. Burnett (1957) similarly found a progressive and rapid loss of resistance to cold in teneral tsetse flies, *Glossina morsitans.* For example, at an age of 7 days, 42% survived exposure to 2.5°C, whereas at 10 days of age only 37% survived, and at 14 days all died. Similar effects are found in mosquitoes, whose temperature relations have been reviewed by Clements (1963).

A fall, with age, in tolerance to high temperatures has been observed in the chalcid *Dalhbominus fuscipennis.* In wasps acclimated to 17°, 23°, and 29°C, the time of survival at 42°C fell from 210 minutes at an age of 15 hours to 62 minutes at an age of 4 days. Wasps acclimated at 29°C showed the greatest loss of temperature tolerance, which was attributed to their lower content of body water (Baldwin, 1954). Bowler (1967) and Bowler and Hollingsworth (1966) obtained similar results with *Drosophila subobscura.* They suggested that a decline, with increased age, in the time of survival may be common to all endopterygote insects. If this is so, adult age should always be considered when evaluating the results of survival tests.

Insects may be killed by high temperatures, directly by heat, and indirectly by desiccation. A third factor, starvation, may sometimes also cause death at high temperatures and affect the thermal death point (Mellanby, 1934). For example, unfed lice, *Pediculus humanus,* died in moist air within 24 hours at temperatures lower than those fatal to fed larvae. Desiccation was not the cause of death: at high temperatures their rate of metabolism had been increased and their food reserves were insufficient to last them over a period as long as 24 hours. A similar observation was made with mosquitoes, *Culex fatigans.* The actual mechanism of heat death is discussed below (Section III,F,2,a).

D. Diapause, Estivation, and Hibernation

Many animals are able to exist in inconstant environments that would otherwise be unfavorable for permanent habitation, because their life cycle includes a dormant resting phase, or diapause. The physiology of diapause has been the subject of much research (Andrewartha, 1952; Andrewartha and Birch, 1954; Lees, 1955; Wigglesworth, 1965). It is usually characterized by temporary failure of development, reduced metabolism, and enhanced resistance to heat and cold. Only its thermal aspects will be considered in this chapter.

In Europe, many species of earthworm, such as *Allolobophora longa* and *Eisenia foetida,* estivate during the summer months. Each animal hollows out a small chamber deep down in the soil, curls up in a knotted ball, and surrounds itself with mucus which lines the chamber as it dries. The onset of estivation is associated with low soil humidity, because it is possible to prevent it by keeping worms in a humid atmosphere. At the same time, cyclical neurosecretory processes are probably involved (Michon, 1949). Although related primarily to low humidity, estivation obviously plays an important part in enabling earthworms to avoid high summer temperatures.

Snails also estivate, and this is especially important in desert and semiarid places, again primarily in relation to drought (Cloudsley-Thompson and Chadwick, 1964). During estivation, the mouth of the shell is closed by a thick diaphragm, which reduces water loss by evaporation. Desert snails have been known to remain in such a state of suspended animation for several years, until dormancy was broken by heavy rain.

Diapause is particularly widespread among desert arthropods; Tombes (1965) states that estivation has been recorded in 37 insect species, representing 5 major orders, most of which occur in arid, or semiarid regions.

It has often been said that the fauna of desert regions estivates during the summer, because few animals can be seen (Buxton, 1923). On the other hand, Omer-Cooper (1948) claimed that this apparent state of affairs is due to the seasonal appearance of a vernal rain fauna in regions with seasonal precipitation, and that, in a true desert, no general cessation of activity takes place. Although the larvae of *Polypedilum vanderplanki*, which can tolerate extreme temperatures in a state of desiccation (Hinton, 1960), are not in diapause, this form of suspended animation is uncommon and is primarily a response to the absence of water. In fact, the existence of estivation, in the form of temperature-induced quiescence without diapause, has not been established.

The diapause stage in the life cycle is characteristically a resistant one. Eggs of the Australian grasshopper, *Austroicetes cruciata,* for example, are able to withstand heat and desiccation that would quickly kill the active stages, and eggs firmly in diapause are far more resistant than eggs that have completed, or are not yet in, that phase of development (Birch, 1942). In this species, diapause ensures that the active stages are present only in that season of the year favorable to their development and survival. The hot, dry summer is spent as a diapausing egg, which is remarkably resistant to heat and water loss.

Indeed, diapause is primarily an adaptation to drought, rather than to high temperature. According to de Wilde (1962), experiments show that high temperatures tend to avert diapause in "long-day" insects although they may promote diapause in "short-term" insects. The same argument may perhaps apply to diapause among arctic insects and spiders in winter, when all available water is frozen. Even so, the animals that show the phenomenon of cold-hardiness (described in Section III,E), tolerate supercooling or freezing only in diapause.

E. Cold-hardiness, Supercooling, and Freezing

Terrestrial invertebrate animals of arctic regions often exhibit cold-hardiness as a form of acclimatization to winter conditions. Instances have been cited among pulmonate mollusks, insects, and arachnids. In contrast, few invertebrates of temperate climates can survive exposure to the severe cold that is experienced annually by arctic forms. As Kozhanchikov (1938) recognized, insects can be divided into three groups by their responses to low temperatures: those that cannot survive exposure to cold, those that become quiescent and reassume normal activity as soon as they are warmer, and the diapause stages of forms that hibernate in this condition.

Cold adaptation in the growing season, discussed in Section III,F, contrasts with tolerance of very low temperatures in winter. The latter phenomenon is caused by the slowing down of essential functions to a very low level, and thereby, to some extent, avoiding intracellular ice formation (Downes, 1965).

1. *Supercooling*

Many insects avoid freezing by supercooling, for pure water in a capillary tube or in the tissues of an insect may not freeze until temperatures well below 0°C have been reached. Cloud droplets are common at —20°C and have been observed as water clouds at —35°C. Very pure water in droplets of only a few microns in diameter has been supercooled in the laboratory to temperatures as low as —40°C (Mason, 1956).

The ability of insects to survive temperatures below freezing, through the phenomenon of supercooling, has been known since 1899, when Bachmetjew first investigated the body temperature of *Saturnia pyri* exposed to an air temperature of —13.5°C. The temperature of the insect dropped steadily to —9°C, rose suddenly to about —1.5°C, owing to the liberation of the latent heat of freezing, and then began to fall again. Similar temperature curves have been obtained by other workers such as Siegler (1946). Cold-hardiness often increases during the winter in hibernating insects such as grasshoppers, *Chortophaga* sp., and moths, *Isia isabella* and *Diacrisia virginiea* (Bodine, 1921; Payne, 1927b). Insects that supercool to temperatures below —40°C have all been found to have low freezing points because of high solute concentrations. Thus, Salt (1959a) reported that supercooling of the Canadian hymenopteran, *Bracon cephi,* ranged from —26° to —46°C, and varied in direct proportion to the solute concentration (Fig. 4). Glycerol, which not only lowers the freezing point, but also increases supercooling by at least an equivalent amount, was the most prevalent solute. At the same time, since viscosity increases with falling temperature, nucleation is also inhibited.

The degree of cold-hardiness, as measured by the degree of supercooling, often shows a close correlation with the amount of water present in the tissues (for references, *vide* Andrewartha and Birch, 1954). Thus, many insects preparing for diapause become dehydrated even in moist, cool conditions when there is plenty of food present (Bodine, 1923; Payne, 1926a,b; Salt, 1936; Kozhanchikov, 1938; Ditman *et al.,* 1943). There are, however, a number of exceptions, such as the pyralid flour moth, *Anagasta (Ephestia) kühniella,* the water content of whose larvae shows no change as they pass into the prepupal stage, although the supercooling point decreases from —6° to —21°C (Salt, 1936).

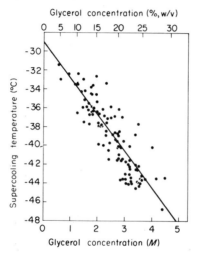

FIG. 4. Relationship between supercooling temperatures and glycerol concentrations in 109 *Bracon cephi* larvae of variable-cold hardiness. From Salt (1959a).

Examples of insects that become dehydrated before diapause are Colorado potato beetles, *Leptinotarsa decemlineata,* the moth, *Diacrisia virginica,* and the oak borer, *Dendroides canadensis.* According to Payne (1927a), these all show seasonal trends in dehydration and cold-hardiness. Payne dehydrated the beetle, *Popilla japonica,* to half its weight, and found a corresponding increase in cold-hardiness. In contrast, Salt (1936) found that adult *Leptocoris* sp. could be desiccated, until they had lost 20% of their weight, without effect upon the supercooling point and that, although the water content of *A. kühniella* larvae, prepupae, and pupae is constant, their supercooling points are —5.8°C, —8.0°C, and —21°C, respectively.

In insects susceptable to freezing, water loss lowers supercooling points to some extent by concentrating solutes, but the amount is usually negligible (Salt, 1956). In any case, most insects cannot tolerate very high electrolytic concentrations, and no cases are known in which insects prepare for hibernation by dehydrating to the extent of lowering their freezing points by several degrees. The water content of hibernating insects is usually lower than in other stages of development because of the decrease in secretory processes and gut evacuation, but this does not allow better survival after freezing. Indeed, in some instances, the reverse may occur (Salt, 1961b).

The supercooling and freezing points of last instar larvae of *A. kühniella* were highest in larvae stored at 20°C and were gradually lowered after storage at 6°, 0°, and —6°C. Depression of supercooling points were, however, much larger than those of freezing points, and, concurrent with this increase in the amount of supercooling, an increase in the concentrations of several hemolymph solutes was found. Hemolymph concentrations could be increased by exposure to anoxia for 12 or 24 hours, which resulted in increased supercooling. Glycerol accounted for only a part of the supercooling of the larvae (Sømme, 1966).

The effects of glycerol on cold-hardiness in insects have been investigated by Sømme (1964), who demonstrated seasonal changes in the concentration of this polyhydric alcohol in the overwintering stages of ten species. In one case, the presence of sorbitol was also observed, and the eggs of two other species contained another polyhydric alcohol, probably mannitol. An increase in glycerol during the fall was observed in insect eggs at temperatures ranging from —5° to 20°C, and the concentration did not diminish in any species as long as it was in diapause. After diapause was broken, however, glycerol was lost in all species, even at temperatures as low as —5°C. An increase in concentration was never found in post-diapause insects.

Although there is no strict correlation between glycerol and freezing tolerance (Sømme, 1965a), the accumulation of glycerol in larvae of the ermine moth, *Hyponomeuta evonymellus,* and of the tortricid, *Lasypeyresia strobilella,* is clearly related to lowered supercooling points during the fall. Moreover, eggs of the tortricid, *Acrolita naevana,* from a location in eastern Norway, accumulated more glycerol than did eggs from a region with a milder climate in western Norway, thus suggesting differences in adaptation to low temperature. Again, overwintering eggs of the European red mite, *Panonychus ulmi,* accumulate sorbitol during the fall, which apparently causes a depression of the supercooling point (Sømme, 1965b). Glycerol accumulates in the tissues of ants, *Camponotus pennsilvanicus,* cooled to 0°–5°C over a period of 6 days (Dubach *et al.,* 1959).

It may therefore be concluded that factors increasing supercooling in insects are not obvious, except for the synthesis of protective solutes before hibernation. These depress the freezing point and the supercooling point by at least an equal amount and sometimes more. The physiology of glycerol, sorbitol, and other cryoprotective compounds has been reviewed by Umminger (1968), who gives detailed references. In several species, however, it has been shown that the synthesis of glycerol in the fall has little effect upon supercooling (Salt, 1964).

Indeed, other factors may be more important. The effects of food and other foreign material in larvae of *A. kühniella* and *Agrotis* sp. have been investigated by Salt (1953), who found that these insects go through a cycle of hardiness which corresponds to their feeding periods. They are much less hardy when food is in the gut. The inoculation of small quantities of plant materials or inert substances, such as glass or cork, into the hemocele were all found to inhibit supercooling. Whereas earlier workers, such as Payne, thought that the hardiness of tissues could be altered by changes in the water content or the concentration of solutions present, Salt believes the hardiness of the tissues to be unchangeable. The process of gradual hardening is unproven, and hardiness of the whole insect is determined by the presence of foreign bodies. The clue to the problem of supercooling is therefore most likely to be found by an investigation of biological nucleating agents (Salt, 1964).

2. *Freezing Tolerance*

The ability of some insects, especially lepidopterous larvae, to withstand being frozen to the point of brittleness has been known for over 200 years. The earlier literature is reviewed by, among others, A. V. Smith (1958), Salt (1961b), and Wigglesworth (1965). Nevertheless, until recently, many entomologists assumed that insects were killed if ice formed within their tissues and that tolerance of low temperature always depended upon supercooling. It is now well established, however, that insects of several genera can survive, even when their body fluids have been supercooled before freezing. For example, larvae of the corn borer, *Pyraustia nubilis,* collected during winter and early spring, survived supercooling to $-29°C$ and subsequent freezing to the same temperature (Barnes and Hodson, 1956, 1957). Similar results have been obtained in northern Japan with hibernating prepupae of the moth, *Monema flavescens,* which survive atmospheric temperatures of $-20°$ to $-30°C$ during the winter. Under laboratory conditions, these become supercooled to temperatures as low as $-20°C$, below which freezing began (Asahina *et al.,* 1954).

Glycerol accumulates in many insects during the winter, as mentioned above, but there is no correlation between this and freezing tolerance. Thus some insects, like the gallflies, *Euura nodis* and *Eurosta solidaginis,* which contain 15% or more glycerol, are killed by freezing, while others that contain less than 3% are unharmed (Sømme, 1964). On the other hand, *Antheraea polyphemus* has a high glycerol content and is able to withstand freezing (Salt, 1957). Indeed, seasonal changes in glycerol content seem to follow a similar pattern in all diapausing insects so far investigated. Thus glycerol alone cannot protect insects against freezing damage, although it increases cold-hardiness to some extent by depressing the supercooling point. Moreover, there is a remarkable uniformity in the melting points of the fats of insect tissues, whether the insects show cold-hardiness or not (Salt, 1956).

The various theories of freezing tolerance and freezing injury have been reviewed by Salt (1961b) and earlier ideas, by Uvarov (1931), so they will not be discussed in detail here. Briefly they can be summarized as follows.

According to the *bound water theory,* bound water is considered to be oriented as layers of hydrogen and hydroxyl ions, which are alternately adsorbed on the colloid miscelles, and hence are compressible (Robinson, 1927, 1928). Therefore, when the free water freezes, there is more space for expansion without causing injury. This explanation could only hold, however, if water binding occurs simultaneously with freezing. Moreover, the space would have to remain empty in order to be available for future expansion when the free water freezes (Salt, 1961b). This theory has also been criticized by Andrewartha and Birch (1954), who claim that bound water is merely supercooled water.

The *electrolyte concentration theory* suggests that if the electrolyte concentration of a cell or tissue is increased, it eventually becomes lethal, and this is what occurs on freezing.

According to the *mechanical theory,* injury is caused by the stresses and strains imposed by ice formation. When fully hydrated larvae of the Nigerian chironomid, *Polypedilum vanderplanki,* are frozen, they recover temporarily, but fail to complete their development, owing to breakdown of the fat body. Since they can tolerate complete dehydration, and hence extreme electrolyte concentration, in the later stages of this process, it cannot be assumed that this is the cause of the freezing damage in these experiments. It is equally unlikely that the damage is caused by the mechanical effect of ice formation. In fact, the damage caused by freezing is apparently identical with that caused by too rapid drying. This suggests that water is being lost from the cells so rapidly that the stresses set up cause the disruption of protoplasmic bonds (Leader, 1962).

The *site-of-freezing theory* maintains that intracellular freezing is fatal, whereas extracellular freezing is comparatively innocuous. The ultimate cause of injury is not explained, but the suggestion is more compatible with the theory of mechanical freezing injury than with the electrolyte concentration theory. Studies on the isolated tissues and organs of *Monema flavescens* suggested that ice crystals were extracellular in prepupae that subsequently revived, and that intracellular crystallization in the heart resulted in disruption of that organ (Asahina *et al.*, 1954). On the other hand, Salt (1961a) produced extracellular freezing in the larvae of the wheat stem sawfly, *Cephus cinctus*, at $-2.5°C$. Slow further cooling to $-10°$, $-15°$, or $-20°C$ was then used to cause intracellular freezing. Comparison of the two types of freezing were therefore possible at the same temperatures. The level of activity after thawing was then used as a criterion of injury, and it was found that intracellular freezing was more harmful at $-15°$ and $-20°C$, but not at $-10°C$, above which injuries decreased to insignificance. Although larvae frozen extracellularly held an initial advantage over those frozen intracellularly, survivors of the latter group retained their vitality better, probably because they lost weight more slowly. Again, cells of the fat body of *Eurostia solidagenis* larvae are very large, yet they can withstand intracellular freezing many times (Salt, 1959b).

Scholander *et al.* (1953a) found that chironomid larvae in Alaska, which, under natural conditions, survive in frozen mud or ice at temperatures as low as $-40°C$ for many months at a time, can, in the laboratory, withstand repeated freezing and thawing to and from $-16°C$. The amount of ice present was determined by a microflotation method, and was found to be such that the unfrozen water remained approximately inversely proportional to the temperature below $0°C$. At $-10°C$, some 90% of all the water was frozen, but the unfrozen water was not held in a supercooled state. A little free water was present even at $-35°C$, the lowest temperature investigated, and respiration continued down to $-26°C$, the lowest temperature at which it could be measured.

If the surface of an insect is dry when it is exposed to falling temperatures, its tissues will supercool until the formation of an ice crystal in its body liquids causes freezing. Such endogenous freezing is termed nucleative. In contrast, an insect in external contact with ice or freezing water may freeze as a result of inoculation of its body liquids by the external ice. Such exogenous freezing is termed inoculative. Two hypotheses have been proposed to account for delayed inoculative freezing, but neither is wholly satisfactory. The first postulates that the outer extremities of the pathways, through the epicuticle, are hydrophobic and contain air which temporarily separates contact moisture from pore liquids. After freezing of the contact moisture, a vapor pressure differential results in a flow of vapor outwards. This freezes on the ice and builds up on its inner surface until the ice front touches liquid in a space large enough to allow freezing.

This hypothesis assumes the existence of at least one pathway large enough to permit the penetration of ice without hindrance: the second assumes that no such unrestricted pathways are present. Differences in chemical potential between the ice and the liquid in the pore canals would then cause the latter to move outwards to the contracting ice layer and accrete on its inner surface. The motive force would have to be great enough to dilate the pathways and thus allow penetration of ice into the interior of the body (Salt, 1963).

With regard to endogenous freezing, Salt (1966a,b,c) has recently proved that the general temperature range within which an insect nucleates is determined by intrinsic factors—nucleating agents and body water—whereas

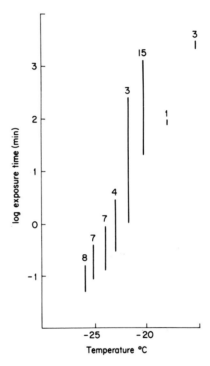

Fig. 5.   The duration of exposure required to freeze 50% of the larvae of *Cephus cinctus* at different temperatures. The range of values obtained in different experiments is shown by vertical lines; the number of experiments carried out at each temperature is given at the top of each line. Redrawn from Bursell (1964).

the specific freezing temperature within this range is determined by extrinsic factors, such as the cooling pattern and the element of chance that attends nucleation.

The probability of nucleation is strongly temperature-dependent, and time plays a dominant role (Fig. 5), because nucleation depends upon chance favorable molecular orientations (Salt, 1958). No substance has yet been identified as the primary nucleating agent of an insect, but a variety of tissue substances possess this potentiality, and those in the hemolymph are most likely to initiate freezing. In feeding insects, foreign nucleating agents in the digestive tract are usually more efficient than are indigenous agents (Salt, 1966a). Indeed, it can be assumed that gut contents are the source of ice nucleation in feeding insects, while residual food in the gut is the main source in nonfeeding forms. When freezing is confined to tissues with no digestive elements, such as excised appendages, preferred nucleation sites have been observed, but the structures involved have not been identified. The fact that hemolymph and intracellular matter are improbable as functional nucleating sites greatly reduces the anatomical possibilities available (Salt, 1968).

The question as to why some insects are tolerant of freezing, while others are killed, is clearly of fundamental importance, but it has not yet been answered. As the temperature is lowered below freezing point, however, the molecular arrangement of water becomes more like that of ice. Aggregations of molecules are produced in great numbers, but, because of the low temperature, are denied time to grow. The viscosity also increases so that vitrification, rather than freezing in the usual sense of the word, takes place (Salt, 1961a). Glycerol may assist in this to some extent and it may be that survival after freezing depends upon vitrification.

F. Acclimation to Heat and Cold

Characteristic of many invertebrates is the ability to acclimate—often surprisingly rapidly—to heat and cold. The lethal temperature of a species is not absolute, therefore, but depends upon the past thermal history of each particular organism. Consequently, figures for lethal temperature are usually not significant unless the previous temperature of acclimation is also given. Moreover, acclimation influences not only the upper and lower incipient lethal temperatures, but also the duration of exposure to a lethal temperature that an animal can withstand (Andrewartha and Birch, 1954; McWhinnie, 1967). There is also variation between species, in the length of time taken to acclimate to a particular temperature, and variation within a species, in the time taken to acclimate to different temperatures. In general, the lower the acclimating temperature, the longer the process of acclimation takes.

Another complication lies in deciding the criteria to be used in assessing the results of experiments. There are several complicating factors: determining whether the times of exposure to lethal temperatures (Fig. 6) are constant or changing; determining the percentage of animals killed (LT_{50}—the temperature at which 50% of the experimental animals die within a specified period is a usual figure); or determining whether an animal is actually dead. For this reason, the figures given in Table I should be regarded as approximate only.

Metabolic adaptations of poikilotherms to temperature differences occur through shifts of the metabolism–temperature curve (to the left in the cold and to the right in heat) or by changes in the slope of the metabolism–temperature curve (that is, in Q_{10}) (Prosser, 1955). Terrestrial animals show very much less metabolic adaptation than do aquatic animals (see Chapter 1). Many insects and arachnids, for example, merely exhibit diminished metabolism as the temperature falls, and enter a dormant state in

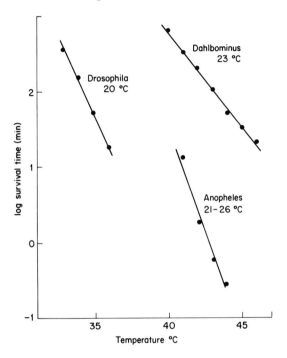

Fig. 6.   The relation between survival time and temperature in three species of insect reared at temperatures between 20° and 26°C and tested at high relative humidity. Redrawn from Bursell (1964).

winter (Scholander *et al.*, 1953b). When the regression of metabolism with body size is taken into account, however, some metabolic adaptation may may be demonstrated (Rao and Bullock, 1954). The Q_{10} for metabolism tends to be less for cold-adapted than for warm-adapted animals. It has also been found by G. A. Edwards (1946) that arthropods not only show sex differences in oxygen consumption, but that smaller individuals respond to temperature changes more markedly than do larger animals of the same species. Whether such slight metabolic adaptations have much ecological significance, however, is perhaps doubtful.

The general effect of reduced temperature is to decrease the rates of all metabolic activities. An exception is the temporary stimulation of the central nervous system (Kerkut and Taylor, 1956, 1958), resulting in locomotory activity in slugs (Dainton, 1943, 1954), millipedes (Cloudsley-Thompson, 1951a,b), and other arthropods. This probably operates over a limited temperature range and is associated with nocturnal activity. It may also accentuate the differences between the rates of different metabolic activities. Certain enzyme systems and metabolic pathways may even be blocked or changed, resulting in faulty development, development without molting, and so on (Salt, 1961c).

1. *Annelida and Mollusca*

In an investigation of the heat–death temperature of two earthworms, *Allolobophora terrestris* and *Eisenia foetida,* Miles (1966) found that, under the conditions chosen, *E. foetida* could survive temperatures up to 33.3°C, while for *A. terrestris,* the limiting temperature was 25.7°C (Table I). These figures were based on a 12-hour exposure, leaving 80% of the animals still alive 48 hours after the end of exposure (LT_{20}); all the worms had been previously acclimated at 15°C for a few weeks. As pointed out above, it is probable that if any of these conditions had varied, the lethal temperatures obtained would have been different.

Although the frequency with which the dorsal blood vessel and pseudo-hearts of the earthworm pulsate varies according to the temperature (Rogers and Lewis, 1914), metabolic acclimation nevertheless occurs in these animals (Precht, 1958). The heat tolerance of *Pheretima* sp. increases 0.3° per 1°C rise in conditioning temperature (W. C. Grant, 1953).

Saroja and Rao (1965) have recently shown that thermal acclimation in the Indian earthworm, *Lampito mauritii,* is accompanied by changes in the inorganic ions, glycogen, RNA, protein nitrogen, and water content of the tissues. They suggest that the activity of the neurosecretory cells increases during acclimation, thereby affecting metabolism and tissue respiration, and resulting in the changes observed.

Gelineo and Kolendig (1953) kept five snails, *Helix pomatia,* for two months at 6°C and five others between 16° and 20°C, after which they measured their oxygen consumption at 6° and 30°C. The animals that had been acclimated to cold showed a respiration rate 19% higher at 6°C and 40% higher at 30°C than the specimens acclimated to the higher temperature. On the other hand, Mellanby (1961) found that although the slugs, *Agrolimax reticulatus* and *Arion hortensis,* had different chill–coma temperatures—about 0° and 5°C, respectively—they did not appear to show any low temperature acclimation at all. However, Roy (1963) acclimated slugs of the species *Arion circumscriptus* to temperatures of 5°, 8° 10°, 20°, and 25°C. After acclimation, metabolic rate was deter-

mined, either as oxygen consumption at 20° and 30°C or by direct calorimetry at 1.25° and 25°C. Roy found that at all given exposure temperatures
the average metabolic rate was lower by 1–1.5% for each degree of increase
in the temperature of acclimation (Fig. 7).

When the logarithms of total oxygen consumption or heat production
per hour were plotted against the logarithms of body weight, the regression
line obtained for the slugs acclimated to heat stood below that for animals

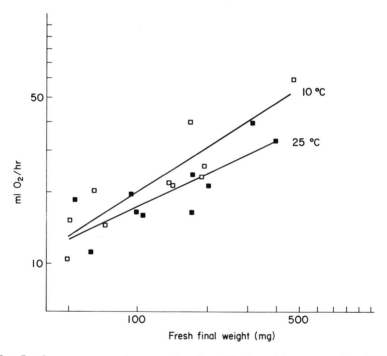

Fig. 7.   Oxygen consumption, as a function of body weight, measured at 20°C in
Arion circumscriptus acclimated at 10° and 25°C. ■ = data for slugs acclimated at 25°C;
□ = data for slugs acclimated at 10°C. Redrawn from Roy (1963).

acclimated to cold. The slope was also slighter for the warm-acclimated
slugs, so that the distance between corresponding points of two such curves
was larger on the right side of the graph, where the larger specimens
were represented, than on the left side where the small specimens were
shown (Fig. 7). This would imply that an increase in the acclimation
temperature reduces metabolic rate to a proportionately greater extent in
larger than in smaller specimens. The value of the slope, which was inversely
correlated with acclimation temperature, was also inversely correlated with
the experimental temperature at which metabolism was determined. Roy's

results therefore confirm those of Gelineo and Kolendig (1953), and add yet one more species to the presently somewhat restricted list of terrestrial poikilotherms known to show acclimation to temperature. No doubt this list will be greatly increased in the near future, and species that do not acclimate will be found to be exceptional.

2. *Arthropoda*

a. Heat. Acclimation to temperature is better known in arthropods than in annelids and mollusks. It has been demonstrated in wood lice, insects, and arachnids. For example, Edney (1964a) found that the lethal temperature (LT_{50}) for an exposure of 30 minutes in saturated air was 41.6°C for *Porcellio laevis* and *Armadillidium vulgare* preconditioned for 14 days at 30°C; the lethal temperatures for animals preconditioned at 10°C were 37.4° and 38.3°C, respectively. The low lethal temperatures were also affected by acclimation, being 5.5 and −2.4°C in *P. laevis* preconditioned at 30° and 10°C, and 3.0° and −2.7°C for *A. vulgare*. The effect of acclimation was also seen in the heart beat and standard metabolic rate (Edney, 1964b).

Mellanby (1954) showed that the heat–coma and thermal death points of insects could be rapidly changed by keeping the animals at different temperatures for only 20 hours; longer exposure gave no further adaptation. According to Cloudsley-Thompson (1962b), preconditioning for 24 hours resulted in enhanced resistance to high temperatures for as much as 4 hours in the scorpion, *Leiurus quinquestriatus,* and the tenebrionid desert beetles, *Ocnera hispida* and *Pimelia grandis.* In the chalcid wasp, *Dahlbominus fuscipennis,* thermal adjustment to high temperature is also a rapid process. The maximal resistance to 43°C for starved adults held at 36°C and 32°C was reached after exposure to these temperatures for 2 and 3 hours, respectively; it was suggested that the decrease in resistance after longer exposure might have been caused by changes in the specific gravity of the hemolymph (Baldwin and Riordan, 1956). House *et al.* (1958) also found that the preconditioning of fly larvae, *Pseudosarcophaga affinis,* for only 2 hours at 39°C could increase the period required to give 50% mortality by nearly 50% as compared with larvae reared at 23°C. Conditioning of honeybees to 35°C resulted in increased survival at 45°C, 46°C, and 47°C compared with survival of bees conditioned to 20°C (Free and Spencer-Booth, 1962).

Respiratory function and thermal acclimation have been studied in a number of tropical invertebrates including Mollusca, wood lice, beetles, scorpions, and Solifugae. While the different species showed widely different levels of respiration, they had several features in common. Oxygen consumption measured at 20°C was, in all individuals, 10 or 15% lower after acclimation to 34°C than after acclimation to 20°C, but the respiratory quotient was about the same, lying in the range of 0.8 to 0.9. Measured at 34°C, however, oxygen consumption was about 30% lower in animals acclimated to this temperature than in animals acclimated to 20°C (Carlisle and Cloudsley-Thompson, 1968).

Applebaum *et al.* (1964) investigated the effect of temperature acclimation on the digestive enzymes of *Tenebrio molitor* larvae *in vitro.* In larvae acclimated to low temperatures, they found a homeostatic tendency with regard to proteolytic, but not to amylase, activity. The absolute amount of proteolytic enzyme, as assayed *in vitro,* decreased sharply at higher temperatures, whereas that of amylase remained constant.

The mechanism of such temperature acclimation is, however, little known. In the past, death by heat has been attributed to the coagulation of protein, destruction of enzymes, asphyxiation, and disturbances in the equilibrium of protoplasm through the accumulation of toxic waste products (Bělehrádek, 1935, 1957; Larsen, 1943). G. S. Fraenkel and Herford (1940) concluded that death at high temperatures was not due merely to lack of oxygen. They suggested, however, that it might have been caused by the accumulation of metabolic waste products. Hopf (1940) found that blowfly larvae kept at 39°C accumulated organic and inorganic phosphorus compounds in their hemolymph.

Heat death in the Saharan scorpion, *Leuirus quinquestriatus,* and the beetle, *Ocnera hispida,* is associated with a decrease in blood pH, and may therefore be due to the accumulation of acid metabolic waste products more rapidly than they can be eliminated (Cloudsley-Thompson, 1962b). In animals less well adapted to survive high temperatures, death is probably due to some other cause.

Larsen (1943) showed that, in five species of Diptera, death from heat often does not occur during or immediately after exposure, but occurs later in development. She advanced the hypothesis that injury might consist of a total or partial destruction of induction substances in the labile periods, so that the consequences of the heat exposure do not appear until the processes normally induced are about to begin. If then the equilibrium is seriously disturbed, development will stop and the animal dies; but if the disturbance is less serious, development continues in a more or less defective way.

It is clear therefore that heat death and temperature acclimation cannot be attributed to any single factor. The only other hypothesis supported by experimental evidence is that of lipoid liberation, for it has been shown by various authors that the melting points of the fats in organisms may vary with the temperatures at which they were laid down (Bělehrádek, 1935). Yet here again the evidence is conflicting.

G. S. Frankel and Hopf (1940) found that the amount of heat adaptation and the degree of unsaturation of the phosphatides of blowfly larvae, measured by their iodine values, is dependent on the temperature at which breeding occurrred. House *et al.* (1958) found that by feeding larvae of *Calliphora erythrocephala* on a diet of highly saturated lipid, it was possible to increase their heat resistance. Cherry (1959) showed that, when larvae of the fly, *Phormia terraenovae* were fed on diets containing fats with different melting points and different degrees of saturation, the fat laid down was affected, though the range of the melting points of this depot fat was much narrower than that of the fat in the diet. At the same time, larvae reared at high temperatures laid down fat that had a higher melting point and a lower iodine number than did larvae reared at lower temperatures. No relation between the properties of the fat and the thermal death point was discovered, although the temperature of rearing had an effect on the lethal temperature. Rainey (1938) found insignificant differences in the iodine numbers of the lipids from larvae of the fly *Lucilia sericata* reared at 15°C, 25°C, and 35°C; while Ditman and Weiland (1938) found only a slight effect in the corn ear worm *Heliothus zea.*

Since acclimation to heat can take place within an hour or two, the hypothesis of lipoid liberation cannot be accepted as a general explanation of temperature adaptation, for it seems unlikely that the composition of the body fat could be altered within such a brief period.

According to Okasha (1968), the effects of sublethal high temperature on *Rhodnius prolixus* are probably due to direct action on the brain, thus inhibiting hormone secretion.

A marked similarity has been found to exist between the lethal effects of excessive heat and of x-rays. Baldwin (1956) showed that, in *Dahlbomius fuscipennis,* the immediate consequence of both is a coma from which the insects may, or may not recover. Tolerance diminishes rapidly with age, but prior acclimation increases tolerance. The similarities between heat and radiation killing may, however, be peculiar to organisms such as arthropods, in which cell division is absent or nearly so, and in which very high doses of x-rays are required to kill.

b. Cold. The chill-coma temperature (that is, the temperature at which an animal is immobilized by cold) was investigated by Mellanby (1939) in five species of insect, *viz. Blatta orientalis, Cimex lectularius, Rhodnius prolixus, Lucilia sericata, Calliphora erythrocephala,* and *Glossina palpalis.* It was found to be affected considerably by the temperature at which the insects had been living: individuals from warm conditions were immobilized at higher temperatures than those from cool conditions. During chill–coma, however, insects from high temperatures did not become acclimated to the low temperature. Both cold-hardiness and the threshold for spontaneous movements were similarly affected by the temperature of pre-conditioning. Acclimation usually occurred within 20 hours (as in the case of acclimation to high temperatures).

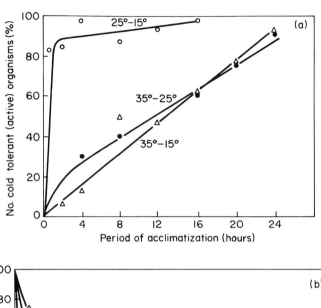

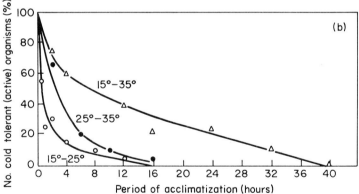

FIG. 8.   (a) Rate of gain of cold tolerance following a step transfer of *Blattella germanica* from a high to a low temperature. (b) Rate of loss of cold tolerance following a step transfer from a low to a high temperature in *Blattella germanica*. From Colhoun (1960).

In *Blatella germanica*, Colhoun (1954, 1960) measured the relationship between acclimation temperature and activity at low temperature. He found that insects kept at 15°C were able to remain active at temperatures at which insects from cultures maintained at 25°C and 35°C were immoblized (Fig. 8). Acclimation to cold is not an unlimited process, however, and

is only possible within a certain range: for example, the chill–coma temperature for *B. germanica* was the same whether the insects were acclimated
at 10°C or at 15°C. Survival at 7°C was also longer in cold-adapted insects:
the cause of death was not ascertained, but appeared to be related to
nervous disturbances, for the level of acetylcholine in male *Periplaneta
americana* increased at higher temperatures (Colhoun, 1958). Scholander
et al. (1953b) measured the oxygen consumption at graded temperatures
of various species obtained in Alaska, and compared them with tropical
forms from the Panama Canal. In contrast to the aquatic animals studied,
the terrestrial species revealed very slight adaptations to temperature and
only in the range 10° to 20°C. Below 10°C, the activity of arctic insects
declines much as in tropical species, and insects tend to crawl rather than
fly. Deal (1941) found no difference in the behavior of wireworms in
a temperature gradient after keeping them at 5°C for a fortnight; and
Hafez (1950) found no difference in the reactions to temperature of
housefly larvae preconditioned to 12°C and 35°C for 5 hours.

Poljakov (1937) and Scholander *et al.* (1953b) were likewise unable
to find any modification of metabolism in relation to appreciable differences
in environmental temperature. G. A. Edwards and Nutting (1950) showed
that the curves of oxygen consumption and heart rate were similar in two
insects of the same order, the snow-dwelling *Grylloblatta campodeiformis,*
and the firebrat *Thermobia domestica.* Whereas *T. domestica* prefers a
temperature of 32°–44°C, *G. campodeiformis* is normally active from —2.5°
to 11.3°C. Activity decreases below and increases above these temperatures
until the insect becomes stuporous at 18°C and irreversibly damaged at
20.5°C. *T. domestica* is active from 12° to 50°C: activity decreases at
50°C, and heat injury becomes apparent at 51.3°C. The temperature characteristic for the oxygen consumption of *G. campodeiformis* in the range
—2.5° to 20.5°C is 14,600 cal, of *T. domestica* between 12° and 50°C,
it is 15,100 cal. Both these insects appear to be strictly poikilothermic in
that they make no metabolic adaptation to offset unfavorable temperatures.
Again, *Tribalium confusum* acclimated at 18° to 38°C shows little Q_{10}
adaption (D. K. Edwards, 1958a).

These seem to be exceptional cases, however, and transition of the
rate–temperature curve without change in slope—that is, shifting upward
or to the left after cold acclimation is shown in oxygen consumption of
several beetles (Marzusch, 1952). Adults of *Blastophagus piniperda* acclimated to 5°C were more tolerent of —5° and —10°C than beetles acclimated in 25°C, but at —20°C no such effect was observed. Acclimation
to both heat and cold in this species has important ecological significance
(Annila and Perttunen, 1964).

On the other hand, grasshoppers, *Mecostethus grossus,* kept at 12°C and 95% relative humidity, had a higher temperature preference than the same individuals kept at 25°C and 95% relative humidity. Evaporation preferences were the same in both experiments, however, and it seems probable that the animals may have a more stable reaction with regard to the combined effects of temperature and humidity than to temperature alone (Coulianos, 1958). The preferred temperature of fifth instar hoppers of *Locusta migratoria* is a function of preconditioning temperature (R. F. Chapman, 1955), and the temperature tolerance zone of oribatid mites also depends upon the temperature of acclimation (Wallwork, 1960).

In a study of the effect of hibernation and seasonal variation of temperature on the respiratory exchange of *Formica ulkei,* Dreyer (1932) found that the rate of respiration and the respiratory quotient varied directly with environmental temperature. The R.Q. was 0.866 for active ants at 22°C and 0.500 for hibernating ants at 4°C. Starvation produced a reduction of 92% in the volume of carbon dioxide produced, and 85% in the volume of oxygen consumed. Dryer suggested that hibernation normally protects ants from starvation during their inactivity at low temperatures and that the analogous effects of low temperature and starvation on respiratory exchange indicated that abnormal and incomplete oxidations, due to low temperature, caused the reduced metabolism occuring during hibernation.

More recently, Atwal (1960a) demonstrated rapid cold acclimation in pupae of the pyralid moth, *Anagasta kühniella.* When these were conditioned at various temperatures between 5° and 25°C for different periods of time ranging from 1 to 16 hours, the mortality due to subsequent exposure at —15°C for 4 hours was found to be affected by each of three factors: age, temperature, and duration of conditioning. Acclimation was maximal in 4 hours, and deteriorated after 16 hours. It increased as the temperature was lowered to 10°C, but was less at 5°C when the injurious effects of chilling began to offset the advantages of acclimation.

Atwal (1960b) also found that acclimation of *A. kühniella* pupae within the range of normal temperatures was not associated with changes in the rate of oxygen consumption or in the specific gravity of the hemolymph. Only when pupae were conditioned at the extreme temperatures of 5° and 35°C for about 16 and 8 hours, respectively, did their hemolymph become more concentrated, and this was not due to desiccation. Consequently, it was concluded that the theory of osmoregulation does not satisfactorily explain the phenomenon of thermal acclimation.

The heart beat frequency of *Periplaneta americana* gives a linear plot against temperature over the range 12° to 40°C, but below 12°C, the frequency deviates considerably from linearity. The heart continues beating well below the cold stupor temperature of the animal: to 1.8°C in cold-adapted and to 4°C in warm-adapted individuals (Richards, 1963). There is a positive correlation between the chill–coma temperature of insects, and both ATPase activity and its temperature coefficients. Such relationships probably contribute to the ability of cold-tolerant species to maintain muscle activity at temperatures which would normally inactivate less tolerant species. Higher temperature coefficients also facilitate muscular activity at temperatures close to those which induce chill–coma (Mutchmor, 1967).

G. Seasonal Acclimatization

Seasonal acclimatization probably occurs in most poikilotherms and sometimes have a genetic basis, as will be seen below (Section IV,B). Saroja (1961) demonstrated a homeostatic mechanism by which the oxygen consumption of the tropical earthworm, *Megascolex mauritii,* is higher in winter than in summer at various ambient temperatures. The difference in the slopes of his regression curves for winter and summer animals indicates that the effect of weight on oxygen consumption varies with the season. In other words, the degree of acclimatization to temperature varies with weight and is greater in smaller worms, which generally consume oxygen at a higher rate per unit body weight than do larger specimens.

The rate of heart beat of snails, *Helix* sp., and slugs, *Limax* sp., shows seasonal shifts when compared under standard laboratory conditions (Crozier and Stier, 1924, 1926). In December and January, the frequency of heart beat in *Limax maximus* exhibits a temperature characteristic of $11,500 \pm 250 \mu$. The ingestion of a small volume of sugar solution results in a temporary change to $16,200 \pm 320 \mu$, which agrees quantitatively with the value obtained from these slugs in spring: the effect is reversible (Crozier and Stier, 1926).

More recently, G. A. Edwards and Irving (1943) have shown indirectly that the beach flea *Talorchestia megalopthalma* (Amphipoda) differs in standard metabolism in a homeostatic direction when winter and summer samples are compared in the field. These authors, however, did not take into account the fact that their winter samples were larger in size.

According to Rao and Bullock (1954), it is plain, on constructing metabolism–weight curves, that the slopes for the animals in winter lie entirely above those of the summer animals, measured either at 12° or at 22°C. There are also differences in slope due to differences in Q_{10}, which may also change with adaptation.

Edney (1964a) demonstrated seasonal acclimatization in the California wood lice, *Porcellio laevis* and *Armadillidium vulgare,* which showed differences of 3.0° and 2.4°C, respectively, between their summer and winter upper lethal temperatures. Similar results have been obtained in Sudan with *Metoponorthrus pruinosus* and *Periscyphis jannonei* (Cloudsley-Thompson, 1969). Collembola are more resistant to cold in winter than in summer (Agrell, 1941), and Lees (1948) found that nymphs of the sheep tick *Ixodes ricinus* collected in the field in winter become immobilized by cold at about 1°C, while specimens maintained at 25°C, had a chill–coma temperature of 7°C. The degree of saturation of fatty acids in insects (Section III,F,2,a) has been observed to vary with the season (Timon-David, 1930), diet, and the stage in the life history (Yuill and Craig, 1937).

Larvae of the European corn borer, *Pyraustia* sp., collected in Minnesota in the fall were found not to be cold resistant and there was a correlation between the age composition of the population and the ability to overwinter. Climatic conditions preceding the fall affected survival far more than conditions during the winter or in the following spring (Barnes and Hodson, 1956). Seasonal metabolism in tropical insects has been discussed by G. A. Edwards and Gonzales (1954).

Scholander *et al.* (1953a) claimed that, in the few cases in the literature where seasonal adaptations have been found, they take place by displacement of the metabolic temperature curve. In no case, according to these authors, has it been found that organisms are adapted to seasonal or other fluctuations in temperature by having a low respiratory Q_{10}, that is, by being insensitive to temperature changes.

Seasonal changes in glycerol concentration in diapausing species, described by Sømme (1964), have already been mentioned (Section III,E,2). Seasonal adaptation in nondiapausing insects in most cases probably results from simple acclimation to ambient air temperature. Thus, Free and Spencer-Booth (1960) found that honeybees in winter had a lower chill–coma temperature than did bees in summer; but after acclimation to 35°C there was no difference. In Florida, the temperature preferred by the pierid butterfly, *Ascia monuste,* is also correlated with seasonal changes in temperature, with a difference of about 5°C between summer and winter (Nielsen and Nielsen, 1958).

Since acclimation to high and low temperatures is extremely rapid, lethal and chill–coma temperatures can be established only in the laboratory with animals kept under constant conditions. In the field, where the temperature is fluctuating all the time, the position of these points will also fluctuate. For instance, as Mellanby (1939) emphasizes, when the day is warm, an insect will more easily be immobilized by cold and more easily killed by freezing. When the day is cool, the reverse will be the case. Whether or not these changes affect the economy of the species depends on the speed of acclimatization and the rapidity with which the temperature changes.

IV. Genetic Adaptations

A. GENETIC BASIS OF DIAPAUSE

Many invertebrate species exhibit geographical races that differ in the character of their diapause. In many, the potentialities for diapause are not realized in each generation. Diapause is then said to be facultative. Such races commonly complete two or more generations annually, while those with obligatory diapause exhibit a strictly univoltine life cycle with only one generation per year.

These are expressions of the genetic constitution of the different races. The inheritance of diapause has been described by Lees (1955) with especial reference to the silkworm, *Bombyx mori,* and it will not be discussed here except to point out that natural selection has often tended to favor the evolution of species with genetic strains that respond differently to the environment. In such species, both heredity and environment are concerned in the determination of voltinism. Thus, Le Berre (1953) was able to select a strain of *Locusta migratoria gallica* which would produce no diapause eggs at 33°C, but still yielded some at lower temperatures. Again, Waloff (1949) was able to breed from a strain of the pyralid moth, *A. elutella,* with obligatory diapause, another which developed without interruption at 25°C. At 21°C, however, 92% of the larvae entered diapause, so the temperature range at which diapause did not occur was not very wide.

In many older studies (e.g, Uvarov, 1931), it was assumed that diapause is a manifestation of some deep-seated internal rhythm, moulded by natural selection until it matched the rhythm of the environment. Although this possibility cannot be ignored, there does not appear to be any very strong evidence in favor of it (Lees, 1955). What is clearly inherent is the ability to respond in a particular way to specific environmental stimuli such as temperature, drought, length of day, and so on. And one of the results of such responses is the ability to withstand unfavorable climatic conditions that might otherwise prove fatal.

B. SEASONAL CYCLES

Most invertebrate animals have life cycles of a year's duration, and show seasonal reproductive rhythms which result in the most resistant stages appearing when climatic conditions are least favorable. In hot, dry deserts, developmental stages appear at the time of the rains, when the weather is cooler and there is abundant food: in arctic regions, during the spring and summer. Periods of extreme heat and cold are usually passed in some resting stage, or diapause, which is resistant to adverse conditions.

Quiescence and diapause usually occur in that stage of the life cycle best adapted to resist the rigors of the climate. Thus, among insects, it may occur in the egg before the embryo has completed segmentation and also when the embryo is mature and apparently ready to hatch, as well as in a number of intermediate stages. For any one species, however, the stage is uniform and under genetic control. In the larva or nymph, diapause may occur at the close of any instar, but it is more frequent in the early instars or the last one: it is also common in pupae and can occur in adults (Andrewartha, 1952).

Seasonal genetic changes in resistance to high temperatures have been studied in fruitflies. Populations of *Drosophila pseudoobscura* at Mt. San Jacinto, California maintain three types of third chromosome at more or less equal frequencies: the so-called standard (ST), arrowhead (AR), and Chiricahua (CH). There is, however, a marked seasonal cycle. Standard decreases from 47% in April to 29% in June and returns to 47% in September with compensating changes in other types, but especially in Chiricahua. When artificial populations were cultured under various conditions and the frequencies followed for several months, no significant change occurred at 16.5°C irrespective of initial frequency, but, at 25°C, the populations of ST and CH shifted rapidly toward an equilibrium at 70% ST and 30% CH (Wright and Dobzhansky, 1946; Dobzhansky, 1947). At 30°C, ST pupae were more viable than CH or heterozygotes and adults of ST or heterozygotes lived longer at 25° and 30°C than did adults of CH (Levine, 1952).

C. Latitudinally Separated Populations

Many poikilothermic animals exhibit in their metabolism or activity some degree of independence of their temperature. One aspect of this appears in the temperature adaptation of latitudinally separated populations of the same species (Bullock, 1955; see also Chapter 1). Many examples are known among marine animals and some studies have been conducted on terrestrial invertebrates. One of the earliest of these was by Goldschmidt (1918) who showed that genetic differences in pigment production and growth rate occur in natural populations or races of the gypsy moth, *Lymantria dispar*. Later, Goldschmidt analyzed clinal geographic variation in *L. dispar* in great detail and showed that northern races have dark brown hairs and a short larvae period, whereas southern races are light yellow and have a longer larvae period (Goldschmidt, 1940).

A more recent example is afforded by the work of Elens (1953a,b), who found in three species of pine needle wasp, *Diprion pini, D. pallidum,* and *D. sertifer,* that high rates of egg development were directly correlated with a cooler habitat, both between species and within a species. Moreover, the populations from colder habitats showed a lower Q_{10}, especially at the time of eclosion. The honeybee, *Apis mellifera,* is more adapted to temperature climates than is *A. indica* which, however, does not show any corresponding adaptation to the tropics. Both species respond to low temperatures by increased food consumption and metabolism, while, above 40°C, little food and much water is taken. *A. indica* is the more sensitive to cold (Free and Spencer-Booth, 1961).

Cold tolerance in the mosquito *Culex tarsalis* increases with shorter photoperiod (Anderson and Harwood, 1966). Newly emerged females from latitude 35°N. exposed to an 8-hour photoperiod had 62% unsaturated fatty acids compared with 52% in insects exposed to a 16-hour photoperiod (Harwood and Takata, 1965). Short photoperiod therefore acts as a factor accessory to low temperature in the accumulation of unsaturated fatty acids.

In the case of *Drosophila funebris,* Timoféeff-Ressovsky (1940) tested 34 populations from various parts of Europe at 15°, 22°, and 29°C, and found that northern populations survived better at low and southern populations were more resistant to higher temperatures. Dobzhansky (1935) compared the fecundity of two races of *D. pseudoobscura,* which are identical morphologically but differ in the shape of the Y-chromosome. He found that the race which normally inhabits cool, moist regions had a greater fecundity at 14° and 19°C, while that found in warmer, more continental climates was the more fecund at 25° and 27.5°C. Thus the geographical distribution of the two races conforms to their physiological peculiarities. A parallel situation occurs at different altitudes in the Sierra Nevada Mountains. When several different strains and clones of *D. persimilis* were reared together in cages at different temperatures, all chromosome arrangements were equal at 25°C, but at 16°C, the high altitude type was more successful (Spiess, 1950).

Tantawy and Mallah (1961) collected natural populations of *Drosophila melanogester* and *D. simulans* from different geographical regions in Lebanon, Egypt, and Uganda, and reared the offspring of such populations under various temperatures ranging from 10° to 31.5°C. They found that, not only did the temperature of rearing affect various morphological characters such as wing and thorax length, but that northern populations were more vigorous, less variable, and more viable than all others at almost every temperature: populations from Uganda showed superiority only at the higher temperatures which approximated to their original climatic conditions.

Hartmann-Goldstein and Sperlich (1963) crossed a northern strain of *D. subobscura* with a strain from temperate regions and varied the temperature of development of different series of F2 individuals. One series was kept at 19°C and another at 23°C throughout development: two other series were kept at one temperature during their larval instars and at the other as pupae. It was found that high temperatures, particularly during the pupal stage, favored heterozygotes, but that a change in temperature during development favored homozygotes. The effects of temperature on the embryonic development of insects have been reviewed by Howe (1967).

Adaptations to temperature in geographic races of the Queensland fruit fly *Dacus* (*Strumeta*) *tryoni* appear chiefly to affect fecundity, longevity, and the survival rates of immature stages, but not the speed of development (Bateman, 1967).

Eggs of the tortricid moth *Acrolita naevana* from a location in eastern Norway accumulated more glycerol than did eggs from a region with a milder climate in western Norway (Sømme, 1965a). Accumulation of glycerol is clearly an adaptation to low temperature in winter and is presumably under genetic control since the eggs were treated similarly before being tested for glycerol content.

Experiments undertaken to determine the temperature–respiration curves and survival at extreme temperatures of *Tribolium confusum* and a black mutant of the same species showed that the curve of the latter differed from that of the normal, red insects in that there was no definite trend in females toward higher oxygen consumption over the temperature range investigated. No difference in survival time was apparent at −3°C between black and red male *T. confusum,* but black females were not able to survive at this temperature to the same degree as the normal, red females (Edwards, 1958b).

Bowler and Hollingsworth (1965) measured gain and loss of acclimation to temperature in males from two inbred lines of *Drosophila subobscura* and their hybrids by recording the time of survival in dry air at a lethal temperature of 34°C. Hybrid males lost acclimation more quickly than inbred males, but also gained it more quickly. The results suggest that hybrids can produce the enzymes necessary for temperature acclimation more rapidly than inbreds and confirm the hypothesis that hybrids are biochemically more stable.

Many arctic insects are more hairy and darker in color than their relatives from more temperate regions (Downes, 1962, 1964). This character is, of course, under genetic control. Church (1960b) has shown that the coats of hair on bumblebees, hawk moths, and noctuid moths are excellent insulators against convective heat loss (Section III,B,1). The habit of basking, observed so frequently among arctic Lepidoptera and Diptera, and the prevalence of melanic forms (Downes, 1962) indicate the significance of direct sunlight in the physiology of the insects. Although Digby (1955) did not obtain any very definite relationship between color and the temperature excess of insects exposed to sunshine, Downes (1964) suggested that perhaps there may be additional factors operating in the field. Moreover, most arctic insects and spiders have a lower temperature threshold of activity than have their southern relatives (Bertram, 1935).

West African species of oribatid mites have a tolerance zone of 18° to 36°C compared with 16° to 28°C in North American species. The former also have an upper critical temperature (at which they are immobilized) of 37°C and a lethal temperature (50% mortality within 30 minutes) of 38° to 40°C; compared with 30°C and 30° to 32°C, respectively, in North American species. The difference between the two groups depends very largely on the previous environmental temperature to which the mites have been exposed (Wallwork, 1960). Thus, preconditioning of the West African *Galumnella areolata* for 4 hours at 23°C, compared with 30°C, had a marked effect on the tolerance zone, which decreased to 16°C to 30°C, and on the upper critical limit, which was lowered to 32°C. The upper lethal temperature (42°C) was not affected. The mite, *Tetranychus urticae*, may have a diapausing stage which is very resistant to cold, whereas the related *T. cinnabarinus* does not have a diapause and is not cold-hardy (Van de Bund and Helle, 1960). This genetic character is presumably responsible for the distribution of the two species.

Speed of development may also be regarded as an adaptation to temperature. For example, the chief adaptation enabling certain species of Ephemeroptera to inhibit colder situations is their ability to develop more rapidly at low temperatures, and thus complete their life cycle within a year (Ide, 1935). Other genetic adaptations to temperature have been discussed by Clarke (1967).

V. Conclusions

In this chapter the ways in which terrestrial invertebrate animals combat the thermal demands placed on them by the environment in which they live have been outlined. True thermoregulation is achieved chiefly by behavioral mechanisms which result in the avoidance of extreme temperatures. Temperature regulation is also achieved by means of transpiration and metabolic heating. This is most obvious in the case of social insects, where the effects are enhanced by mutual cooperation. Other physiological adaptations include estivation and hibernation. In summer diapause, invertebrates are resistant to high temperature: extreme cold is countered in the diapausing arthropod by supercooling and the ability to withstand freezing. Most invertebrates show acclimation to temperature. This may result in seasonal acclimatization, although it is sometimes masked by size differences. Finally, it is shown that many of these adaptations are hereditary. Although no attempt has been made to compile a complete bibliography, the following list of references is probably sufficiently comprehensive to act as a basis for further research.

REFERENCES

Abushama, F. T. (1964). *Animal Behaviour* **12**, 140.
Adams, P. A., and Heath, J. E. (1964). *Nature* **201**, 20.
Agrell, I. (1941). *Opuscula Entomol.* Suppl. 3, 1.
Allee, W. C., Emerson, A. E., Park O., Park, T., and Schmidt, K. P. (1949). "Principles of Animal Ecology," Saunders, Philadelphia, Pennsylvania.
Alexander, A. J., and Ewer, D. W. (1958). *J. Exptl. Biol.* **35**, 349.
Anderson, A. W., and Harwood, R. F. (1966). *Mosquito News* **26**, 1.
Andrewartha, H. G. (1952). *Biol. Rev. Cambridge Phil. Soc.* **27**, 50.
Andrewartha, H. G., and Birch, L. C. (1954). "The Distribution and Abundance of Animals," Univ. of Chicago Press, Chicago, Illinois.
Annila, E., and Perttunen, V. (1964). *Ann. Entomol. Fenn.* **30**, 35.
Applebaum, S. W., Jankovíc, M., Grozdonovíc, J., and Mavenkovíc, D. (1964). *Physiol. Zool.* **37**, 90.
Ardo, P. (1957). *Opuscula Entomol.* Suppl. 14, 1.
Asahina, E., Aoki, K., and Shinozaki, J. (1954). *Bull. Entomol. Res.* **45**, 329.
Atwal, A. S. (1960a). *Can. J. Zool.* **38**, 131.
Atwal, A. S. (1960b). *Can. J. Zool.* **38**, 143.
Bachmetjew, P. (1899). *Z. Wiss. Zool.* **66**, 520.
Bair, T. D. (1950). *Ecology* **31**, 474.
Baldwin, W. F. (1954). *Can. J. Zool.* **32**, 157.
Baldwin, W. F. (1956). *Radiation Res.* **5**, 46.
Baldwin, W. F., and Riordan, D. F. (1956). *Can. J. Zool.* **34**, 565.
Barnes, D., and Hodson, A. C. (1956). *J. Econ. Entomol.* **49**, 19.
Barnes, D., and Hodson, A. C. (1957). *Rev. Appl. Entomol.* **45A**, 93.
Bateman, M. A. (1967). *Australian J. Zool.* **15**, 1141.
Bauer, K. (1955). *Zool. Jahrb., Abt. Allgem. Zool. Physiol. Tiere* **65**, 267.
Beall, G. (1941). *Can. Field Nat.* **55**, 123.
Bĕlehrádek, J. (1935). *Protoplasma-Monograph. (Berlin)* **8**, 1.
Bĕlehrádek, J. (1957). *Ann. Rev. Physiol.* **19**, 59.
Bernard, F. (1951). *Bull. Soc. Hist. Nat. Toulouse* **86**, 88.
Bernard, J., Gahery, Y., and Boistel, J. (1965). *In* "Physiology of the Insect Central Nervous System" (J. E. Treherne and J. W. L. Beament, eds.), pp. 67–72. Academic Press, New York.
Bertram, G. C. L. (1935). *J. Animal Ecol.* **4**, 35.
Birch, L. C. (1942). *Australian J. Exptl. Biol. Med. Sci.* **20**, 17.
Bodenheimer, F. S. (1929). *Z. Angew. Entomol.* **15**, 435.
Bodenheimer, F. S. (1934a). *Zool. Jahrb., Abt. 1. Syst.* **66**, 113.
Bodenheimer, F. S. (1934b). *Bull. Soc. Entomol. Egypt* p. 211.
Bodenheimer, F. S. (1935). "Animal Life in Palestine. An Introduction to the Problem of Animal Ecology and Zoogeography." L. Mayer, Jerusalem.
Bodenheimer, F. S., and Klein, H. J. (1930). *Z. Verglich. Physiol.* **11**, 345.
Bodine, J. H. (1921). *J. Exptl. Zool.* **32**, 137.
Bodine, J. H. (1923). *J. Exptl. Zool.* **37**, 457.

Bolwig, N. (1957). *J. Entomol. Soc. S. Africa* **20,** 454.
Bowler, K. (1967). *Entomol. Exptl. Appl.* **10,** 16.
Bowler, K., and Hollingsworth, M. J. (1965). *Genet. Res.* **6,** 1.
Bowler, K., and Hollingsworth, M. J. (1966). *Exptl. Gerontol.* **2,** 1.
Bullock, T. H. (1955). *Biol. Rev. Cambridge Phil. Soc.* **30,** 311.
Burnett, G. C. (1957). *Proc. Roy. Entomol. Soc. London* A**32,** 53.
Bursell, E. (1964). *In* "The Physiology of Insecta" (M. Rockstein, ed.), Vol. 1, pp. 290, 294, and 303. Academic Press, New York.
Buxton, P. A. (1923). "Animal Life in Deserts," Arnold, London.
Buxton, P. A. (1924a). *Entomol. Monthly Mag.* **60,** 3.
Buxton, P. A. (1924b). *Proc. Roy. Soc* B**96,** 123.
Callahan, P. S. (1965a). *Nature* **207,** 1172.
Callahan, P. S. (1965b). *Ann. Entomol. Soc. Am.* **58,** 727 and 746.
Cappe de Baillon, P. (1936). *Bull. Biol. France Belg.* **70,** 1.
Carlisle, D. B., and Cloudsley-Thompson, J. L. (1968). *Nature* **218,** 684.
Carthy, J. D. (1958). "An Introduction to the Behavior of Invertebrates." Allen & Unwin, London.
Chapman, L. N., Michel, J. K., Parker, Y. R., Miller, G. E., and Kelly, E. G. (1926). *Ecology* **7,** 416.
Chapman, R. F. (1955). *J. Exptl. Biol.* **32,** 126.
Cherry, L. (1959). *Entomol. Exptl. Appl.* **2,** 68.
Church, N. S. (1960a). *J. Exptl. Biol.* **37,** 171.
Church, N. S. (1960b). *J. Exptl. Biol.* **37,** 186.
Clarke, K. V. (1967). *In* "Thermobiology" (A. H. Rose, ed.), pp. 293–352. Academic Press, New York.
Clements, A. N. (1963). "The Physiology of Mosquitoes," Pergamon Press, New York.
Cloudsley-Thompson, J. L. (1950). *Quart. J. Microscop. Sci.* **91,** 453.
Cloudsley-Thompson, J. L. (1951a). *Proc. Zool. Soc. London* **121,** 253.
Cloudsley-Thompson, J. L. (1951b). *J. Exptl. Biol.* **28,** 165.
Cloudsley-Thompson, J. L. (1956). *Ann. Mag. Nat. Hist.* [12] **9,** 305.
Cloudsley-Thompson, J. L. (1958). "Spiders, Scorpions, Centipedes and Mites." Pergamon Press, New York (rev. ed., 1968).
Cloudsley-Thompson, J. L. (1959). *Entomol. Exptl. Appl.* **2,** 249.
Cloudsley-Thompson, J. L. (1960). *Entomol. Monthly Mag.* **96,** 49.
Cloudsley-Thompson, J. L. (1961a). *Cold Spring Harbor Symp. Quant. Biol.* **25,** 345.
Cloudsley-Thompson, J. L. (1961b). "Rhythmic Activity in Animal Physiology and Behaviour," Academic Press, New York.
Cloudsley-Thompson, J. L. (1962a). *Ann. Rev. Entomol.* **7,** 199.
Cloudsley-Thompson, J. L. (1962b). *Entomol. Exptl. Appl.* **5,** 270.
Cloudsley-Thompson, J. L. (1963a). *Entomol. Monthly Mag.* **98,** 243.
Cloudsley-Thompson, J. L. (1963b). *Entomol. Exptl. Appl.* **6,** 75.
Cloudsley-Thompson, J. L. (1964a). *In* "Handbook of Physiology" (Am. Physiol. Soc., D. B. Dill, ed.), Sect. 4, pp. 451–65. Williams & Wilkins, Baltimore, Maryland.
Cloudsley-Thompson, J. L. (1964b). *Entomol. Monthly Mag.* **100,** 148.
Cloudsley-Thompson, J. L. (1965). "Desert Life," Pergamon Press, New York.
Cloudsley-Thompson, J. L. (1968). *Sci. Progr. (Oxford)* **56,** 499.
Cloudsley-Thompson, J. L. (1969). *J. Zool.* **158,** 267.
Cloudsley-Thompson, J. L., and Chadwick, M. J. (1964). "Life in Deserts," Dufour, Philadelphia, Pennsylvania.
Colhoun, E. H. (1954). *Nature* **173,** 582.
Colhoun, E. H. (1958). *J. Insect Physiol.* **2,** 108.

Colhoun, E. H. (1960). *Entomol. Exptl. Appl.* **3**, 27.
Coulianos, C-C. (1958). *Entomol. Tidskr.* **78**, 265.
Cowles, R. B. (1962). *Science* **135**, 670.
Crozier, W. J., and Stier, T. B. (1924). *J. Gen. Physiol.* **7**, 705.
Crozier, W. J., and Stier, T. B. (1926). *J. Gen. Physiol.* **9**, 547.
Dainton, B. H. (1943). *Nature* **151**, 25.
Dainton, B. H. (1954). *J. Exptl. Biol.* **31**, 165.
Deal, J. (1941). *J. Animal Ecol.* **10**, 323.
de Wilde, J. (1962). *Ann. Rev. Entomol.* **7**, 1.
Digby, P. S. B. (1955). *J. Exptl. Biol.* **32**, 279.
Ditman, L. P., and Weiland, G. W. (1938). *Ann. Entomol. Soc. Am.* **31**, 578.
Ditman, L. P., Vogt, G. B., and Smith, D. R. (1943). *J. Econ. Entomol.* **36**, 304.
Dobzhansky, T. (1935). *J. Exptl. Zool.* **71**, 449.
Dobzhansky, T. (1947). *Evolution* **1**, 1.
Dotterweich, H. (1928). *Zool. Jahrb., Abt. Allgem. Zool. Physiol. Tiere* **44**, 399.
Downes, J. A. (1962). *Can. Entomol.* **94**, 143.
Downes, J. A. (1964). *Can. Entomol.* **96**, 279.
Downes, J. A. (1965). *Ann. Rev. Entomol.* **10**, 257.
Dreyer, W. A. (1932). *Physiol. Zool.* **5**, 301.
Dubach, P., Smith, F., Pratt, D., and Stewart, C. M. (1959). *Nature* **184**, 288.
Dunham, J. (1962). *Physiol. Zool.* **35**, 297.
Dunham, W. (1931). *Ohio J. Sci.* **31**, 181.
Edney, E. B. (1951a). *J. Exptl. Biol.* **28**, 91.
Edney, E. B. (1951b). *J. Exptl. Biol.* **28**, 271.
Edney, E. B. (1952). *Nature* **170**, 586.
Edney, E. B. (1953). *J. Exptl. Biol.* **30**, 331.
Edney, E. B. (1957). "The Water Relations of Terrestrial Arthropods," Cambridge Univ. Press, New York.
Edney, E. B. (1958). *Proc. 10th Intern. Congr. Entomol., Montreal, 1956* Vol. 2, p. 709. 10th Intern. Congr. Entomol., Ottawa.
Edney, E. B. (1964a). *J. Exptl. Zool.* **37**, 364.
Edney, E. B. (1964b). *J. Exptl. Zool.* **37**, 378.
Edney, E. B. (1967). *Science* **156**, 1059.
Edney, E. B., and Barrass, R. (1962). *J. Insect Physiol.* **8**, 469.
Edwards, D. K. (1958a). *Can. J. Zool.* **36**, 363.
Edwards, D. K. (1958b). *Physiol. Zool.* **31**, 323.
Edwards, G. A. (1946). *J. Cellular Comp. Physiol.* **27**, 53.
Edwards, G. A., and Gonzales, M. D. (1954). *Acta Physiol. Latinoam.* **4**, 121.
Edwards, G. A., and Irving, L. (1943). *J. Cellular Comp. Physiol.* **21**, 183.
Edwards, G. A., and Nutting, W. L. (1950). *Psyche* **57**, 33.
Elens, A. A. (1953a). *Agricultura (Louvain)* [2] **1**, 19.
Elens, A. A. (1953b). *Agricultura (Louvain)* [2] **1**, 78.
Ellis, P. E., and Ashall, C. (1957). *Anti-Locust Bull.* **25**, 1.
Evans, W. G. (1964). *Nature* **202**, 211.
Evans, W. G. (1966a). *Ann. Entomol. Soc. Am.* **59**, 873.
Evans, W. G. (1966b). *Ecology* **47**, 1061.
Falconer, D. S. (1945). *J. Exptl. Biol.* **21**, 17.
Flemister, L. J. (1964). *In* "Handbook of Physiology" (Am. Physiol. Soc., D. B. Dill, ed.), Sect. 4, pp. 593–602. Williams & Wilkins, Baltimore, Maryland.
Fraenkel, G. (1929). *Biol. Zentr.* **49**, 657.
Fraenkel, G. (1930). *Z. Vergleich. Physiol.* **13**, 300.

Fraenkel, G. S., and Gunn, D. L. (1961). "The Orientation of Animals: Kineses, Taxes and Compass Reactions," 2nd ed. Dover, New York.

Fraenkel, G. S., and Herford, G. V. B. (1940). *J. Exptl. Biol.* **17**, 386.

Fraenkel, G. S., and Hopf, M. S. (1940). *Biochem. J.* **34**, 1085.

Franz, H. (1930). *Biol. Zentr.* **50**, 158.

Free, J. B., and Spencer-Booth, Y. (1958). *J. Exptl. Biol.* **35**, 930.

Free, J. B., and Spencer-Booth Y. (1960). *Entomol. Exptl. Appl.* **3**, 222.

Free, J. B., and Spencer-Booth, Y. (1961). *Nature* **190**, 933.

Free, J. B., and Spencer-Booth, Y. (1962). *Entomol. Exptl. Appl.* **5**, 249.

Garrett-Jones, C. (1951). *Bull. Entomol. Res.* **41**, 679.

Gebhardt, H. (1953). *Zool. Jahrb., Abt. Allgem. Zool. Physiol. Tiere* **63**, 558.

Geist, R. M. (1928). *Ann. Entomol. Soc. Am.* **21**, 614.

Gelineo, S., and Kolendig, M. (1953). *Bull. Acad. Sarb. Sci., Cl. Sci. Math. Nat.* [12] **3**, 1.

Goldschmidt, R. (1918). *Am. Naturalist* **52**, 28.

Goldschmidt, R. (1940). "The Material Basis of Evolution," Yale Univ. Press, New Haven, Connecticut.

Grant, G. R. M. (1950). *Proc. Roy. Soc. Queensland* **60**, 89.

Grant, W. C. (1953). *Anat. Record* **117**, 561.

Green, G. W. (1955). *Can. Entomol.* **87**, 441.

Gunn, D. L. (1934). *Z. Vergleich. Physiol.* **20**, 617.

Gunn, D. L. (1935). *J. Exptl. Biol.* **12**, 185.

Gunn, D. L. (1942). *Biol. Rev. Cambridge Phil. Soc.* **17**, 293.

Gunn, D. L., and Hopf, H. S. (1942). *J. Exptl. Biol.* **18**, 278.

Gunn, D. L., and Notley, F. B. (1936). *J. Exptl. Biol.* **13**, 28.

Guthrie, F. E., and Decker, G. C. (1954). *J. Econ. Entomol.* **47**, 882.

Hafez, M. (1950). *Parasitology* **40**, 215.

Hafez, M. (1953). *J. Exptl. Zool.* **124**, 199.

Hafez, M., and Ibrahim, M. M. (1964). *Bull. Soc. Entomol. Egypte* **48**, 193.

Hartmann-Goldstein, I., and Sperlich, D. (1963). *Genetics* **48**, 863.

Harwood, R. F., and Takata, N. (1965). *J. Insect Physiol.* **11**, 711.

Haufe, W. O. (1957). *Can. Entomol.* **89**, 120.

Hazelhoff, E. H. (1954). *Physiol. Comparata Oecol.* **3**, 343.

Heath, J. E. (1967). *Am. Midland Naturalist* **77**, 64.

Heath, J. E., and Adams, P. A. (1965). *Nature* **201**, 20.

Heath, J. E., and Adams, P. A. (1967). *J. Exptl. Biol.* **47**, 21.

Heran, H. (1952). *Z. Vergleich. Physiol.* **34**, 179.

Herter, K. (1923). *Biol. Zentr.* **43**, 282.

Herter, K. (1924). *Z. Vergleich Physiol.* **1**, 221.

Herter, K. (1953). "Der Temperatursinn der Insekten." Dunber & Humbolt, Berlin.

Hesse, R., Allee, W. C., and Schmidt, K. P. (1951). "Ecological Animal Geography," 2nd ed. Wiley, New York.

Heusner, A., and Stussi, T. (1964). *Insectes Sociaux* **11**, 239.

Himmer, A. (1932). *Biol. Rev. Cambridge Phil. Soc.* **7**, 224.

Hinton, H. E. (1960). *Nature* **188**, 336.

Hogben, L., and Kirk, R. L. (1944). *Proc. Roy. Soc.* B**132**, 239.

Holdaway, F. G., and Gray, F. J. (1948). *Australian J. Sci. Res.* **1**, 464.

Homp, R. (1938). *Z. Vergleich. Physiol.* **26**, 1.

Hopf, H. S. (1940). *Biochem. J.* **34**, 1936.

House, H. L., Riordan, D. F., and Barlow, J. S. (1958). *Can. J. Zool.* **36**, 629.

Howe, R. W. (1967). *Ann. Rev. Entomol.* **12**, 15.

Ide, F. P. (1935). *Univ. Toronto Studies Biol.* **39**, 1.

Jack, R. W. (1939). *Mem. Dept. Agr., S. Rhodesia* 1, 1.
Jackson, W. B. (1957). *Ecology* 38, 276.
Katô, M. (1939). *Sci. Rept. Tôhoku Univ., Fourth Sen.* 14, 53.
Kennedy, J. S. (1939). *Trans. Roy. Entomol. Soc. London* 89, 385.
Kerkut, G. A., and Taylor, B. J. R. (1956). *Nature* 178, 426.
Kerkut, G. A., and Taylor, B. J. R. (1957). *J. Exptl. Biol.* 34, 486.
Kerkut, G. A., and Taylor, B. J. R. (1958). *Behaviour* 13, 259.
Koidsumi, K. (1935). *Mem. Fac. Sci. Agr. Taihoku* 12, 281.
Kozhanchikov, I. V. (1938). *Bull. Entomol. Res.* 29, 253.
Krogh, A., and Zeuthen, E. (1941). *J. Exptl. Biol.* 18, 1.
Krumbiegel, I. (1932). *Zool. Jahrb. Abt. 1. Syst.* 63, 183.
Lacher, V. (1964). *Z. Vergleich. Physiol.* 48, 587.
Larsen, E. B. (1943). *Kgl. Danske Videnskab. Selskab, Biol. Medd.* 19, No. 3, 1.
Laverack, M. S. (1961). *Comp. Biochem. Physiol.* 3, 136.
Laverack, M. S. (1963). "The Physiology of Earthworms," Pergamon Press, New York.
Leader, J. P. (1962). *J. Insect Physiol.* 8, 155.
Le Berre, J. R. (1953). *Bull. Biol. France Belg.* 87, 227.
Lees, A. D. (1948). *J. Exptl. Biol.* 25, 145.
Lees, A. D. (1955). "The Physiology of Diapause in Arthropods." Cambridge Univ. Press, New York.
Leigh, T. F., and Smith, R. F. (1959). *Hilgardia* 28, 569.
Lensky, Y. (1964a). *J. Insect Physiol.* 10, 1.
Lensky, Y. (1964b). *Insects Sociaux* 11, 293.
Levine, R. P. (1952). *Evolution* 6, 216.
Lindauer, M. (1954). *Z. Vergleich. Physiol.* 36, 391.
Lindauer, M. (1955). *Bee World* 36, 62.
Loftus, R. (1966). *Z. Vergleich. Physiol.* 52, 380.
Luscher, M. (1951). *Nature* 167, 34.
Macfadyen, A. (1967). *In* "Thermobiology" (A. H. Rose, ed.), pp. 535–553. Academic Press, New York.
Mc Iver, S. B., and Harwood, R. F. (1966). *J. Kansas Entomol. Soc.* 39, 535.
McWhinnie, M. A. (1967). *In* "Thermobiology" (A. H. Rose, ed.), pp. 353–373. Academic Press, New York.
Madge, D. S. (1961). *Nature* 190, 106.
Mail, G. A. (1930). *J. Agr. Res.* 41, 571.
Mail, G. A. (1932). *J. Econ. Entomol.* 25, 1049.
Mail, G. A., and Salt, R. W. (1933). *J. Econ. Entomol.* 25, 1068.
Makings, P. (1964). *J. Exptl. Biol.* 41, 473.
Makings, P. (1968). *J. Exptl. Biol.* 48, 247.
Marzusch, K. (1952). *Z. Vergleich. Physiol.* 34, 75.
Mason, B. J. (1956). *Sci. Prog. (London)* 44, 479.
Mellanby, K. (1932). *J. Exptl. Biol.* 9, 222.
Mellanby, K. (1933). *Proc. Roy. Entomol. Soc. London* C8, 22.
Mellanby, K. (1934). *J. Exptl. Biol.* 11, 48.
Mellanby, K. (1939). *Proc. Roy. Soc.* B127, 473.
Mellanby, K. (1954). *Nature* 173, 582.
Mellanby, K. (1958). *Nature* 181, 1403.
Mellanby, K. (1961). *Nature* 189, 944.
Michon, J. (1949). *Compt. Rend.* 228, 1455.
Miles, H. B. (1966). *School Sci. Rev.* 48, 55.
Murray, R. W. (1962). *Symp. Soc. Exptl. Biol.* 16, 244.

Mutchmor, J. A. (1967). *In* "Molecular Mechanisms of Temperature Adaptation," Publ. No. 84, pp. 165–176. Am. Assoc. Advance. Sci., Washington, D.C.

Necheles, H. (1924). *Arch. Ges. Physiol.* **204,** 72.

Nicholson, A. J. (1934). *Bull. Entomol. Res.* **25,** 85.

Nielsen, E. T. (1938). *Videnskab. Medd. Dansk Naturh. Foren. Kbh.* **102,** 1.

Nielsen, E. T., and Nielsen, H. T. (1958). *Ecology* **40,** 181.

Nørgaard, E. (1948). *Flora Fauna* **54,** 1.

Nørgaard, E. (1951). *Oikos* **3,** 1.

Nørgaard, D. (1956). *Oikos* **7,** 159.

Okasha, A. Y. K. (1968). *J. Exptl. Biol.* **48,** 455, 465, and 475.

Omer-Cooper, J. (1948). *Proc. Egypt. Acad. Sci.* **3,** 1.

Oosthuizen, M. J. (1939). *J. Entomol. Soc. S. Africa* **2,** 63.

Palmén, E. (1954). *Ann. Entomol. Fenn.* **20,** 1.

Parker, A. H. (1948). *Bull. Entomol. Res.* **39,** 387.

Parker, A. H. (1952). *Bull. Entomol. Res.* **43,** 221.

Parry, D. A. (1951). *J. Exptl. Biol.* **28,** 445.

Payne, N. M. (1926a). *Quart. Rev. Biol.* **1,** 270.

Payne, N. M. (1926b). *Ecology* **7,** 99.

Payne, N. M. (1927a). *Biol. Bull. Marine Biol. Lab.* **52,** 449.

Payne, N. M. (1927b). *J. Morphol.* **43,** 521.

Pepper, J. H., and Hastings, E. (1952). *Ecology* **33,** 96.

Perttunen, V. (1958). *Ann. Entomol. Fenn.* **24,** 12.

Perttunen, V. (1959). *Ann. Entomol. Fenn.* **25,** 65.

Perttunen, V., and Paloheimo, L. (1963). *Ann. Entomol. Fenn.* **29,** 171.

Peterson, D. G., and Brown, A. W. A. (1951). *Bull. Entomol. Res.* **42,** 535.

Pierre, F. (1958). "Écologie et peuplement entomologique des sables vifs du Sahara Nord—Occidental." C. N. R. S., Paris.

Platt, R. B., Collins, C. L., and Witherspoon, J. P. (1957). *Ecol. Monographs* **27,** 303.

Poljakov, J. D. (1937). *Bull. Soc. Nat. Moscou, Sect. Biol* [N. S.] **46,** 291.

Precht, H. (1958). *In* "Physiological Adaptation" (C. L. Prosser, ed.), pp. 50–78. Am. Physiol. Soc., Washington, D.C.

Prosser, C. L. (1955). *Biol. Rev. Cambridge Phil. Soc.* **30,** 229.

Prosser, C. L. (1961). *In* "Comparative Animal Physiology" (C. L. Prosser and F. A. Brown, Jr., eds.), pp. 238–284. Saunders, Philadelphia, Pennsylvania.

Raignier, A. (1948). *Cellule Rec. Cytol. Histol.* **51,** 281.

Rainey, R. C. (1938). *Ann. Appl. Biol.* **25,** 822.

Rao, K. P., and Bullock, T. H. (1954). *Am. Naturalist* **88,** 33.

Richards, A. G. (1963). *J. Insect Physiol.* **9,** 597.

Rivnay, E. (1932). *Parasitology* **24,** 121.

Robinson, W. (1927). *J. Econ. Entomol.* **20,** 80.

Robinson, W. (1928). *J. Econ. Entomol.* **21,** 897.

Rogers, C. G., and Lewis, E. M. (1914). *Biol. Bull. Woods Hole* **27,** 262.

Roth, L. M. (1951). *Ann. Entomol. Soc. Am.* **44,** 59.

Roy, A. (1963). *Can. J. Zool.* **41,** 671.

Salt, R. W. (1936). *Tech. Bull. Minn. Agr. Expt. Sta.* No. 116, 1.

Salt, R. W. (1953). *Can. Entomol.* **85,** 261.

Salt, R. W. (1956). *Can. J. Zool.* **34,** 1.

Salt, R. W. (1957). *Can Entomol.* **89,** 491.

Salt, R. W. (1958). *J. Insect Physiol.* **2,** 178.

Salt, R. W. (1959a). *Can. J. Zool.* **37,** 59.

Salt, R. W. (1959b). *Nature* **184,** 1426.

Salt, R. W. (1961a). *Can. J. Zool.* **39**, 349.
Salt, R. W. (1961b). *Ann. Rev. Entomol.* **6**, 55.
Salt, R. W. (1961c). *Brit. Med. Bull.* **17**, 5.
Salt, R. W. (1963). *Can. Entomol.* **95**, 1190.
Salt, R. W. (1964). *In* "Handbook of Physiology" (Am. Physiol. Soc., J. Field, ed.), Sect. 4, pp. 449–355. Williams & Wilkins, Baltimore, Maryland.
Salt, R. W. (1966a). *Can. J. Zool.* **44**, 117.
Salt, R. W. (1966b). *Can. J. Zool.* **44**, 655.
Salt, R. W. (1966c). *Can. J. Zool.* **44**, 947.
Salt, R. W. (1968). *Can. J. Zool.* **46**, 329.
Saroja, K. (1961). *Nature* **190**, 930.
Saroja, K., and Rao, K. P. (1965). *Z. Vergleich. Physiol.* **50**, 35.
Schneirla, T. C., Brown, R. Z., and Brown, F. C. (1954). *Ecol. Monographs* **24**, 269.
Scholander, P. F., Flagg, W., Hock, R. J., and Irving, L. (1953a). *J. Cellular Comp. Physiol.* **42**, Suppl. 1, 1–56.
Scholander, P. F., Flagg, W., Hock, R. J., and Irving, L. (1953b). *Physiol. Zool.* **26**, 67.
Shepherd, R. F. (1958). *Can. J. Zool.* **36**, 779.
Siegler, E. H. (1946). *J. Agr. Res.* **72**, 329.
Sioli, H. (1937). *Zool. Jahrb., Abt. Allgem. Zool. Physiol. Tiere* **58**, 284.
Slifer, E. (1951). *Proc. Roy. Soc.* B**138**, 414.
Smith, A. C. (1902). *Am. J. Physiol.* **6**, 459.
Smith, A. U. (1958). *Biol. Rev. Cambridge Phil. Soc.* **33**, 197.
Solomon, M. E. (1937). *Australian J. Exptl. Biol. Med. Sci.* **15**, 1.
Sømme, L. (1964). *Can. J. Zool.* **42**, 87.
Sømme, L. (1965a). *Can. J. Zool.* **43**, 765.
Sømme, L. (1965b). *Can. J. Zool.* **43**, 881.
Sømme, L. (1966). *J. Insect Physiol.* **12**, 1069.
Sotavolta, O. (1954). *Ann. Zool. Soc. Zool.-Botan. Fennicae Vanamo* **16**, No. 8, 1.
Spiess, E. B. (1950). *Evolution* **4**, 14.
Stahel, G., and Geijskes, D. C. (1940). *Rev. Entomol.* **11**, 766.
Steiner, A. (1926). *Mitt. Naturforsch. Ges. Bern* p. 1.
Steiner, A. (1929). *Z. Vergleich. Physiol* **9**, 1.
Steiner, A. (1930a). *Naturwissenschaften* **18**, 595.
Steiner, A. (1930b). *Z. Vergleich. Physiol.* **11**, 461.
Stower, W. J., and Griffiths, J. F. (1966). *Entomol. Exptl. Appl.* **9**, 127.
Strebel, O. (1932). *Z. Morphol. Oekol. Tiere* **25**, 31.
Strel'nikov, I. D. (1936). *Trav. Inst. Zool. Acad. Sci. USSR* **2**, 637.
Sweetman, H. L. (1938). *Ecol. Monographs* **8**, 285.
Sweetman, H. L. (1939). *J. Econ. Entomol.* **32**, 698.
Tantawy, A. O., and Mallah, G. S. (1961). *Evolution* **15**, 1.
Thomsen, E., and Thomsen, M. (1937). *Z. Vergleich. Physiol.* **24**, 343.
Thomson, R. C. M. (1938). *Bull. Entomol. Res.* **29**, 125.
Timoféeff-Ressovsky, N. W. (1940). *In* "The New Systematics" (J. Huxley, ed.), pp. 73–136. Oxford Univ. Press (Clarendon), London and New York.
Timon-David, J. (1930). *Ann. Fac. Sci. Marseille* **4**, 29.
Tombes, A. S. (1965). *Proc. 12th Intern. Congr. Entomol., London, 1964* p. 183.
Totze, R. (1933). *Z. Vergleich. Physiol.* **19**, 110.
Umminger, B. L. (1968). *Yale Sci. Mag.* **42**, 6.
Uvarov, B. P. (1931). *Trans. Entomol. Soc. London* **79**, 1.
Van de Bund, C. F., and Helle, W. (1960). *Entomol. Exptl. Appl.* **3**, 142.
Verrier, M. L. (1932). *Bull. Biol. France Belg.* **66**, 200.

Wallwork, J. A. (1960). *Proc. Zool. Soc. London* **135,** 619.

Waloff, N. (1949). *Trans. Roy. Entomol. Soc. London* **100,** 147.

Warburg, M. R. (1965). *Physiol. Zool.* **38,** 99.

Wellington, W. G. (1949). *Sci. Agr.* **29,** 201.

Wellington, W. G. (1950). *Sci. Agr.* **30,** 209.

Weyrauch, W. (1936). *Z. Vergleich. Physiol.* **23,** 51.

Wigglesworth, V. B. (1941). *Parasitology* **33,** 67.

Wigglesworth, V. B. (1965). "The Principles of Insect Physiology," (6th rev. ed.). Dutton, New York.

Wigglesworth, V. B., and Gillett, J. D. (1934). *J. Exptl. Biol* **11,** 120.

Wilkinson, P. R. (1953). *Australian J. Zool.* **1,** 345.

Williams, C. B. (1930). "The Migration of Butterflies." Oliver and Boyd, New York.

Williams, C. B. (1938). *Ann. Entomol. Soc. Am.* **31,** 211.

Wohlgemuth, R. (1957). *Z. Vergleich. Physiol.* **40,** 119.

Wright, S., and Dobzhansky, T. (1946). *Genetics* **31,** 125.

Yuill, J. S., and Craig, R. (1937). *J. Exptl. Zool.* **75,** 169.

Chapter 3 FISH

F. E. J. Fry and P. W. Hochachka

I. Introduction

Many observations on the resting metabolism of various species of fish in relation to temperature (e.g., Scholander *et al.,* 1953, Arctic and tropical; Wohlschlag, 1960, Antarctic) show the range of adaptation of these poikilotherms to temperature. Species active at the poles have as high metabolic

rates at the appropriate low temperatures as do tropical species at the
much higher temperatures appropriate to them. There can be said to be
a continuum of metabolism–temperature curves for various fishes whereby
each reaches its maximum at its own point between −2°C to 40°C. A
comparison of the tissue metabolism of two species well toward the two
ends of the spectrum is given by Somero and deVries, (1967). The respiration of tissue preparations from an Antarctic fish, *Trematomus,* is as high
at 0°–5°C as the rate of comparable tissues from goldfish at 20°–25°C.

We shall take for granted this wide adaptive radiation shown in the
temperature relations of the species and deal here with acclimative changes
displayed by the individual. Fish are continuously adjusting to changes
in temperature as shown in the example in Fig. 1. Here, the irregularities

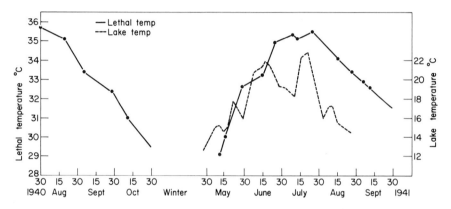

Fɪɢ. 1.   Seasonal change in the 14-hour upper lethal temperature of the bullhead in
relation to changes in water temperature of its habitat. Modified from Brett (1944).

in the curve are not the result of experimental error, but are responses
to the vagaries of the weather superimposed on the annual climatic cycle.
Adjustment may be reactionary, that is, a response to the immediate effect
of the environment, or it may be anticipatory. In anticipatory thermoadjust-
ment, the organism responds to some aspect of the environment linked
with the temperature cycle so as to predispose it to the change in
temperature.

Adjustments to temperature of the whole organism are first described
and a brief account then given of the effect of thermal history on organs
and tissues. However, the shifts in metabolism of tissues are not considered
at all exhaustively particularly in view of Precht's major review on the
subject (1968). Instead, emphasis is placed on the possibilities for adjustment in the activity of the respiratory enzymes, together with an hypothesis
for regulation that will account for anticipatory as well as reactionary
adjustment.

A few species of fish have the ability to regulate their body temperature at least to some degree. Such physiological regulation is summarized briefly.

II. The Whole Organism

A. TEMPERATURE COMPENSATION

1. *Resistance Adjustment*

The most fundamental adjustment is that which extends the range of temperature over which the animal can live: Precht's resistance adjustment (1949). Figure 2 shows a typical thermal tolerance diagram for a fish, the example shown being chosen for the completeness of the data. Figure 2 is an oversimplification in that no account is taken in this diagram of

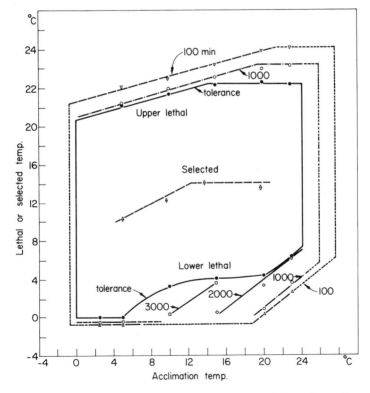

Fig. 2. Lethal temperature and temperature preference of the sockeye salmon, *Oncorhynchus nerka*, in fresh water, in relation to acclimation temperature. The central line is the modal selected temperature. The two lines labeled "tolerance" represent the incipient lethal temperatures—the temperatures at which 50% of the sample survives on indefinitely continued exposure. The remaining lines show the temperatures which kill 50% of the sample in a given length of time. From Brett (1952) and Brett and Alderdice (1958).

any aspect of the environment other than the thermal regime, and thus only reactionary adjustment is displayed.

There can be substantial anticipatory adjustment in the lethal temperature. For example, Hart (1952) found summer—winter differences clearly expressed in the upper lethal temperatures at a given acclimation temperature of four species of minnows. Day length has been shown to have an effect on upper lethal temperature independent of the normal seasonal change (Hoar and Robinson, 1959; Tyler, 1966). In these various cases, the upper lethal temperature is higher in summer or after prior exposure to longer days. Hart also found some evidence of a reciprocal effect in the lower lethal temperature. However, major consideration of anticipatory adjustment will be left until the section on behavioral thermoregulation (Section II,B,2).

In the sockeye salmon (Fig. 2), the upper lethal temperature changes approximately 1°C for every 4°C change in the acclimation temperature. The latter term refers to a constant temperature to which the fish have been exposed for a sufficient time to bring about a stable response. At a certain high acclimation temperature—the level being related to the length of time that the fish can withstand a given temperature—there is no further change in lethal temperature with changing acclimation temperature. Thus, in Fig. 2, the upper tolerance temperature, the temperature at which the animal can live for an indefinitely prolonged period, does not change with rising acclimation temperature beyond 14°C. There is no further adjustment in the ability to resist an upper lethal temperature for 1000 minutes above an acclimation temperature of approximately 18°C. The upper lethal temperature that can be resisted for 100 minutes continues to rise, however, with increasing acclimation temperature up to 22°C. Hence, resistance adjustment is complex, short-term resistance to high temperature being adjusted over a wider range than long-term resistance. The adjustment in the lower lethal temperature in relation to changes in acclimation temperature is reciprocal, but still more complex. The low temperature which a sockeye can resist for a given length of time changes by approximately 1°C for a 1.5°C change in acclimation temperature. Again, a point is reached where a further change in acclimation temperature brings no further change in the lethal temperature. Lower lethal temperatures for short-term resistance are stabilized at higher acclimation temperatures than are those for long-term resistance. The further complexity in the response of the lower lethal temperature to acclimation temperature appears to be due to a discontinuity in the time at which the fish passes from the zone of thermal resistance to the zone of tolerance, that is from a temperature at which the fish dies in a determinate time to one at which it can live indefinitely. It can be taken then that the leveling of the response to acclimation temperature in the tolerance of the sockeye to low temperature is analogous to the plateau in the response of the upper lethal temperature.

Such complexities in the relation of lethal temperature to acclimation temperature are not yet understood but must indicate a complexity in the causes of death under thermal stress, so that the adjustive response is not necessarily the same one at all acclimation temperatures. A recent paper commenting on such complexities in the upper lethal temperature is that of Tyler (1966), and the general subject is reviewed briefly in Fry (1967).

Much of the literature on lethal temperatures of fish is reviewed by Brett (1956) and Fry (1964, 1967). Many species, for example the bullhead, for which the seasonal change in the upper lethal temperature is shown in Fig. 1, and the goldfish (Fry *et al.*, 1942) have a greater range of compensation than does the sockeye. Observations on marine species are rare, but recently Hoff and Westman (1966) have given complete thermal tolerance diagrams for three temperate marine species, all of which follow the typical pattern shown in Fig. 2. The lower incipient lethal temperatures of two of these, the flounder, *Pseudopleuronectes americanus,* and the silverside, *Menidia menidia,* level off at approximately 1°C at relatively high acclimation temperatures. The third species, the northern swellfish, *Spheroides maculatus,* has a single phase in the response of the lower lethal to acclimation temperature, changing linearly from 14°C at an acclimation temperature of 32.5°C to 8°C at an acclimation temperature of 8°C.

2. *Capacity Adjustment*

Figure 3 shows the effect of acclimation temperature on the ability of a fish to be active. The attribute displayed is the so-called cruising speed, which is measured by inducing the fish to swim either in a rotating chamber or against a current in a flume or pipe. In the example shown, as in the same type of measurement in other species (see Fry, 1967, for earlier references), a fish can ordinarily swim at its best at any given temperature when acclimated to that temperature. In the cruising speed of the green sunfish, there is little acclimation effect except at the extreme temperatures. Roots and Prosser (1962) were of the opinion that the muscles and nerves can bring about swimming over the whole range of temperature within the lethal limits at a given acclimation level, but that the usual response is blocked at the extremes. At low temperatures, a strong stimulus would bring about a short swimming response. At high temperatures, the fish appeared to be trying to escape from the warm water, and Roots and Prosser suggest its attitude with the spines of its dorsal fin held stiffly erect indicated a fright reaction.

Brett (1967) concluded that acclimation of *Oncorhynchus nerka* to 15°C allowed that species to cruise somewhat faster at 10°C and 20°C than when acclimated to the latter temperatures. A similar slight advantage was shown at 38°C by the goldfish acclimated to 35°C over the extrapolated response for those acclimated to the higher temperature (Fry and Hart, 1948). However, neither of these differences are large. Brett (1967) points out that the precipitous decrease in swimming speed at high temperatures

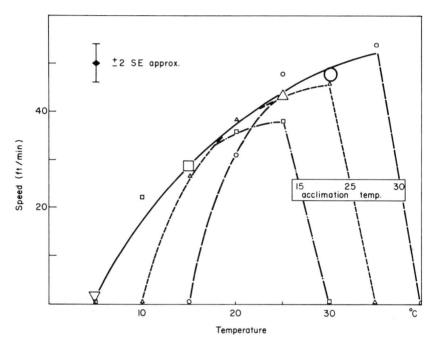

Fig. 3.   Sustained swimming speed of the green sunfish in relation to test and acclimation temperature. From Roots and Prosser (1962). Large symbols denote tests at acclimation temperatures.

comes in the range of the temperature that is lethal. Roots and Prosser (1962) had no measure of the upper lethal temperature of the green sunfish, but from comparison with other centrarchids, it seems probable that the same case applies to their data also.

3. *Adjustment in Metabolic Rate*

As is the case for other organisms, numerous investigations, perhaps the earliest being those of Wells (1935), have shown that after a sudden change to a new temperature, the metabolism of intact fish adjusts upwards or downwards—appropriate to the direction of the temperature shift—so that the result is a reduction of the Q_{10} for the acclimated, as opposed to the unacclimated animal. There are some exceptions to this generalization, for example, Christophersen and Precht (1952) and Roberts (1966) found that the crucian carp, *Carassius carassius,* did not have as high a metabolic rate at an intermediate temperature when acclimated to a low temperature as when acclimated at a higher one. However, whatever the change, it is probable, both from the nature of the experiments performed and from the magnitude of the metabolic rates found, that the preponderance of adjustment in the metabolism of the intact fish is due to changes in the degree of locomotor activity, as indeed Wells suggested. Unfortunately, although occasionally given specific mention (Roberts, 1961), the possibility that changes in locomotor activity may be the ruling factor in the changes in metabolism during adjustment to temperature appears to have been largely overlooked in the physiological literature. Most investigators have relied on a quiet, darkened chamber, and the circumstance that the fish must confine its movements to a small compass, in order to reduce the metabolism due to spontaneous activity to a negligible minimum, a faith that has usually been misplaced. The use of anaesthetics (Christophersen and Precht, 1952) or surgical immobilization (Suhrmann, 1955) has, in general, been avoided because of undesirable side effects (McFarland, 1959; Schultze, 1965b).

The definitive experiment, which has interpreted all the previous numerous investigations on the effect of sudden shifts of temperature on the metabolic rate of fish, is Precht's two-temperature experiment on the eel (Precht, 1961; Schultze, 1965a,b). In this experiment, an eel is confined to a narrow tube, not much longer than the fish itself, which is supplied with water at a different temperature from either end. The water is drained out midway along the tube, and thus the anterior half of the eel can be acclimated to one temperature and the posterior to another. Schultze demonstrated that the metabolic rate of eels so treated responded in a manner characteristic of the thermal history of the eel's anterior end. Hence he concluded, after Fisher (1958), that thermal acclimation in this respect was a function of the central nervous system. In the light of Schultze's findings, most further consideration of adjustment in the metabolism of the whole fish will be confined to a consideration of the order of magnitude of the metabolic rate of the goldfish under the various pertinent experimental conditions (Fig. 4).

The active and standard rates of metabolism (Fig. 4) indicate the limits to the rates of oxygen consumption so far found for goldfish at the various temperatures. The active rate is found by inducing the fish to swim steadily while its oxygen consumption is measured. The classical work on active metabolism of fish is that of Brett (1964). References to later papers will

be found in Kutty (1968) or G. M. M. Rao (1968). The standard rate
shown in Fig. 4 was determined by simultaneously measuring the oxygen
consumption of the fish and the turbulence of the water in the respiration
chamber. The degree of turbulence is taken to be a measure of the physical
activity of the fish. A series of such pairs of measurements were taken
for a given fish, and its standard metabolism was found, from the relation

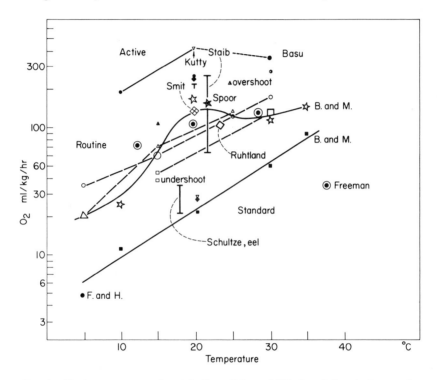

Fɪɢ. 4. Various measures of metabolism of the goldfish in relation to temperature.
From Basu (1959), Beamish and Mookherjii (1964), Freeman (1950), Fry and Hart (1948),
Klicka (1965), Kutty (1968), Ruhland (1965), Smit (1965), Spoor (1946), and Staib
(1962). Klicka's data are represented by open circles, upright triangles, and squares. For
routine metabolism, large symbols represent tests at acclimation temperatures. Active and
standard metabolism were always measured at the acclimation temperature. The range of
Schultze's data (1965b) for the eel is shown for comparison.

between the metabolic rate and the degree of turbulence, as the rate at
zero turbulence. Thus, in this instance, standard metabolism represents the
resting metabolism of the cells, the cost of muscle tone to retain posture,
and the cost of the supporting organ activities to maintain metabolism
at this level. The cost of locomotory activity and of irrigation of the gills
is eliminated. The method was pioneered by Spoor (1946), and the latest

refinement is that of Heusner and Enright (1966). References to most methods used up to now to measure activity in fishes may be found in de Groot and Schuyf (1967).

Standard metabolism has also been estimated by extrapolation to zero speed from measurements on fish swimming intermittently (Smit, 1965; Muir *et al.,* 1965) or steadily at various given or observed speeds (Wohlschlag, 1957; Brett, 1964). In these cases, standard metabolism includes the cost of irrigation and in Wohlschlag's method perhaps also the cost of excitement (see Smit, 1965; Kutty, 1968). The various methods all give standard metabolic rates of the same order if appropriate precautions are taken to ensure that the fish is not excited. Smit's measure of standard metabolism, given in Fig. 4, was determined by the swimming speed method and approximates that obtained by Beamish and Mookherjii (1964) by the turbulence method.

The central solid line in Fig. 4 passes through measurements of the routine metabolic rate of the goldfish, that is, the oxygen consumption of the fish as ordinarily measured—undisturbed in a darkened or shaded chamber during the ordinary working day. With some individual exceptions, the goldfish appears to be a diurnal animal. The various symbols represent the observations of various workers with some correction, for fish of different sizes, to values representative of a fish of 100 gm. The curve is continued only to 35°C. Freeman's point at 35°C was not used, since it diverges so widely from the rest of the data and there do not appear to be any confirmatory observations in the literature. The line for the routine metabolism of the goldfish lies well above the line describing the standard metabolic rate and follows a sigmoid course on a semilogarithmic plot, with little change in the rate with respect to temperature above 20°C. Such a zone of relatively constant metabolic rate over a certain range of temperature has commonly been found (e.g., Meuwis and Heuts, 1957) and is without doubt due to systematic changes in the degree of spontaneous activity in relation to level of temperature. Many of these changes have been related to the phenomenon of temperature selection (Schmein-Engberding, 1953; Sullivan, 1954; personal communication in Fry, 1964; Fisher and Sullivan, 1958; Ivlev, 1960). The order of magnitude of the metabolic rate along the routine curve, 21 to 142 ml O_2/kg/hr, is at the general level reported in most experiments on temperature compensation of the metabolism of intact fish, and indeed is shown by Klicka's measurements which are included in the figure and discussed below.

To show that fish which display only spontaneous activity have metabolic rates approaching the maximum at times, the range of values found by Staib (1962) is given. The line describing the range of Staib's values also approximately describes Spoor's range (1946) as well. Thus, in the case of these two investigators, the peak metabolic rates for spontaneous activity approach the active rate. The peak rate for spontaneous activity found by Smit again approaches the active rate. The chamber used by Smit was an annulus so that the fish could swim continuously, but the chambers used by Spoor and Staib were of the type ordinarily used, in which the fish is relatively restricted in its movement. Fish can show such high metabolic rates in small chambers because of the high cost of continual small accelerations.

Klicka's experiments (1965) on the response of the resting metabolism of the goldfish to temperature shifts are also shown in Fig. 4. Besides showing the typical pattern of response reported for such experiments (with the exception of an anomaly at 5°C), it will also be seen that these values all cluster closely about the line for routine metabolism. Moreover, the overshoot and undershoot for metabolism that are characteristic of the first response to a sudden increase or decrease in temperature also lie well within the curves for active and standard metabolism for acclimated animals, and thus can also be accounted for by changes in physical activity, in the absence of evidence to the contrary.

It cannot be said, therefore, from evidence such as is presented by Klicka's data, that any fundamental change in the metabolism of the aggregate of the individual cells of the goldfish has brought about the changes observed in the metabolism of the whole organism or that the converse is true. The conclusion drawn from this detailed consideration of the goldfish data probably holds for the various other observations on other species. Indeed, Peterson and Anderson (1969) have provided direct measurements of the effect of temperature on spontaneous activity in relation to acclimation temperature for the Atlantic salmon (Fig. 5), which show shifts of the type shown by curves for metabolism such as Klicka's.

However, while the conclusion voiced above, namely that investigations of the metabolism of intact fish have generally failed to show compensations that can be unequivocally ascribed to the resting metabolism of the major mass of cells, is a negative one, this is not to say that the experiments have not demonstrated temperature compensation. There has certainly been compensation, but the compensation in spontaneous activity has probably overshadowed the physiological compensation that undoubtedly underlies it. The remarkable thing about the data on routine metabolism in Fig. 4 is the consistency in the values found by the various authors, which forces one to the conclusion that thermal history has a profound influence on behavior. Looked at in this light the typical pattern of metabolic compensation to changes in temperature must represent capacity adjustments in the central nervous system.

With the adoption of the oxygen electrode, a partial allowance for activity has been made, in that immediate observations of short-term fluctuations in oxygen consumption are possible, and the metabolic rate is measured only when the oxygen consumption has been steady and low, relative to the fluctuating values. Schultze's data (1965b), found in this way, are plotted in Fig. 4. His data for the eel are of the same order as those for the standard metabolism of the goldfish, but of course, still show temperature compensation under the influence of the anterior end of the ani-

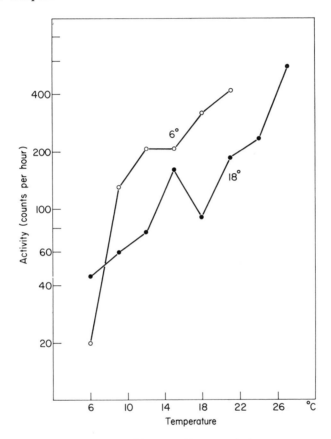

Fɪɢ. 5.   Effect of acclimation to 6°C and 18°C, respectively, on spontaneous activity in relation to temperature in Atlantic salmon, *Salmo salar*. The activity shown is the rate 1–6 hours after the change in temperature. Modified from Fig. 9, Peterson and Anderson (1969).

mal. Schultze's data are better compared with the routine metabolism of the eel determined by Boetius and Boetius (1967).

The question remains then as to whether, when techniques are sufficiently refined, temperature compensation will be found in the standard metabolism of the intact fish. The experimenter, of course, faces other difficulties, beyond the assessment of physical activity, in looking for capacity adjustment in the standard metabolic rate of the intact fish. The fish as an aquatic animal must meet the cost of osmoregulation. For a 100-gm rainbow trout in fresh water, the cost of osmoregulation is about 20% of its metabolic rate, whether the fish is acclimated to either 5°C or 15°C (G. M. M. Rao, 1968). There appear, therefore, to be adjustments in the permeability of the fish with thermal acclimation. A rapid change in temperature might lead to a transitory change in the cost of osmoregulation, while the permeability of the integument was being readjusted. An obvious desirable modification of experimental techniques is the control of the osmotic pressure of the medium, as well as control of spontaneous activity.

Beamish (1964b) found a clearly expressed annual variation in the standard metabolism of the eastern brook trout, *Salvelinus fontinalis,* maintained throughout the year at 10°C under natural daylight at Lat 45N. The standard metabolic rate in the late fall spawning period was approximately double the minimum rate for the year, which was found in March and April.

An impression that may be gained from the literature concerning metabolism of the whole organism is that temperature compensation may greatly reduce the Q_{10} below 2. When standard metabolism has been measured in fish acclimated to each test temperature, such is not the case. The Q_{10} for standard metabolism of the goldfish acclimated to each test temperature is approximately 2 throughout the range. Similar values, but with some variation of Q_{10} over the temperature range, are given for other species by Beamish (1964a) and Brett (1964). The relation of active metabolism to temperature is complicated by the limiting effect of the oxygen supply at higher temperatures, a point well discussed by Brett (1964), but again in his data for the sockeye, which are the most reliable available, the Q_{10} for active metabolism does not depart greatly from 2 where oxygen is not limiting.

While most work in capacity adjustment has been concerned with routine metabolism, Kanungo and Prosser (1959) measured the effects of sudden shifts of temperature on active metabolism. Although they did not get such high values as those for the active line shown in Fig. 4, they did get a clear shift of metabolic rate in the direction required to be consonant with the adjustments in cruising speed, such as are shown in Fig. 3. Their data are shown in relation to the data of various other authors (Fry, 1967; his Fig. 11). It is to be hoped that more such work will be done.

B. TEMPERATURE REGULATION

1. *Introduction*

Fish, in common apparently with all motile organisms, respond to a temperature gradient by selecting, with more or less precision, a particular temperature (Fig. 6). To a large degree, the phenomenon of temperature selection explains the distribution of fish in nature (Ferguson, 1958; Alabaster and Downing, 1966). It seems to hold that the final preferendum, the point at which the selected temperature coincides with the acclimation temperature (e.g., 14°C for the sockeye salmon in Fig. 2) represents an optimum as measured by various activities (Sullivan, 1954; Fry, 1964). However, there are no exhaustive series of comparisons of final preferenda with optima for various activities, and even acceptance of those reported must be provisional until the effect of season on the final preferendum has been well explored (Fig. 7). Probably the most impressive demonstration of behavioral thermoregulation in fish is that of Rozin and Mayer (1961), who trained individual goldfish to maintain the temperature of their aquarium water by actuating a valve to introduce cool water as the temperature rose. Such fish maintained the aquarium temperature at about 34°C with a precision equivalent to that achieved by the rat in a similar performance.

In two groups of fish, the tunas and the lamnid sharks (Carey and Teal, 1969a), it has been demonstrated that there is some physiological thermoregulation by local conservation of muscular heat.

The temperature sense, which is acute in fish (Bull, 1936; Bardach, 1956; Bardach and Bjorklund, 1957), is generally attributed to the undifferentiated nerve endings in the skin. Murray (1965) concluded that the temperature response of the ampullae of Lorenzini (Sand, 1938) is an incidental one. Murray (1965, 1967) considers that the biologically important function of the ampullae is to detect faint electric currents, and he argues that, in particular, the canal which intervenes between the ampulla and the surface is evidence against the temperature sense being of primary significance. In any event, the ampullae are present only in relatively few forms. Späth (1967) measured the impulses carried by the maxillary nerve when a 1-mm diameter sphere of glass (at skin temperature) or silver (heated or cooled) was pressed lightly on the skin over the free endings of the nerve. If the sphere and the skin were at the same temperature, the impulses rose to a maximum with increasing temperature and decreased with decreasing temperature, thus, with the expected temperature effect. On the other hand, if the sphere was at a temperature different from that of the skin the impulses were more frequent when it was colder than the skin and less frequent when it was warmer, in proportion to the temperature difference. Späth therefore considers that a combination of temperature difference and pressure is necessary to provide the sensory information for thermokinetic behavior. If, however, a concurrent stimulus of pressure is essential for the fish to interpret changes in temperature, the necessary pressure effect must be exceedingly small. Bardach and Bjorklund (1957) report that a convection current descending from an ice cube, at a temperature difference of approximately 0.5°C in the range of 20°C, brought a sharp reaction from a yellow bullhead, *Ameiurus natalis*. Sullivan (1954) points out that temperature selection by fish in a gradient requires the central nervous system as well as the surface receptors.

2. *Behavioral Regulation*

Thermoregulatory behavior in fish is not yet well understood, nor indeed adequately described. The purpose of what follows is simply to give notice

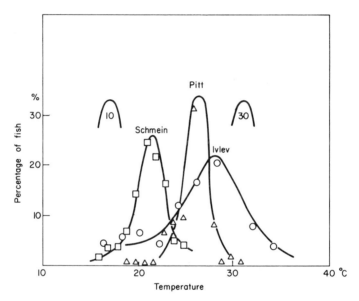

FIG. 6. Various measures of distribution of carp, *Cyprinus carpio*, in temperature gradients. Data of Pitt *et al.* (1956), Ivlev (1960), and Schmein-Engberding (1953). For explanation see text. Ten and thirty are modes for those acclimation temperatures.

of the phenomenon with particular reference to anticipatory thermoregulation. Figure 6 shows three examples of how fish distribute themselves in a gradient. All groups were acclimated to approximately the same temperature. In each instance, as is generally the case, there is a clearly defined clustering of the observations about some central temperature. In two cases—the data of Ivlev (1960) and Pitt *et al.* (1956)—whereas there is a difference in dispersion, which might easily be attributed to differences in the conditions of the experiments, the mean selected temperatures are similar. In the third (Schmein-Engberding), although the acclimation temperature is essentially the same, a considerably lower temperature was selected. Thus, while the thermal history may have a major effect on the position of the temperature preferendum, as is indicated in Fig. 6 by the modes for 10°C and 30°C acclimation temperatures, other circumstances have their influence.

Season may exert a major, and possibly the paramount, influence on the temperature preferendum. Sullivan and Fisher (1953) reported that the preferred temperature of the brook trout, *Salvelinus fontinalis*, increased in late winter, although the water in which their stock was kept was then at its coldest point. Figure 7 shows Zahn's data (1963) for the

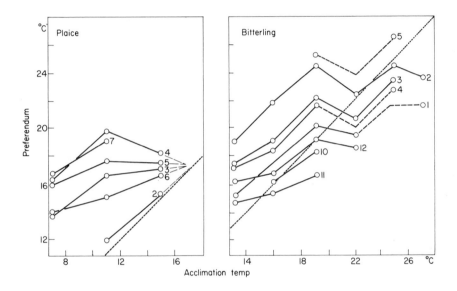

Fig. 7.   Effect of season and acclimation temperature on temperature selection in the plaice, *Pleuronectes platessa*, and bitterling, *Rhodeus sericeus*. From Zahn (1963). Numbers refer to months.

mean selected temperature of the plaice and the bitterling in relation to acclimation temperature and time of year. In both species, the general picture is one of a major interaction between season and acclimation temperature, so much so that in the summer months the temperature selected by the plaice is essentially independent of the acclimation temperature. Otherwise, in late fall and early winter, the temperature preferendum is probably low in relation to acclimation temperature and rises from late winter to early summer. There are some irregularities in the data presented for the bitterling, the more extensive series, which suggest that there may be two peaks, one in February and the other in May, but Zahn had two series of fish. He began in September with three fish taken near Berlin in July and added a further ten to his stock in February. These latter were from a fish farm. In his laboratory, the fish were exposed to natural daylight plus a supplement of artificial light from 8:00 to 18:00 hours. Thus the minimum photoperiod to which they were subjected was approximately 10 hours, which would provide a constant day from late October to early February at Lat 53N. The new stock, which came from a fish farm, may well have passed the winter at the natural photoperiod for the region. Thus the March–April observations are more likely to represent the natural cycle than those for January and February.

In contrast to the extensive anticipatory adjustment shown by the temperate species of the plaice and bitterling, Zahn states that two tropical species, a barb, *Puntius conchonius,* and the guppy, *Lebistes reticulatus,* showed no seasonal effect. Similarly, Garside and Tait (1958) found no seasonal effect in the rainbow trout, but they made only summer–winter comparisons.

Since time of year has been shown to have such a profound effect in a substantial fraction of the cases where it has been taken into account, there seems little profit in dealing at any length with the effect of thermal history alone. It has been observed that there is a wide variety of response in the thermal preferendum in relation to the thermal history (Ferguson, 1958; Zahn, 1962), under what may be termed, without further definition, the laboratory photoperiod. Such responses have gone from a slightly negative relation between acclimation temperature and selected temperature, as was reported for the rainbow trout by Garside and Tait (1958), to that of such species as the pink salmon, *Oncorhynchus gorbuschka,* (Brett, 1952), where the acclimation temperature and the preferendum may be almost the same over a wide range. The variety of responses shown in the observations of the thermal preferendum of the rainbow trout in the three major reports that present this subject (Mantelmann, 1958; Garside and Tait, 1958; Javaid and Anderson, 1967), little of which can be explained at present by seasonal change or otherwise, suggests that inadequacies in our approach to such a behavioral manifestation as temperature selection may still often prejudice our observations. Such a reservation applies, though, only to detail. Two principles are clear, fish do display a thermal preferendum, and the choice can be responsive to other factors besides the thermal history.

In Fig. 7 (bearing in mind Zahn's supplement of artificial light), the temperature selected by the bitterling at a given acclimation temperature in midwinter would differ little from the acclimation temperature. In spring, however, at low acclimation temperatures, the temperature selected would be some 6°–8°C above the acclimation temperature. The data for the plaice show an even greater seasonal shift. In that case, the curves between acclimation temperature and selected temperature appear to fan out from a common final preferendum of approximately 18°C, so that in late spring, the preferendum is almost independent of the acclimation temperature. In the few data presented for February, acclimation temperature and selected temperature are essentially identical.

It is tempting to interpret such changes in the relation of the preferendum to the acclimation temperature as a predisposition toward cold temperatures in winter and warmer ones in summer, which occurs some time before the event is realized. No doubt such an interpretation was in the minds of Sullivan and Fisher (1953), who first described a seasonal shift in the thermal preferendum and commented on its relation to the seasonal light cycle. These authors later demonstrated that the temperature for peak spontaneous activity, when temperature is changed by rapid steps, shifted with season, in order to correspond with the shift in the preferendum. Roberts (1964) stated the proposition explicitly.

Figure 8 shows two examples of probable anticipatory thermal adjustment that may be reflected by seasonal changes in behavioral thermoregulation. Figure 8A displays Roberts' data (1964) for the routine metabolism of the pumpkinseed. Here, fish exposed to short days for some time show a higher spontaneous activity relative to acclimation temperature than do fish previously exposed to long days. Figure 8B shows a seasonal effect on what is, probably, to a considerable degree, a forced activity. The upper level of metabolism shown there has been designated "paced," since the values were obtained by Wohlschlag's method (1957). In his method there is an input into the situation by the experimenter, since the chamber is rotated counter to the direction in which the fish is swimming. Thus, although the speed of rotation is set by the speed at which the fish starts to swim spontaneously, the backward displacement of the fish relative to its surroundings may tend to perpetuate the movement. The order of magnitude of the values for the paced metabolism in the pinfish is that for the active metabolism of the goldfish, as the comparison in Fig. 8B shows.

In both examples, at temperatures above 10°C, the individuals previously exposed to short, or shortening, days show a higher activity at a given acclimation temperature. However, the data are not displayed here to comment on the direction of the change, but merely to point out the order of magnitude of the adjustments that are independent of the direct influence of temperature. In the data of Wohlschlag *et al.* (1968), the response brought about by season is equivalent to a difference in acclimation temperature of about 7°C. Change in day length gives about an equivalent effect in Roberts' data. A feature of his data that Roberts (1964) stresses is the lack of a photoperiod effect below 10°C, which he attributes to the fact that this species is in a state of hibernation at those temperatures.

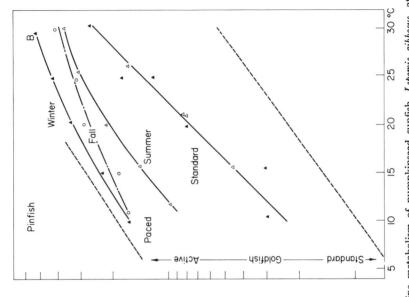

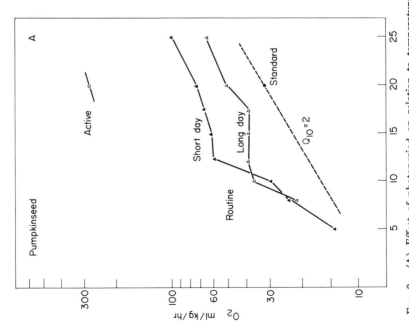

Fig. 8. (A) Effect of photoperiod on relation to temperature of routine metabolism of pumpkinseed sunfish, *Lepomis gibbosus*, at various acclimation temperatures. From Roberts (1964). Points for standard and active metabolism at various acclimation temperatures. From Brett and Sutherland (1965). (B) Paced metabolism of the pinfish in relation to season and acclimation temperature. Data of Wohlschlag et al. (1968). Goldfish data are from Fig. 4.

Wohlschlag *et al.* found no seasonal variation in their measure of standard metabolism.

3. *Physiological Regulation*

A partial regulation of the body temperature has been found in two groups of fishes, the tunas and the lamnid sharks. In these, the red lateral muscles largely receive their blood supply from the lateral artery through an extensive rete formed with the tributaries of the lateral vein, which forms an efficient countercurrent heat exchanger. There are some differences in the organization of the retia among the various tunas, and in some, the muscle may be served by a dorsal as well as a lateral rete (Kishinouye, 1923). The red lateral muscles in these fishes extend deep between the main masses of body muscle, which receive their main blood supply through vessels not associated with retia. The case is best known for the tunas and has only recently been described for lamnid sharks (Carey and Teal, 1969a). The red muscle is the muscle used in steady swimming, and thus in both these groups, which must swim continuously, it is continuously producing heat. The heat conserved by the rete warms the major muscle mass, presumably by conduction. The temperature is not constant throughout the main muscle (Carey and Teal, 1966), but shows the appropriate gradients to the surface and to the dorsal aorta, where the heat sinks are. The viscera receive less of the conserved heat—in some species there is a visceral rete (Kishinouye, 1923)—and the heart least of all. Data for the brain are lacking.

The muscle heat conservation system can be extremely effective, as Fig. 9 shows. The bluefin tuna are the most effective conservers of the species investigated, possibly because of the large size of the individuals under observation, but other species maintain considerable temperature differentials between their muscles and the water in which they are found. There are also regressions of muscle temperature on ambient for the skipjack, *Katsuwonus pelamis,* and the yellowfin, *Thunnus albacares* (Barrett and Hester, 1964). These have lesser powers of conservation in terms of the slope of regression of body temperature on ambient temperature. The mako shark, *Isurus oxyrhynchus,* regulates to a somewhat lesser degree than the tuna, but over water temperatures from 22°C to 15°C maintained a temperature differential of approximately 5°C (Carey and Teal, 1969a).

The temperature excess achieved by these fish appears to be attained by conservation through heat exchange in the retia and not by increased thermogenesis, as is indicated by the data for the active bluefin (Fig. 9). Those fish which had been played on hook and line for long periods, and which would have been expected to have had a higher metabolic rate in the time immediately preceding observations, showed a lowering of the body temperature in comparison to those fish which had been taken quietly in traps.

Control of temperature in these fish is best looked at as control of the upper limit, as Carey and Teal (1969b) comment. When the water temperature is below the optimum for the muscle, the fish conserves heat either to the extent that is necessary or to that which is within its capability. Presumably, no conservation is practiced at all at temperatures above the optimum and muscle temperature will then equal ambient temperature. The temperatures at which extrapolation predicts the muscle temperature

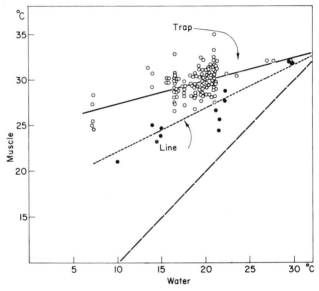

Fig. 9.   Maximum muscle temperatures in bluefin tuna, *Thunnus thynnus*, in relation to water temperature. Open circles—fish shot in traps without struggling; dots—fish taken by angling; lowest line indicates equality of body and water temperature. Modified from Carey and Teal (1969b).

to equal the ambient are about 33°C for the bluefin and 39°C for the skipjack and the yellowfin (Barrett and Hester, 1964). In the mako shark, Carey and Teal (1969a) indicate that a similar equivalence of temperatures would be found at approximately 28°C.

Another physiological response to temperature change which may be related to temperature regulation, or at least foreshadow events in the higher vertebrates, is the change in circulation which apparently accompanies a sudden change in ambient temperature. Pegel' and Remorov (1963) deduced that the circulation through the gills is restricted, at least for a short term, after a temperature change. Their interpretation is that the circulation through the gills is restricted to reduce the rate of heat exchange. The difference in the rate of heat transfer between heating and cooling (see Ihssen's data for the goldfish in Fry, 1967) is possibly another indication of the same response. An extreme case of the constriction of the branchial blood vessels is reported by Potts and Morris (1968) for the Antarctic fish. *Trematomus bernachii.* In this species, the gills are normally gorged with blood, but at extremely low temperatures, they are almost bloodless. The constriction is considered to be related to osmotic control, and perhaps it helps to resist freezing of the blood.

III. Organ Systems

Tissues, or organs dealt with as aggregations of cells, have been the components of fish most widely examined for evidence of temperature adjustment. Some changes, however, that might explain temperature adjustment, have also been looked for in the capacities of the organ systems. None of these investigations can be considered conclusive, but there has been preliminary work on the circulatory, nervous, and digestive systems. Of these, the most recent is the work of Smit (1967) on the digestive system, in which he measured the rate of secretion of acid and pepsin in relation to acclimation temperature. He found little adjustment at 15°C. Above that temperature he found Precht's type 3 compensation complicated by the circumstance that the curve for fish acclimated to each test temperature showed an optimum at 25°C. Smit did not measure actual digestion rates, but he infers that the rate of digestion is also most rapid at 25°C. In support of this he cites Gomazkov's finding (1959) that the ling, *Lota lota,* has a higher rate of digestion at 10°C than at 21°C.

The work of Prosser and his associates on adjustment in the nervous system is illustrated in Fig. 10, together with the relation of the lower incipient lethal temperature. The most significant feature in this comparison is that the slopes of the various lines are essentially parallel, indicating that the quantitative response to thermal acclimation is similar in cold block, minimum conditioning temperature, and the lower lethal temperature. Further, the cold-block temperature for the simple reflex—a twitch of the caudal fin as the result of an electric shock administered to the isthmus—is at about the same absolute level of temperature as the lethal temperature. The most cold-sensitive relation of the nervous system shown on the graph is that between conditioning temperature and cold-block temperature, which, if the conditioning temperature is the acclimation temperature, lies about 13°C above the lethal temperature, where the lines are parallel. However, without any change in thermal acclimation, a conditioned reflex can be established down to the broken line running through point *C* (Fig. 10). The minimum cold block line approaches 0°C at an acclimation temperature of 10°C, and thus it would appear that goldfish can function adequately at the near freezing temperatures of winter, as indeed experience shows.

Cold block of the nervous system is not likely to be responsible for all acclimative changes in lower lethal temperature. With respect to the lower lethal temperatures of the sockeye salmon illustrated in Fig. 2, it may be surmised that cold block of simple reflexes might be related to lower lethal temperature at acclimation temperatures above 20°C. If such is the case,

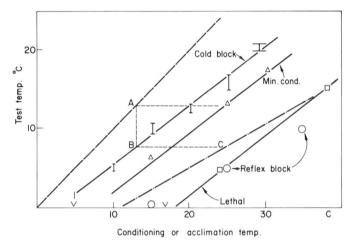

Fig. 10.   Various measures of the response of the central nervous system of the goldfish to acclimation temperature. The uppermost, dashed, line is a construction line which indicates when acclimation and test temperature are equal, and was used to determine the position of the dotted line. The dotted line indicates the minimum cold-block temperature for forming a conditioned reflex at a given acclimation temperature and was arrived at by proceeding through points such as are indicated by A, B, and C; v indicates the lethal temperature was below 0°C. Data of Prosser and Fahri (1965) and Roots and Prosser (1962). Lethal temperatures from Fry *et al.* (1942).

then at lower acclimation temperatures, survival must be limited by the functioning of some other system, which breaks down in advance of the cold block of the nervous system. Loss of ability to osmoregulate is a possibility (Doudoroff, 1945).

Acclimation responses of the circulatory system have been looked for particularly in the transport capacity of the blood, but to date, the findings have been generally negative. For example, Anthony (1961a), found no difference in the oxygen capacity of blood between goldfish acclimated to 5°C and those acclimated to 30°C. Again Black and his colleagues (1966a,b) found no changes in the dissociation curves for the blood of brook trout and Atlantic salmon. However, Grigg (1969) found a consistently higher oxygen affinity in the blood of the bullhead, *Ictalurus nebulosus,* acclimated to 24°C as compared with that of fish acclimated to 9°C. He attributed this shift to changes in erythrocytes rather than in the plasma. Hart (1957), in some crude experiments, found that the stroke output of the channel cat, *Ictalurus punctatus,* and the largemouth bass, *Huro salmoides,* in relation to rate of heart beat, was greater in summer than in winter, suggesting that the pumping capacity of the circulatory system might be greater when the fish were acclimated to higher temperatures. Das and Prosser (1967) also suggest that there is a greater blood supply to muscle when goldfish are acclimated to 25°C than when they are acclimated to 5°C. Jankowsky's observations (1968) on the oxygen content of venous blood are also consonant with such a circulatory adjustment.

Now that there are refined methods for measuring blood pressure and stroke output (see e.g., K. Johansen *et al.,* 1966), new experiments based on Hart's preliminary findings may be well worthwhile. Basu (1959) measured the effect of the presence of dissolved carbon dioxide on the active rate of oxygen consumption of three species of fish and found that at high temperatures the pCO_2 had a somewhat less depressing effect. Anthony (1961b) objected to such a conclusion on the grounds that partial pressure may not be the proper expression for the level of carbon dioxide in the environment, presumably since the exchange between the fish and the water takes place through a countercurrent system, so that the significant measure may be concentration. Again, therefore, there is the promise that the new techniques of cannulation, which permit blood samples to be taken from swimming fish, will allow a new understanding of oxygen uptake and transfer under various environmental conditions and levels of activity (Randall *et al.,* 1967).

With regard to resistance adjustment, the succession of failure of various organs remains, at least superficially, unaltered when the upper lethal temperature changes (Precht, 1959; Tsukuda, 1961). Thus, adjustment in the different organ systems to changing temperature is parallel, to a large degree. Nevertheless, the discontinuities in the times to death, such as are shown in the differences of progression of the lines of equal thermal resistance at different acclimation temperatures (Fig. 2), do suggest, however, that the site of first failure can be different at different acclimation temperatures.

IV. Tissues

Isolated brains, livers, and muscles, have been investigated to determine the degree of temperature compensation at the cellular level. Gill filaments have also been studied without reference to the relative amount of the various tissues they contain. The tests on these tissues have been of three types: (1) a direct measurement of the thermal death point in muscle; (2) measurements of the metabolic rate, usually as oxygen consumption; and (3) analysis of metabolic pathways by substrate tests. In this section, a brief survey is presented of the first two approaches. Metabolic pathways are dealt with in Section V,D.

A. Thermal Death Points

The upper lethal temperatures of excised muscle have been found to be remarkably independent of acclimation temperature by Ushakov and his colleagues (Ushakov, 1964; Troshin 1967). While, unfortunately, no real comparisons can be made, it appears likely that the upper lethal temperature of excised muscle approximates the ultimate lethal temperature of the organism.

Data on muscle of the perch, *Perca fluviatilis,* and the roach, *Rutilus rutilus,* obtained by Kusakina (1962), can be compared with the ultimate lethal temperatures of the whole fish, as studied by Weatherley (1963) and Cocking (1959). For the perch, the 10-minute lethal temperatures are approximately 36°C for both muscle and the whole fish, while for the roach, the 100-minute lethal temperature of muscle is 30°C, approximately, and the ultimate lethal tolerance temperature of the fish is 33.5°C. The discrepancy in the case of the roach is perhaps due to poor survival of the muscle for other reasons. The chief environmental influence on the upper lethal temperature of muscle appears to be a brief depression of several degrees associated with the spawning season. In general, acclimation temperature has been found to have no effect, but Altukhov (1963), as well as observing the spawning period depression in resistance, found that survival time of excised muscle of the horse mackerel, *Trachurus mediterraneus,* increased by about 75% as the sea temperature changed from 12°C to 28°C. Studies of the lower lethal temperature of tissues appear to have been confined to studies of resistance to freezing.

B. Metabolic Rates

The metabolic rate of tissue slices, minces, and breis has been widely studied, usually as the rate of oxygen consumption. In general, although not by any means always to the same degree, and sometimes, indeed, with a reversal, the metabolic rates of tissues show a compensation of Precht's type 3 or a greater response. The various findings do not yet provide a consistent point of view, and the whole matter must still be considered unsettled, as are the relations of the metabolism of the whole organism. Thus, Precht (1964b) points out that muscle from bitterling, *Rhodeus amarus* (= *sericeus*), and ide, *Idus idus* (see also Berkholz, 1966), show a marked compensation in their oxygen consumption, while that of the eel shows rather less. The muscle of the tench, *Tinca tinca,* clearly shows still less compensation. Prosser (1967) points out in his summary of temperature compensation in surviving tissues of the goldfish, that gills show good temperature compensation, muscles less, liver still less, and heart and brain tissue virtually none. In the rainbow trout, *Salmo gairdneri,* gills have shown no compensation, brain complete compensation, and liver over-compensation (Evans *et al.,* 1962).

Precht's two-temperature experiment with the eel has demonstrated (Schultze, 1965b) that compensation in muscle (and presumably other tissues) is dependent on local temperatures (Chatfield *et al.,* 1953). However, Prosser *et al.* (1965), through a comparison of the relative frequency of tonic electric spikes in muscle in the anterior and posterior sections of the eel, with the rates of metabolism of muscle minces reported by Schultze (1965b), conclude that the metabolic rate of the excised muscle reflects the level of nervous impulses which have been reaching it. The finding of Wittenberger and Diaciuc (1965) that electrical stimulation of the red muscle of carp prior to excision increased the oxygen consumption of slices is concordant with the conclusion of Prosser *et al.,* as Jankowsky (1968) appreciated. Presumably, in the two-temperature experiment, the spinal cord responds to the temperature of local heating, and we are left uncertain as to whether the change in the metabolic rate of the muscle reflects a direct compensation of the tissue. Some tissue somewhere must compensate directly.

Precht (1964c) summarizes the various behavior of tissues following thermal acclimation as follows.

A. Tissues show capacity adjustment
1. There may be a direct effect of temperature on the tissue tested
2. The first effect may be on a regulatory tissue which then influences the tissue tested. (Precht's *Nacheffect*)
B. Tissues show no capacity adjustment
1. The effect is on the regulatory tissue only, the tissue tested making an immediate response when required but intrinsically not affected
2. The effect of the regulatory system can be transferred to the tissue tested through the circulatory system, the tissue in question again not being permanently affected (Precht's *Direkteffect*)

Precht's possibilities allow for anticipatory as well as reactionary compensation.

Changes in the metabolic rate have also been used to determine resistance adjustment of isolated tissues, as well as their capacity adjustment. The resistance measured has been that of the respiratory enzymes, not the resistance of the intact cell, which has been the subject of Ushakov and his

school. As a comparison, the muscle of *Carassius auratius gibelio* will cease
to respond to a stimulus after a 10-minute exposure at 41°C (Kusakina,
1962), while it requires 10 minutes at about 52°C irreversibly to reduce
the cell respiration (when returned to a more normal temperature), even
when the fish is acclimated to 5°C (Suhrmann, 1955; see Roberts, 1961,
for a note on the taxonomy of Suhrman's fish).

When the respiration of a tissue is measured in relation to temperature,

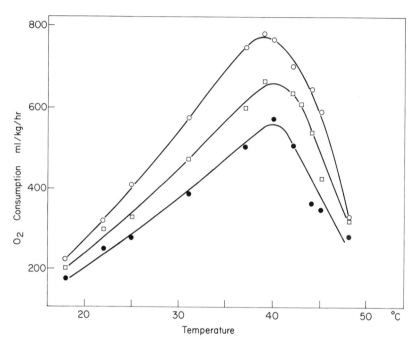

Fig. 11.   Oxygen consumption, during first half-hour, of muscle mince of the ide, *Idus
idus*, in relation to test and acclimation temperature. Acclimation temperatures: open
circles 15°C; squares 12 hours at 15°C, 12 hours at 22°C in alternation; solid circles 22°C.
Experiments Aug.–Oct. From Berkholz (1966).

there is a rising phase with higher temperature, as would be expected.
At a temperature somewhat above the lethal temperature for the fish, a
drop in the rate of respiration begins. At temperatures just above the inversion point, the change is reversible. At higher temperatures, the drop continues and becomes irreversible. The drop has been attributed to the thermal
destruction of enzymes (Ohlenbusch and Precht, 1960). The rate of tissue
respiration in relation to temperature, and the effect of thermal acclimation
on it, is particularly well shown by Berkholz (1966), whose data are presented in Fig. 11.

Precht, in order to get a quantitative measure of the change in the thermal resistance of respiratory enzymes, first measured the metabolic rate of the tissue at a convenient intermediate temperature, such as 22°C, and then exposed the sample in its Warburg vessel, for an appropriate period of time, to a temperature just a little higher than the inversion point. The sample was then returned to the original test temperature and its rate of metabolism was measured again. The proportional difference between measurements before and after exposure to the higher temperature was taken as an expression of the sensitivity of the enzyme system to temperature. In such measurements, muscle cells show clear signs of thermal acclimation (Jankowsky, 1964); there is a lesser proportional change in the metabolic rate for a given heat treatment the higher the thermal acclimation of the cell tested. These experiments, however, would appear to be tests of thermal stability of enzymes rather than of the cells which contain them.

V. Immediate Effects of Temperature on Enzyme Activity

A. SINGLE ENZYME SYSTEMS

Earlier studies of the thermal properties of poikilothermic enzymes have been concerned with heat denaturation or with measurements of activation energies and thermal optima for maximal velocities. Thus, it is sometimes held that enzymes from poikilotherms possess low activation energy characteristics, and therefore function as highly efficient catalysts, despite the low thermal energy available. To be sure, a positive correlation between the habitat temperature of the organism and activation energies of its enzymes sometimes is observed, as is shown in Arrhenius plots of pyruvate kinase (PyK) activity from muscle of trout, a temperate zone species active from 8° to 20°C, and *Trematomus,* an Antarctic fish active at −2° to 0°C (Fig. 12). It is evident that the activation energy of the *Trematomus* PyK is substantially lower than that of the trout. This may be adaptive. On the other hand, the activation energy of the rat muscle PyK, at its biological temperature range, is of the same order as that of *Trematomus* PyK some 40° lower. It is clear from these data alone that activation energy per se need not consistently correlate with the temperature in which any given enzyme must function. We have obtained similar results with several enzyme systems from polar, temperate zone, and tropical fishes. We find that the activation energies for any given enzyme cannot be categorized according to the species habitat temperatures; indeed, variations in activation energies of isozymes within species can be greater than variations between species adapted to distinctly different thermal environments.

We have therefore concluded that measurements of activation energies as
such yield rather little useful insight into compensatory responses to temperature. This problem is discussed further by Behrisch (1969) and Somero
(1969a).

Even less need be said concerning the importance of thermal optima
for maximum velocities (V_{max}) of poikilothermic enzymes. Again, in a

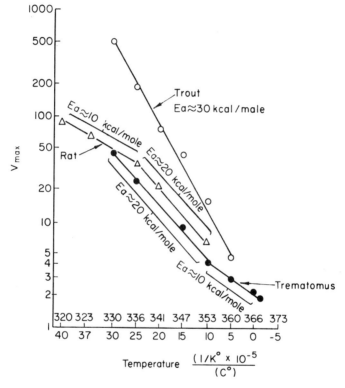

Fig. 12. Arrhenius plots of activity of pyruvate kinase (PyK) from rainbow trout,
Salmo gairdneri (open circles); *Trematomus borchgrevinki* (solid circles); and rat muscle
(triangles) from Somero and Hochachka (1968). For definition of V_{max} see Fig. 13.

small number of instances there appears to be a correlation between habitat
temperature of a given species and the optimum temperature for maximum
velocities of its enzymes. However, this correlation appears to be exceptional.
Usually, Arrhenius plots for V_{max} are linear up to temperatures well above
those which are lethal for the organism. Hence, it is clear that the thermal
optimum for maximal velocities is not a meaningful kinetic parameter for
temperature adaptation in poikilothermic organisms.

The question then arises as to why measurements of activation energy and thermal optima have yielded little insight into mechanisms of temperature adaptation. The difficulty seems to be that these characteristics are based on reaction velocities at saturating substrate concentrations. Such conditions are probably seldom, if ever, found *in vivo*. Modern theories of enzyme regulation all stress that a major kinetic parameter that is modulated is the apparent Michaelis constant, K_m, a measure of the affinity of the enzyme for substrate. This is shown diagramatically in Fig. 13, which is modified from Atkinson's review (1966). When the activity of a regulatory enzyme is measured in the presence of various concentrations of

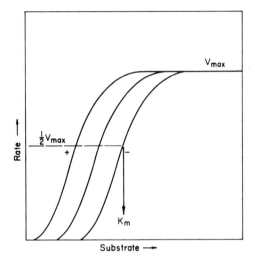

FIG. 13. Effect of positive and negative modulators on substrate saturation curves for regulatory enzymes displaying sigmoidal kinetics. Positive modulators swing the curve to the right. Usually, maximum velocity (V_{max}) is affected less than is the Michaelis constant (K_m). The K_m indicated is for the negatively modulated enzyme.

substrate, over low levels of substrate, there is typically a sigmoidally increasing activity with increasing substrate. Beyond a certain substrate level, further increases bring no increase in enzyme activity (V_{max}). The substrate level at which the rate is $\frac{1}{2} V_{max}$ is K_m. Whereas Fig. 13 refers to an ideal enzyme, it emphasizes that during modulation of enzyme activity, the parameter most likely to be affected is the apparent K_m of the substrate. We, therefore, were not surprised to find that low temperature may affect poikilothermic enzymes in a manner analogous to that of positive modulators. The effect, as seen for lungfish fructose diphosphatase (FDPase), can be dramatic enough so that, where substrate concentrations are within the physiological range, the reaction rate at low temperatures can be higher than at higher temperatures (i.e., the ascending portions of curves in Fig.

14). A similar situation occurs for king crab phosphofructokinase (J. M. Freed, 1969), trout acetylcholinesterase (Baldwin and Hochachka, 1970), lungfish lactate dehydrogenase (LDH) (Hochachka, and Somero, 1968), king crab LDH (Somero and Hochachka, 1969), and lungfish malate dehydrogenase (Hochachka, 1967b). The relationship between temperature and K_m is quite complex. Over the upper temperature range, the K_m varies directly with temperature; at the lower thermal extremes, for any given species, the effect of temperature is often reversed (Fig. 15). In this range, as the temperature is raised, the K_m

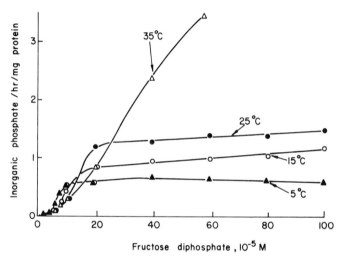

Fig. 14.   Substrate saturation curves of lungfish, *Lepidosiren paradoxa*, liver FDPase at different temperatures at pH 7.5. The saturation curves were carried out in the presence $8 \times 10^{-5}\ M\ \mathrm{Mn^{2+}}$. Figure modified after Behrisch and Hochachka (1969b).

drops. The magnitude of this thermal effect on the K_m varies from enzyme to enzyme, but the general pattern is not violated (see Hochachka and Somero, 1968; Behrisch, 1969; Baldwin and Hochachka, 1970). In consequence, plots of K_m vs temperature yield U-shaped curves, with the minimum K_m closely coinciding with the temperature that is normally encountered by the organism in nature.

A more direct way of illustrating the significance of temperature-dependent changes in enzyme–substrate affinity is shown in Fig. 16, which illustrates the effect of temperature on lungfish LDH activity. Lungfish LDH exhibits the greatest thermal dependence in K_m found for any enzyme we have examined. When temperature is increased from 33° to 45°C, for example, the K_m of pyruvate increases approximately 25-fold (Fig. 15). It is evident that $V_{\max}$ increases with temperature at a proportionately slower rate (the Q_{10} at $V_{\max}$ substrate concentrations is approximately 2.2). An important consequence of this differential change in K_m and $V_{\max}$ with temperature is that at low substrate concentrations, when K_m is of primary importance in determining reaction velocity, catalytic rates are higher at lower temperatures than at higher temperatures (Fig. 16). When substrate concentrations are raised above K_m values, catalytic rates behave

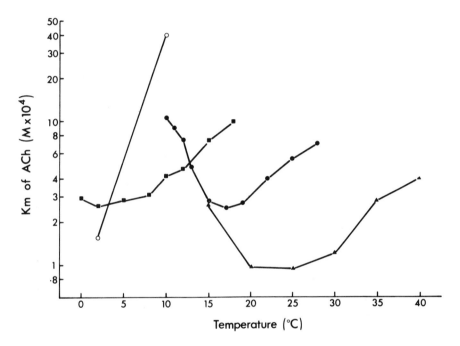

FIG. 15.   Effect of temperature on the K_m of brain AChE of *Trematomus* (open circles), 2° acclimated rainbow trout (solid squares), 17° acclimated rainbow trout (dark circles), and of electric eel (solid triangles). (After Baldwin and Hochachka, 1970; and Baldwin, 1970.)

according to the van t'Hoff law. The result of these $V_{\max}$ and K_m effects is a family of saturation curves for which the thermal optimum gradually shifts upward with increasing substrate concentrations (Fig. 16). It is evident from these considerations that the thermal properties of any given reaction must depend critically on cellular concentrations of substrate. This conclusion is of course consistent with current theories of metabolic regulation.

All of the studies described above were performed with single enzymes. In many poikilotherms, however, several variants (isozymes) of a particular

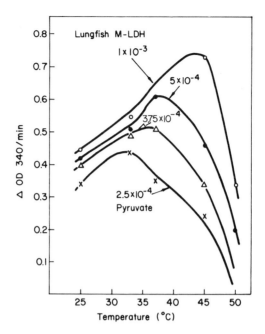

Fig. 16.   Effect of temperature on lungfish muscle lactic dehydrogenase (LDH) reaction velocity at increasing concentrations of pyruvate. Reaction assayed in 10^{-1} M phosphate buffer, pH 7.2, with NADH (nicotinamide adenine dinucleotide, reduced) concentration at 10^{-4} M (from Hochachka and Somero, 1968).

enzyme may be present in a single tissue. The properties of isozymes are discussed below.

B. Isozyme Systems

Although the literature is replete with kinetic comparisons of different isozyme systems, few studies have considered the complex kinetics likely to characterize mixed isozyme systems. We are particularly interested in whether differential temperature-dependent K_m changes can alter the number of isozymes which, at physiological substrate concentrations, are active at different temperatures. That is: can decreases in temperature lead to the activation of additional isozymes that are inactive at higher temperatures?

Two LDH systems of different complexity were considered: king crab (*Paralithodes camtschatica*) leg muscle LDH and rainbow trout epaxial muscle LDH (Somero and Hochachka, 1969). In the former system, two types of kinetic activity were discernible (Fig. 17). However, acrylamide gel electrophoresis revealed five LDH bands, a finding which indicates that the system is one in which two subunit types randomly assemble to

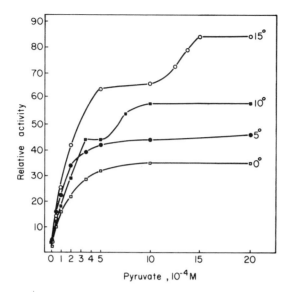

Fɪɢ. 17.   Activity of king crab, *Paralithodes camtschatica*, leg muscle LDH as a function of pyruvate concentration and temperature. The enzyme preparation was a 25–65 % ammonium sulfate precipitate that had been dialyzed exhaustively against $1 \times 10^{-2} M$ tris HCl buffer, pH 7.5, containing 1 mmole EDTA. (After Somero and Hochachka, 1969.)

generate five types of tetrameric LDH molecules. The data suggest that each subunit type largely retains a distinct set of kinetic properties, regardless of its tetrameric combination. This conclusion is consistent with other evidence on LDH function (Fluke and Hochachka, 1965; Kaplan, 1964).

The expected relationship between temperature and K_m of pyruvate is clearly exhibited by the two LDH's of the king crab system (Fig. 17; Table I).

TABLE I

Tʜᴇ Eғғᴇᴄᴛ ᴏғ Tᴇᴍᴘᴇʀᴀᴛᴜʀᴇ ᴏɴ ᴛʜᴇ K_m ᴏғ Pʏʀᴜᴠᴀᴛᴇ
ᴏғ ᴛʜᴇ Tᴡᴏ Kɪɴɢ Cʀᴀʙ LDH Eɴᴢʏᴍᴇs[a]

| Temperature (°C) | K_m of pyruvate (M^{-4}) | |
	"Low K_m" LDH	"High K_m" LDH
0		1.3[b]
5		0.8[b]
10	3.0	7.0
15	3.3	12.0

[a] From Somero and Hochachka (1969).

[b] At these two lower temperatures, the K_m values of the two LDH's are approximately equal (see Fig. 6).

Note, however, that the LDH having the higher K_m of substrate at 10°–15°C exhibits a much sharper temperature dependency in K_m than the other LDH subunit. This differential K_m change may be of great importance to the organism. At physiological pyruvate concentrations (0.1–1.0 M^{-4}) in king crab leg muscle, (J. Freed, 1969), only the low K_m LDH is active at 10°–15°C; the high K_m LDH will be inactive since its K_m of pyruvate is approximately two orders of magnitude greater than

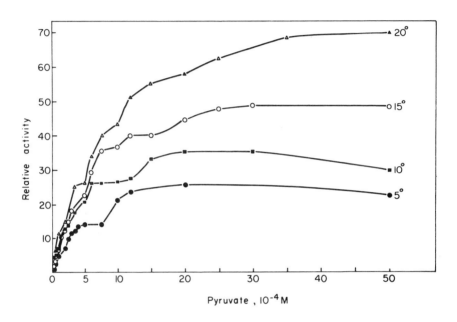

Fig. 18.   Activity of rainbow trout muscle LDH as a function of pyruvate concentration and temperature. Conditions are the same as those for Fig. 17. (After Somero and Hochachka, 1969.)

in vivo pyruvate concentrations (Table I). However, as the temperature decreases, the K_m of this latter LDH decreases sharply, activating the enzyme at physiological substrate levels. Thus, by 5°C, both LDHs are active at physiological pyruvate concentrations, and as a result, LDH activity under these conditions is higher at 5°C, the species' normal habitat temperature, than at 10°C, the approximate upper extreme of the habitat temperature.

Basically similar results were obtained with the more complex LDH isozyme system of rainbow trout epaxial muscle (Fig. 18). In this system, ten LDH's are found, and these appear to be generated by a nonrandom, tetrameric association of four types of subunits (Massaro and Markert, 1968). Even though there are ten electrophoretically distinguishable iso-zymes, only four LDH activities can be observed kinetically (Fig. 18). This finding again suggests that each subunit type retains its kinetic proper-ties, regardless of its particular tetrameric combination.

The complexity of the saturation curves of Fig. 18 precludes accurately estimating K_m values for each LDH activity. However, the same general pattern of differential K_m change found in the simpler king crab system is again observed. Thus, at low pyruvate concentrations, LDH activity is higher at 10°C, the temperature to which the trout were acclimated, than at 15°C.

These two studies indicate that the complex isozyme systems present in many poikilothermic organisms may have a most important role in stabi-lizing catalytic activity in the face of sudden temperature changes. The role of isozymes in thermal acclimation will be discussed in Section VI,A.

Finally, we shall consider one additional mechanism of immediate tem-perature compensation which superficially resembles the isozyme systems discussed above. Pyruvate kinase of the Alaskan king crab appears to exist in two functional forms (Somero, 1969b), one of which has a minimal K_m of phosphoenol pyruvate (PEP) near 5°C, the lower extreme of the animal's habitat temperature, and one which has a minimal K_m near 12°C, the approximate upper extreme of the habitat temperature. Acting together, these two PyK's promote a highly temperature-independent rate of PyK activity over the entire physiological temperature range. In an attempt to resolve the isozyme composition of this system, it was found that only a single protein species is present. The two apparent isozymes appear to be formed through a temperature-dependent interconversion of one protein type. As the temperature is raised, the "cold" PyK is converted to "warm" PyK.

The biological significance of this interconversion is twofold. First, this interconversion provides the animal with two kinetically distinct variants of the enzyme, one of which functions well at the lower habitat tempera-tures, and a second which functions optimally at higher temperatures. If the king crab had to rely on either the "cold" or the "warm" PyK alone, then its ability to convert PEP to pyruvate would be greatly limited at one or the other extremes of habitat temperature. Secondly, as temperature rises, the conversion of progressively more PyK into a form showing sig-moidal saturation kinetics serves to dampen the Q_{10} effect. Thus, in this case at least, low temperature appears to mimic positive modulators (1) by lowering apparent K_m values, as we have already observed for other enzymes, and (2) by promoting interconversion of an enzyme form with sigmoidal saturation kinetics to one showing classical Michaelis kinetics.

These considerations now raise the question of temperature effects on enzyme–modulator interactions.

C. Temperature Effects on Regulatory Properties of Poikilothermic Enzymes

Large and often differential effects of temperature were first observed for enzyme–modulator and enzyme–cofactor interactions of mammalian and bacterial enzymes (Ingraham and Maaløe, 1967; Lowry *et al.,* 1964; Helmreich and Cori, 1964; Taketa and Pogell, 1965; Iwatsuki and Okazaki, 1967). Intuitively, we felt that the types of changes observed for enzymes of homeotherms, as well as their magnitude, would be incompatible with survival in poikilothermic systems. For example, if the magnitude of the change in enzyme–modulator interaction observed for mammalian fructose diphosphatase (FDPase) should occur in poikilothermic systems, then one would expect that gluconeogenesis would be completely "switched-off" at low temperatures (Taketa and Pogell, 1965). A further problem for poikilotherms would appear to be the type of enzyme–modulator response which occurs at different temperatures. For example, in the case of *E. coli* deoxythymidine kinase, deoxythymidine triphosphate inhibits the enzyme at temperatures above 30°C, while at lower temperatures it activates the enzyme. These findings plus similar data from other studies (see Lowry *et al.,* 1964) suggest that enzyme–modulator interactions in poikilothermic organisms, of necessity, would be largely unaffected by temperature, but this expectation has not been realized. Just as enzyme–substrate interactions can be changed by temperature, so also can enzyme–modulator and enzyme–cofactor interactions be temperature sensitive (Behrisch and Hochachka, 1969a,b; Behrisch, 1969; Somero and Hochachka, 1968). It appears, however, *that even though certain regulatory functions of poikilothermic enzymes may be thermally sensitive, the overall regulation of any given enzyme may be highly independent of temperature* (see Hochachka and Somero, 1970; Behrisch, 1969). This conclusion is based on studies of the catalytic and regulatory properties of a small number of enzymes; the underlying arguments have been previously marshaled by Hochachka and Somero (1970) and by Behrisch (1969), and need not be repeated here in detail. To summarize these studies briefly, the properties of enzymes were examined in some detail at important regulatory and branch points in metabolism. Fructose diphosphatase, for example, functions at a branch and regulatory site in the gluconeogenic and glycolytic pathways. In all other systems examined, negative modulation of FDPase by AMP appears to be the major means of controlling the activity of this reaction (Newsholme and Gevers, 1967). Thus, when the energy charge of the cell is

high (AMP levels are very low), FDPase activity is favored and gluconeogenesis is thereby promoted. When the energy charge of the cell is
low, i.e., when AMP levels are high, the FDPase reaction is inhibited.

In our initial studies of trout liver FDPase, we observed that the affinity
of FDPase for AMP increases dramatically at lower temperatures. At 25°C,
the K_i of AMP is approximately 80 M^{-5}; at 15°C a value of 5 M^{-5}
was found; and at 0°C the K_i is 2.5 M^{-5}. In other words, enzyme–AMP
affinity is about twenty to thirty times greater at low temperatures than
at higher ones (Behrisch and Hochachka, 1969a). Since the organism must
be capable of maintaining gluconeogenic activity, and therefore FDPase
activity, even at low temperatures (Hochachka, 1967a), it seemed obvious
that mechanisms must exist for FDPase activation—or at least reversal
of AMP inhibition—at low temperatures.

From detailed consideration of the control of trout FDPase, it has become evident that the increased efficiency of AMP inhibition at low temperatures can be counteracted by a number of mechanisms: (1) increasing
cation concentrations, which decrease AMP site–site interactions; (2) decreasing hydrogen ion concentration, which lowers the K_a values of the
cations and increases the $V_{\max}$ of the reaction; (3) decreasing values of
the free Mg/free Mn ratio, which effectively decreases the K_a value of
the cationic cofactor; (4) decreasing free Ca, which lowers Ca inhibition;
(5) increasing FDP site–site interactions and decreasing AMP site-site
interactions, which activates the enzyme at low temperatures (Behrisch
and Hochachka, 1969a).

If any or all of these control mechanisms are, in fact, operative, one
would predict that the FDPase reaction would be rather insensitive to
temperature. This can indeed be observed. Within the usual biological temperature range, the slopes of Arrhenius plots are quite low, particularly
in the presence of manganese (Behrisch and Hochachka, 1969a; Behrisch,
1969). The optimal velocity seems to be essentially independent of temperature between about 10° and 20°C (Fig. 19). Since most of the above
control mechanisms affect enzyme–ligand affinities or site–site interactions,
the reaction rate is likely to be even more thermally insensitive at low
substrate concentrations. Similar conclusions have been derived for lungfish
liver FDPase (Behrisch and Hochachka, 1969b) and salmon liver FDPase
(Behrisch, 1969).

In the case of PyK, which functions at another branch and control
site in glycolysis and gluconeogenesis, we have found that feed-forward
activation by FDP and feedback inhibition by ATP are both equally effective at all temperatures that the organism experiences in nature (Somero
and Hochachka, 1968). These results, of course, directly support our original hypothesis concerning the temperature independence of enzyme–modula-

tor interactions. However, control of trout muscle PyK by cations is critically dependent upon temperature. To date the probable consequences of these effects on this enzyme have not been completely analyzed (see Somero and Hochachka, 1968).

Support for the hypothesis that regulatory properties are to some extent insensitive to temperature also comes from studies of control of glycolysis in king crab muscle preparations (J. M. Freed *et al.,* 1969). In these studies, it became apparent that the same control sites (hexokinase, phosphofructokinase, and pyruvate kinase) were operative in the regulation of glycolytic flux at all temperatures tested (0°, 8°, and 15°C) within the biological temperature range of the species. Whereas this study clearly

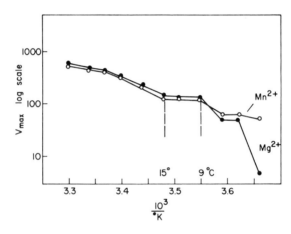

Fig. 19.   Arrhenius plots for activity of salmon FDPase in presence of optimum concentrations of substrate and Mg^{2+} or Mn^{2+}, and at pH 7.4. (After Behrisch, 1969.)

supports the proposition that overall regulatory integrity is maintained irrespective of temperature, it leaves open the possibility that efficiency of control at these sites may vary with temperature. That efficiency of control at these sites does change with temperature is evident in studies of carbon flow through metabolic branch points.

D. Temperature Effects on Carbon Flow through Branch Points in Metabolism

At the outset of this discussion, it is important to stress that the action of temperature on multienzyme processes in poikilotherms has not been widely studied. The data that are available arise from studies of a small number of species, tissues, and metabolic processes. In a number of cases, however, the predictions stemming from the single-enzyme studies discussed

above appear to be realized. Thus, Van Handel (1966) observed that glycogen synthesis can be entirely temperature insensitive over certain temperature ranges; at temperatures below this "plateau" range, the Q_{10} increases
to rather high values. Similarly, Newell (1966) observed that the oxidation
of pyruvate or succinate by mitochondrial preparations from several tissues
and organisms can be independent of temperature over quite broad ranges.
Gordon (1968) has reported low temperature coefficients of oxygen consumption of red and white muscle from tunas over the range of 5°–35°C.
More recently, Dean (1969) has examined the action of temperature on
acetate-1-^{14}C and palmitate-1-^{14}C oxidation in three tissues of the rainbow
trout. In all cases, oxidation rates can show temperature coefficients as
low as unity, at least over certain temperature ranges. Whatever the basic
mechanisms underlying these effects, they seem to be unusually effective
in the oxidation of palmitate by red and white muscle. Thus, between
5° and 18°C, palmitate oxidation rates exhibit a temperature coefficient
less than 1. Similar results are obtained in studies of acetate oxidation
by white muscle of 18°-acclimated trout. In liver from these fish, acetate
oxidation rates show almost complete thermal independence between 10°
and 38°C. In liver, acetate incorporation into lipids also shows thermal
independence over certain thermal ranges; albeit quite high Q_{10} values
are observed at other incubation temperatures.

With the exception of Dean's studies where exogenous substrate levels
were low, exogenous substrate concentrations were high, usually in the
range of 10–50 M^{-4}, in all of the above studies, and hence it was reasonable
to assume that intracellular substrate concentrations were also in this high
range, so that the implication is that the pathways concerned were functioning under saturated substrate concentrations. This need not be the case.
All available evidence on probable intracellular concentrations of metabolites under similar experimental conditions suggest that concentrations are
in the range of the K_m values for the enzymes involved in their metabolism
(Williamson *et al.*, 1967). Also, the distribution of metabolites within the
different intracellular compartments is itself under regulation (see Chappell
and Robinson, 1968, for example). Thus, the alternative assumption, that
substrate concentrations are low, is more consistent with current information
on *in vivo* substrate levels and with our studies on the thermal dependence
of enzyme–substrate affinities of poikilothermic systems.

Interpreting the results of Newell, Van Handel, and Gordon and Dean
is difficult, for these workers have not assessed the effect of temperature
on branch pathways competing for common intermediates. It is clear that
differential effects of temperature on branch point enzymes could greatly
influence the effect of temperature on different metabolic pathways considered *in toto*. Hochachka (1968) examined this problem in an analysis

of the action of temperature on the channeling of carbon through branch points in intermediary metabolism.

Following glucose phosphorylation, three major pathways are present for the further metabolism of G6P: (1) classical Embden-Meyerhof glycolysis; (2) the hexose monophosphate pathway (pentose shunt); and (3) the biosynthetic pathway of glycogen. In liver slices of certain Amazon River fishes (*Symbranchus, Lepidosiren, Electrophorus*), the pentose shunt and the pathway to glycogen become increasingly effective in competing for the common substrate, G6P, when temperature is raised from 22° to 38°C (Hochachka, 1968). Glucose carbon flow to glycogen and through the pentose shunt is consequently strikingly raised; however, carbon flow through glycolysis is not increased at higher temperatures, and may actually exhibit a decrease.

A number of enzymic processes probably account for these observations (Fig. 20): (1) the thermal optimum for G6P dehydrogenase—the first enzyme of the pentose shunt—is high at all G6P levels; hence this enzyme can compete for G6P more effectively at high temperatures; (2) enzyme–substrate affinities of LDH (Hochachka and Somero, 1968) and probably of other glycolytic enzymes increase as the temperature is decreased, thus thermally stabilizing glycolysis; (3) the affinity of glycogen synthetase for the positive modulator G6P is apparently increased at high temperatures; thus, even in the absence of large changes in G6P concentrations, high temperature will favor this pathway; and (4) glycogen phosphorylase is held relatively inactive at high temperatures, possibly by increased affinity of this enzyme for its negative modulators G6P and ATP. This situation would also contribute to the thermal independence of glycolysis. These four conditions are consistent with available information and supply minimal mechanisms for the observed action of temperature on the G6P branching point. In any event, *it must be assumed that efficiency of control at any given site may vary with temperature;* however, as indicated above, the same enzyme reactions serve as control sites (or valves) in any given pathway at all temperatures.

Although further experiments are required for a more complete understanding of these events, the work nonetheless demonstrates that for relatively intact multienzyme systems, the importance of temperature effects on enzyme–substrate and enzyme–modulator affinities is great. As a generalization, it seems reasonable to propose that carbon flow in any given pathway (glycolysis, the Krebs cycle, etc.) can be held independent of temperature by (1) changing sensitivity to modulation of key enzymes in that pathway, and (2) by altering the capabilities of metabolic pathways to compete for common substrates by appropriate thermally dependent changes in enzyme–substrate affinities of key enzymes in the multienzyme sequence.

Control mechanisms such as these would allow certain pathways to remain highly thermally independent, while other branching pathways, e.g., the pentose shunt, glycogen synthesis, and lipogenesis, could alter their activities greatly in response to temperature changes.

This type of differential thermal behavior of different metabolic pathways

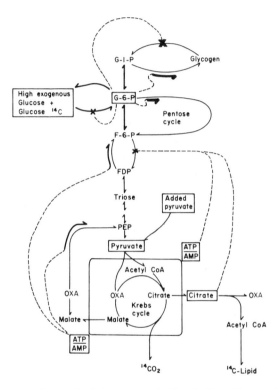

FIG. 20.   Diagram of control of glucose metabolism in liver slices of *Symbranchus* and *Lepidosiren*. Broken lines connect effectors (boxed in metabolites) with the enzyme steps that they modulate. Effector activation is expressed with an arrow; effector inhibition is marked with a cross. Heavy arrows and crosses indicate that the effectiveness of modulation is dependent on temperature; presumably, appropriate enzyme–modulator affinities are increased at high temperatures. (After Hochachka, 1968.)

could be of major significance for poikilotherms. For example, in tuna, the highest and best-regulated intramuscular temperatures occur in the deep red muscle located midway along the bodies of these fishes (Carey and Teal, 1966). In white muscle and the more superficial red muscles, the temperature of the tissue is subject to rapid and large variation. Both ambient water temperature and activity would likely determine the precise temperature of these tissues. In a system such as this, in which large and nonpredictable temperature changes would be expected to occur, a good evolutionary "strategy" would appear to be the development of temperature-independent systems of energy yielding reactions, which would enable the fish to have a constant availability of energy for sudden work efforts such as those involved in prey capture and predator evasion. According to Gordon (1968), aerobic energy metabolism of tuna white muscle appears to conform to this pattern. Unfortunately, we do not know the thermal characteristics of other metabolic sequences in this tissue.

To conclude this section, it seems that three valid generalizations arise from the above studies: (1) enzyme–substrate affinity is an important, and perhaps the crucial, site of natural selection in evolutionary adaptations of enzymes to temperature, (2) appropriate increase in enzyme–substrate affinity at low temperature supplies poikilothermic enzymes with a kind of built-in thermal stability mechanism, which can largely, and often fully, compensate for reduced thermal energy in the environment, and (3) overall regulatory properties of poikilothermic enzymes seem to be rather less sensitive to thermal changes, although it is necessary to assume that efficiency of control at any given site may vary with temperature.

VI. Temperature Acclimation

A. THE PROCESS

Because of the influence of traditional biochemistry, which deals almost exclusively with, and is based upon, mammalian and bacterial systems, the extent to which enzymes of poikilotherms appear tailored for thermally independent function may be somewhat surprising. However, as we have indicated, a direct relationship between K_m and temperature maintained over the entire biological thermal range of the organism is to be seen only in few of the cases thus far observed. At temperatures below a critical minimum, the K_m usually increases dramatically; often the effect is large enough to inactivate the enzyme at all probable physiological concentrations of substrate. Thus, in the case of warm-acclimated trout (18°C), the K_m of brain acetylcholinesterase at 8°C is on the order of 10^{-2} M (Baldwin and Hochachka, 1970); the K_m of muscle LDH at 5°C is about 10^{-1} M (Hochachka and Somero, 1968); the K_m of trout muscle PyK at 0°C, extrapolates to PEP concentrations of over 4×10^{-3} M (Somero and Hochachka, 1968). As far as we can tell, these K_m values may be as much as 100 times higher than probable physiological concentrations, and hence do not even approximate the *in vivo* condition at low temperature. This means that at lower thermal ranges, these enzymes from warm-acclimated trout are highly inefficient, and indeed, except under unusually high substrate concentrations, are essentially inactive. Yet it is common knowledge that this species commonly thrives in waters at these low temperatures after a period of acclimation. How is this paradox resolved?

Many previous studies of cold acclimation imply, and sometimes explicitly suggest, that a basic mechanism of acclimation involves the production of higher quantities of enzymes in order to compensate for the decrease in temperature. Thus, Ekberg (1962) noted that the activities of 6PGDH and aldolase increase during cold acclimation in carp. Jankowsky (1968) found that the activities of aldolase, MDH, and cytochrome oxidase increase in cold acclimation of the golden orfe. Baslow and Nigrelli (1964) reported complete or "perfect" compensation of brain acetylcholinesterase activity in *Fundulus,* and similar data are available for a variety of other enzymes (J. Freed, 1965; Caldwell and Vernberg, 1970). All these studies have measured maximum catalytic activities; none have determined the enzyme forms responsible for the activities in the different acclimation groups of test organisms. *From a functional point of view, the selective or functional advantage of producing increased amounts of inefficient or inactive enzymes is not entirely evident.* It appears therefore that increased enzyme synthesis, as such, is not an adequate mechanism for the kinds of processes we observe in cold acclimation. When this does occur, the kinetic properties of the enzymes concerned probably are temperature insensitive over the entire biological range, or perhaps, exhibit the interconversion phenomena found in king crab pyruvate kinase.

A mechanism involving a special case of enzyme induction, namely isozyme induction, was first recognized in studies of the role of LDH isozymes in thermal acclimation in goldfish (Hochachka, 1965) and later in trout (Hochachka, 1967; Hochachka and Somero, 1968). During cold acclimation in these organisms, new isozymes of LDH appear which differ kinetically from a noninducible set, also present, in having higher absolute affinities for substrate and having minimal K_m values at lower temperatures (Hochachka and Somero, 1968). Essentially identical results are observed in the case of trout muscle PyK. Muscle PyK from warm-acclimated trout shows minimal K_m constants at about 15°–20°. With cold acclimation, a new muscle PyK is induced, which shows minimal values at about 5° (Somero, 1969). In this case, the minimal value of the K_m for both forms of the enzyme is about the same. Baldwin (Baldwin and Hochachka, 1970) has identified two isozymes of acetylcholinesterase in trout brain. Only one of these occurs in warm-acclimated fish, in cold-acclimated (2°), only the other. Both isozymes are present when the trout are acclimated to an intermediate (12°) temperature. Again, the minimal K_m values for the two isozymes are essentially identical, but the minimal occurs at about 18°C for the "warm" enzyme while the minimal occurs at about 2°C for the "cold" form of the enzyme (Fig. 15). In the goldfish, choline acetyltransferase also appears to occur in two forms, the "warm" form of the enzyme having a higher absolute K_m at low temperatures than the "cold" form (Hebb *et al.,* 1969). These data suggest that the crucial process in cold acclimation is not the biosynthesis of more of the same kinds of enzymes that are present in the warm acclimation state, but rather the biosynthesis of new enzyme variants (isozymes) which are better adapted for catalysis at low temperature.

This general conclusion has far reaching implications.

(a) The time course of cold acclimation, which is classically accepted as ranging from about 1 week to several weeks (Brett, 1956; Prosser, 1958) is essentially the same as the time course of isozyme induction. In the case of acetylcholinesterase, Baldwin observed that following transfer to 2°C water, the rainbow trout becomes highly immobile. Normal activity seems to return only with the appearance of a "cold" form of acetylcholinesterase. Clearly, there will be no sharp line in time dividing the cold- and warm-acclimated states, but, in general, the pattern of capacity acclimation and isozyme induction should coincide rather closely.

(b) Any factors or conditions which interfere with isozyme induction will interfere with thermal acclimation. This implication is difficult to test critically. Studies of fishes showing only minor acclimatory capacities might yield useful insight on this matter.

(c) The primary functional and selective advantage of employing "better" isozymes in thermal acclimation—as opposed to producing altered quantities of a single enzyme species—is not Q_{10} reduction (rate compensation), for thermal stability over different temperatures is built into both "cold" and "warm" forms of enzymes. Thus, the types of isozyme changes we have observed in the trout would not, in themselves, promote complete or "perfect" compensation. Indeed, taking the extremes of capacity for metabolism in relation to temperature in fish, as exemplified by the sockeye salmon (Brett, 1964), the Q_{10} for fish acclimated to each temperature is approximately 2, a result within our expectations. For PyK and acetylcholinesterase, the minimal K_m values of the "warm" and "cold" isozymes are essentially equal. Complete rate compensation in activity of these enzymes would conceivably demand that the "cold" isozymes have drastically lower K_m values than the "warm" enzymes. This situation does not seem to be general, and suggests that the primary function of the isozyme changes is the production of enzymes with K_m values in a range likely to be optimal for regulation of catalytic activity. Thus, at low temperatures, small changes in substrate concentration can lead to large changes in the activities of "cold" forms of enzymes (A_4 in Fig. 21), a condition which would appear to be admirably suited to controlling the reaction.

In the case of "warm" forms of these enzymes at low temperatures, very large changes in substrate concentration are required to yield small changes in reaction rate (C_4 in Fig. 21). This condition clearly is not one which allows efficient control of reaction rates. In evolutionary terms, it appears that there is a strong selection for enzymes having K_m values allowing large changes in activity in response to physiological changes in substrate concentrations. This is reflected in the patterns of enzyme variants produced during acclimation and during evolutionary adaptation (see Hochachka and Somero, 1968).

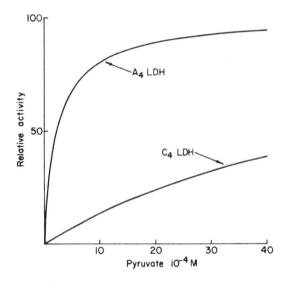

Fig. 21. Theoretical saturation curves for A_4 and C_4 LDH'S of lake and brook trout at 0°C. The K_m of C_4 is about twenty times the K_m of A_4 over all temperatures. (Data of Hochachka and Somero, 1968.)

In these terms, for any given enzymic reaction Q_{10} reduction may be a convenient "spin-off," but not a necessary consequence, of acclimation. One can visualize various kinds of isozyme systems induced during acclimation, which share in common the K_m properties needed to regain, or retain, control of a given reaction; but the effects that these various systems might have on overall rate compensation might vary from isozyme to isozyme. To be sure, Precht arrived at similar conclusions some 20 years earlier; on the basis of strictly empirical data, he was led to categorize five kinds of acclimatory responses (see Precht, 1958; and discussion in Section IV,B). The above considerations appear to provide a formal framework for the enzymic mechanisms underlying Precht's observations.

(d) Finally, for any given reaction, the induction of a new isozyme specifically adapted for function in the cold acclimation state may lead—in the absence of any changes in substrate or modulator concentrations—to the establishment of new steady state conditions because of modified enzyme–substrate and/or enzyme–modulator interactions. This last implication is crucial, for it is consistent with an important end result of the acclimation process—the appearance of new steady state conditions in various metabolic pathways and a general reorganization of cellular metabolism.

B. Basic Metabolic Adjustments

Historically, the first indications of metabolic compensations for thermal changes in the environment were in studies of the activities and respiration of whole animals. Later experiments, utilizing somewhat more sophisticated methodology, indicate that metabolic adjustments during acclimation do not merely change the rates at which given metabolic systems are operating; instead, some metabolic processes are activated to a large extent, others may remain unchanged, still others may be reduced in activity. That is, cold acclimation does not merely speed things up, and warm acclimation does not merely slow things down in a relative or an absolute sense. *Rather, during acclimation, the metabolism of the organism is fundamentally reorganized.* The nature of metabolic reorganization during acclimation has been previously considered in some detail (Hochachka, 1967); hence, we shall at this point only summarize some of the salient features.

In general, the observations can be summarized as follows. In tissues of cold acclimated fish, compared with tissues of warm acclimated ones, (1) glycolysis rate is increased up to fivefold; (2) the participation of the pentose shunt may be increased from negligible contributions to activities accounting for about 10% of glucose metabolism; (3) the Krebs cycle may be decreased, unchanged, or possibly slightly increased (depending upon tissue and species), whereas electron transfer functions are characteristically increased (J. Freed, 1965; Hochachka and Hayes, 1962; Caldwell, 1969); (4) lipogenesis is activated, in some cases by only a small factor (Hochachka and Hayes, 1962; Dean, 1969), but in other cases the activation of synthesis of unique fatty acids may increase during cold acclimation by factors as high as twelve-fold (Knipprath and Mead, 1968); (5) glycogen synthesis rate appears to be increased; (6) protein synthesis rates appear to be generally higher during cold acclimation, at least in certain species and certain tissues (Das and Prosser, 1967; Haschemeyer, 1968, 1969a,b); (7) synthesis rates of nucleic acids (RNA in particular) and their turnover rates are higher in cold acclimated fishes (Das, 1967); and (8) the ionic microenvironment may alter during acclimation (Heinicke and Houston, 1965). On examination of the evidence upon which the above summary rests, it is evident that in any given tissue, not all of the above processes necessarily occur. Most of them probably occur in liver, in which metabolic organization is unusually complex. In tissues such as gill, muscle, and brain, exergonic reactions are coupled to highly specialized work functions; hence, metabolic organization may be abbreviated. It is not surprising therefore, that some of the above changes are not as evident in these tissues. The shunt, for example, is not important in the metabolism of brain or muscle; clearly, adjustments in its participation in glucose metabolism would not be relevant and indeed do not occur in these tissues during acclimation.

A mechanistic model attempting to account for changes in participation of the above processes has been considered in some detail previously (Hochachka, 1967). This model proposes that metabolic adjustments during cold acclimation depend upon an initial induction of a number of new isozymes which are sufficiently sensitive to control so as to be activated or inhibited by preexisting levels of modulators. All other effects are assumed to follow as a consequence of the establishment of a new steady state.

Although relatively successful in explaining a large amount of data, the model has rather severe shortcomings. Firstly, in a simple system of the type assumed, Lardy (1965) argues strongly that a given condition would favor gluconeogenesis *or* lipogenesis but not both; yet, as has been seen, both processes are apparently increased in cold acclimation. Secondly, the model does not account for an increased turnover of glucose in cold-adjusted liver. The data suggest increased glycolytic *and* gluconeogenic flux, but the model only accounts for increased gluconeogenesis. Finally, since the model says nothing about integration, it fails to provide a mechanism for anticipatory adjustment. These shortcomings of the enzyme model suggest that other factors are involved in metabolic adjustment to temperature. Moreover, some of the adjustments are similar to mammalian response to insulin. Hence, the second model derives in large measure from the experiments of Lardy, Weber, and others on the mechanism of action of insulin and the glucocorticoids, and depends on the antagonistic action of these hormones on the activities and concentrations of enzymes affecting directions of net metabolic flow (see Lardy *et al.,* 1965, for related literature).

In the regulation of glucose metabolism, according to this model, glucocorticoids initiate two basic events. The first is to release gluconeogenic precursors (such as free amino acids) from the peripheral tissues into the general circulation. These activate preexisting gluconeogenic enzymes in the liver, and thereby yield an increased product without measurable synthesis of enzyme. Secondly, glucocorticoids induce *de novo* synthesis of key gluconeogenic enzymes (FDPase, G6Pase, PEP-carboxykinase, and transaminases), and thus further activate gluconeogenesis. As far as we can interpret the evidence currently available, the enzymes induced during cold acclimation are isozymic variants of those present in warm acclimation. These two events can account for increased gluconeogenic flux in cold acclimation. The end product of the gluconeogenic pathway is glucose. However, glucose does not "turn off" the gluconeogenic enzymes as one might expect for a simple feedback system. Instead, it activates the release of insulin from pancreatic β-cells which suppresses FDPase, G6Pase, and PEP-carboxykinase (Lardy *et al.,* 1965) and so slows up gluconeogenic flux. At the same time, insulin induces or activates glucokinase, pyruvate kinase, and phosphofructokinase (which activities channel glucose into glycolysis), glycogen synthetase (which, along with glucokinase, channels glucose into glycogen), and malic enzyme (which generates the bulk of TPNH for fat synthesis). The consequences of these events are observed empirically in cold acclimation. Again, different isozymes presumably must show different sensitivities to insulin, a situation in fact well documented in studies of insulin induction of hexokinase (Katzen *et al.,* 1968).

A second model thus proposes that the adjustments which are seen in fish liver are those which would be predicted on the assumption that gluconeogenesis is activated by glucocorticoids, and glycolysis and lipogenesis by insulin. A common feature of control systems is the property of "hunting" for, or oscillating around, some homeostatic condition. The expectation here is precisely that kind of oscillation; at times, gluconeogenic flux exceeds glycolytic flux, but when control is transferred to insulin, glycolytic exceeds gluconeogenic flux. Thus, by this view, a basic process of metabolic adjustment to cold is the appearance of unique isozymes and consequent establishment of new steady state conditions in response to changed hormonal titer. Implicit in these considerations is the assumption that during acclimation, metabolic responses in target and nontarget tissues should be quite distinct—a conclusion likewise reached by Precht (see p. 103).

A second major difficulty with the first model, which is not encountered if two antagonistically acting hormones are involved, concerns the concomitant activation of gluconeogenesis and lipogenesis. Consider the pathways for glucose and lipid syntheses from amino acids yielding pyruvate. Liver mitochondria carboxylate pyruvate to form OXA (oxalacetic acid), but the latter does not diffuse to the cytosol. Part of the OXA condenses with the acetyl-CoA to form citrate; part is reduced to malate. Both malate and citrate can diffuse from the mitochondria.

Under conditions of gluconeogenesis, the malate must be oxidized by DPN and MDH and the OXA converted to PEP by PEP-carboxykinase. In contrast, during fatty acid synthesis, OXA produced by the citrate-cleavage reaction in the cytosol is *reduced* by DPNH and MDH. The malate is converted to pyruvate and CO_2 by malic enzyme, in the process generating TPNH which is the bulk source of reducing power for fatty acid synthesis (Lardy, 1965).

These considerations illustrate that a matter of some major importance in determining whether a liver cell synthesizes fat *or* carbohydrate is the direction taken by the extramitochondrial MDH reaction. The point is that both the malate → OXA reaction of gluconeogenesis and the OXA → malate reaction coupled to fat synthesis cannot run maximally at the same time in the same cell compartment. Yet, as was seen above, the empirical evidence suggests active carbohydrate and lipid synthesis during cold acclimation. This apparent paradox between theory and observation can be resolved by the second model.

When under insulin control, lipogenesis is active, DPNH is depleted by the MDH reaction, and the DPN/DPNH ratio rises. At the same time, glucose is decreasing, through activation of glycogen synthetase and glycolysis, to some critical level at which control is transferred to the glucocorticoids. Subsequent activation of gluconeogenesis restores the DPN/DPNH ratio by reversing the direction of the MDH reaction and "pulling" OXA to PEP.

This model, then, also predicts an oscillation between maximal gluconeogenesis and maximal fat synthesis (Fig. 22), but glycogen and lipid syntheses would be in phase. The process of cold adjustment again involves an establishment of different steady state conditions, owing to different hormone titers. Since time lags could displace these curves, the model only predicts that maximal gluconeogenesis and maximal lipogenesis are not likely to be occurring simultaneously. Either at any time, however, would be higher in cold-acclimated than in warm-acclimated fish.

Finally, it could be argued that a spatial separation of enzymes of lipogenesis and glucogenesis could account for both processes functioning at maximal rates at the same time. Different forms of MDH are well known (Thorne *et al.,* 1963). Some or one of these could be associated with the malate → OXA reaction in carbohydrate synthesis; some or one of these could be associated with the OXA → malate reaction on which fat synthesis depends. Very little is known about cellular compartmentation, and this is clearly an area which will be receiving further and more intense analysis (Williamson, 1965). This hypothesis of separation of lipogenic and glucogenic enzymes makes two predictions that are quite different from any which derive from the hormone model. First of all, there is no requirement for DPN/DPNH oscillations associated with the MDH reaction, and secondly, the hypothesis requires differentiated loci within the cytoplasm to which are attached unique MDH isozymes.

What is the evidence on the mode of action of insulin and the glucocorti-

coids in fishes? At the outset, it must be stressed that there is no direct
evidence in support of the second model as mapped above. As regards
insulin, the most comprehensive study remains that of Falkmer (1961).
The β-cells constitute a good portion of the total volume of islet tissue.
The nature of reactions to the usual hyperglycemic and hypoglycemic agents
and procedures indicates that blood sugar regulation is qualitatively similar

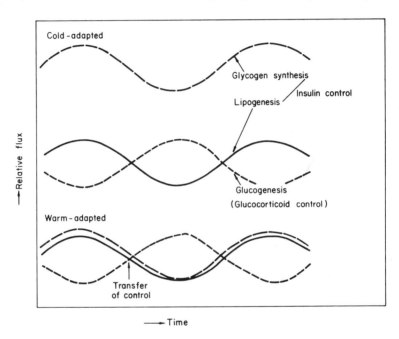

Fig. 22. Diagram of control of gluconeogenesis and lipogenesis by insulin and glucocorticoids. When the system is under insulin control, lipogenesis is active and NADH is
depleted by the MDH reaction. At the same time, glucose is depleted (by activation of
glycolysis) to some critical level at which control is transferred to the glucocorticoids.
Subsequent activation of gluconeogenesis restores the NAD/NADH ratio by reversing the
direction of the MDH reaction and "pulling" OXA to PEP.

to that of mammals. Direct treatment of fishes with hydrocortisone, however, only on occasion induced a hyperglycemia along with β-cell necrosis.
    Two lines of evidence indicate that hormone effects are indeed involved
in adjustments to temperature. P. H. Johansen (1968) demonstrated that
goldfish cannot increase their thermal resistance unless the pituitary is intact.
Secondly, blood serum contains a factor related to the acclimation temperature of the animal from which it has been drawn and which can bring
about compensatory effects in excised muscle, as was first found by
K. P. Rao (1962). Precht (1964a,b) and Jankowsky (1964) give data for

such experiments on fish. Serum from cold-acclimated fishes, when added to muscle brei or muscle homogenates, produces a consistent increase in respiration. The active factor is not present in blood from warm-acclimated fishes in sufficiently high concentrations to alter the respiration of muscle preparations. Identification attempts thus far have been of a preliminary nature but they have ruled out thyroid hormones.

All of the above studies suggest the kinds of mechanisms which appear fundamental to altering participation of different metabolic pathways. However, the adaptive significance of metabolic reorganization has remained unexplained, and indeed, is usually avoided in discussions of thermal acclimation (see Hochachka, 1967; Precht, 1968).

C. BIOLOGICAL SIGNIFICANCE OF METABOLIC REORGANIZATION

Empirically, we know that two kinds of processes often occur during acclimation: (a) compensatory adjustments in metabolic rate, which tend to free the organism from the stringencies of the outer environment; and (b) biophysical and biochemical restructuring of many cellular and tissue components for operation under the new thermal regime imposed on the organism. Previous workers have, by and large, emphasized the first of these processes. We believe that it is the less fundamental, it need not necessarily occur, and when it does, it may indeed be a consequence of the second process of rebuilding. Thus, the synthesis of new enzyme variants in relatively large amounts appear to promote (1) some *stability in rates of enzyme catalyzed reactions,* and (2) *maintenance of metabolic control.* The synthesis of other kinds of proteins, such as membrane proteins, blood proteins, and specific transport proteins may also be an essential part of the restructuring process which occurs during acclimation.

Lipids, particularly membrane-based lipids, appear to play an equally important role in acclimation. Although the literature here is vast (see Johnston and Roots, 1964; Knipprath and Mead, 1968; Roots, 1968), there is universal agreement that in responding to cold exposure, organisms tend to increase the degree of unsaturation of their fatty acids. Earlier it was believed that by altering the degree of unsaturation of fatty acid chains, an organism is able to adjust lipid viscosity to a variety of thermal conditions. Recent data do not contradict this thesis but indicate that the adjustments in lipid composition are far more complex than would be required simply for viscosity regulation.

In addition to simple changes in saturation of fatty acids, very specific changes in lipid composition of different tissues occur during acclimation (Johnston and Roots, 1964; Roots, 1968; Knipprath and Mead, 1968). In the case of goldfish brain, total lipids tend to increase during cold acclimation, but the magnitude of this change is slight and may not be significant. Similarly, the total content of the major membrane-based phospholipids in goldfish CNS (choline glycerophosphatides and ethanolamine phosphatides) is not influenced by temperature acclimation, *but the specific species of phospholipids that occur depend critically upon the acclimation state* (Roots, 1968). These complexities are recognized by Roots (1968); she suggests that the significance of these changes may relate to effects on membrane functions, particularly of nerve membrane (Roots, 1968; Johnston and Roots, 1964). That unsaturated fatty acids form expanded monomolecular films and cannot be as closely packed as saturated fatty acids has long been known; these conditions could lead to important adjustments in various membrane functions (transport, impulse transmission, electron transfer, etc.). Many enzymes, such as those of the electron transfer system, are critically dependent upon the membrane–lipid milieu in which they normally function; acclimation changes in membrane structure may be closely related to associated changes in the activities of these enzymes. It seems clear that just as unique isozyme systems seem to be requisite for activity at certain temperatures, unique membrane composition and membrane architecture also are basic to the acclimatory process. As many enzymes are membrane-bound, it is possible that production of new membrane-based lipids and new isozymes during acclimation may be closely integrated aspects of a single rebuilding process. These kinds of events require energy, fundamental building blocks, synthetic subcellular machinery, unique ionic microenvironments, etc., and may be central to the observed adjustments in cellular metabolism that occur during acclimation (Hochachka, 1967). In this view, reorganization of metabolism is not the essence of acclimation, but rather it is a part of the process of cellular restructuring, allowing maintenance of controlled catalytic functions.

REFERENCES

Alabaster, J. S., and Downing, A. L. (1966). *Min. Agr. Fish Food, U.K. Fish. Invest., Ser. I* **6**, No. 4, 1–42.

Altukhov, J. P. (1963). *Tsitologiya* **5**, 241.

Anthony, E. H. (1961a). *J. Exptl. Biol.* **38**, 93.

Anthony, E. H. (1961b). *J. Exptl. Biol.* **38**, 109.

Atkinson, D. E. (1966). *Ann. Rev. Biochem.* **35**, 85.

Baldwin, J. (1970). Ph.D. Dissertation, Univ. of British Columbia, Vancouver, Canada.

Baldwin, J., and Hochachka, P. W. (1970). *Biochem. J.* (in press).

Bardach, J. E. (1956). *Am. Naturalist* **90**, 309.

Bardach, J. E., and Bjorklund, R. G. (1957). *Am. Naturalist* **91**, 233.

Barrett, I., and Hester, F. J. (1964). *Nature* **203**, 96.

Baslow, M. H., and Nigrelli, R. F. (1964). *Zoologica* **49**, 41.

Basu, S. P. (1959). *J. Fisheries Res. Board Can.* **16**, 175.

Beamish, F. W. H. (1964a). *Can. J. Zool.* **42**, 177.
Beamish, F. W. H. (1964b). *Can. J. Zool.* **42**, 189.
Beamish, F. W. H., and Mookherjii, P. S. (1964). *Can. J. Zool.* **42**, 161.
Behrisch, H. W. (1969). *Biochem. J.* **115**, 687.
Behrisch, H. W., and Hochachka, P. W. (1969a). *Biochem. J.* **111**, 287.
Behrisch, H. W., and Hochachka, P. W. (1969b). *Biochem. J.* **112**, 601.
Berkholz, G. (1966). *Z. Wiss. Zool.* **174**, 377.
Black, E. C., Kirkpatrick, D., and Tucker, H. H. (1966a). *J. Fisheries Res. Board Can.* **23**, 1.
Black, E. C., Tucker, H. H., and Kirkpatrick, D. (1966b). *J. Fisheries Res. Board Can.* **23**, 1187.
Boetius, I., and Boetius, J. (1967). *Medd. Danmarks Fiskeri-og Havunders.* [*N.S.*] **4**, 339.
Brett, J. R. (1944). *Univ. Toronto Studies Biol.* **52**, *Publ. Ontario Fisheries Res. Lab.* **63**, 1.
Brett, J. R. (1952). *J. Fisheries Res. Board Can.* **9**, 265.
Brett, J. R. (1956). *Quart. Rev. Biol.* **31**, 75.
Brett, J. R. (1964). *J. Fisheries Res. Board Can.* **21**, 1183.
Brett, J. R. (1967). *J. Fisheries Res. Board Can.* **24**, 1731.
Brett, J. R., and Alderdice, D. F. (1958). *J. Fisheries Res. Board Can.* **15**, 805.
Brett, J. R., and Sutherland, D. B. (1965). *J. Fisheries Res. Board Can.* **22**, 405.
Bull, H. O. (1936). *J. Marine Biol. Assoc. U.K.* **21**, 1.
Caldwell, R. S., (1969). *Comp. Biochem. Physiol.* **31**, 79.
Caldwell, R. S. and Vernberg, R. J. (1970). *Comp. Biochem. Physiol.* (in press).
Carey, F. G., and Teal, J. M. (1966). *Proc. Natl. Acad. Sci. U.S.* **56**, 1464.
Carey, F. G., and Teal, J. M. (1969a). *Comp. Biochem. Physiol.* **28**, 199.
Carey, F. G., and Teal, J. M. (1969b). *Comp. Biochem. Physiol.* **28**, 205.
Chappell, J. B., and Robinson, B. H. (1968). *In* "Metabolic Roles of Citrate" (T. W. Goodwin, ed.), pp. 123–133. Academic Press, New York.
Chatfield, P. O., Lyman, C. P., and Irving, L. (1953). *Am. J. Physiol.* **172**, 639.
Christophersen, J., and Precht, H. (1952). *Biol. Zentr.* **71**, 313.
Cocking, A. W. (1959). *J. Exptl. Biol.* **36**, 203.
Das, A. B. (1967). *Comp. Biochem. Physiol.* **21**, 469.
Das, A. B., and Prosser, C. L. (1967). *Comp. Biochem. Physiol.* **21**, 449.
Dean, J. M. (1969). *Comp. Biochem. Physiol.* **29**, 185.
de Groot, S. J., and Schuyf, A. (1967). *Experientia* **23**, 1.
Doudoroff, P. (1945). *Biol. Bull.* **88**, 194.
Ekberg, D. R. (1962). *Comp. Biochem. Physiol.* **5**, 123.
Evans, R. M., Purdie, F. C., and Hickman, C. P., Jr. (1962). *Can. J. Zool.* **40**, 107.
Falkmer, S. (1961). *Acta Endocrinol.* Suppl. 59, 1–122.
Ferguson, R. G. (1958). *J. Fisheries Res. Board Can.* **15**, 607.
Fisher, K. C. (1958). *In* "Physiological Adaptation" (C. L. Prosser, ed.), pp. 3–48. Am. Physiol. Soc., Washington, D.C.
Fisher, K. C., and Sullivan, C. M. (1958). *Can. J. Zool.* **36**, 49.
Fluke, D. J., and Hochachka, P. W. (1965). *Radiation Res.* **26**, 395.
Freed, J. (1969), Personal communication.
Freed, J. (1965). *Comp. Biochem. Physiol.* **14**, 651.
Freed, J. M. (1969). Unpublished data.
Freed, J. M., Prosser, C. L., and Hochachka, P. W. (1969). Unpublished data.
Freeman, J. A. (1950). *Biol. Bull.* **99**, 416.
Fry, F. E. J. (1964). *In* "Handbook of Physiology" (Am. Physiol. Soc., J. Field, ed.), Sect. 4, pp. 715–728. Williams & Wilkins, Baltimore, Maryland.
Fry, F. E. J. (1967). *In* "Thermobiology" (A. H. Rose, ed.), pp. 375–409. Academic Press, New York.
Fry, F. E. J., and Hart, J. S. (1948). *J. Fisheries Res. Board Can.* **7**, 169.

Fry, F. E. J., Brett, J. R., and Clawson, G. H. (1942). *Rev. Can. Biol.* **1,** 50.
Garside, E. T., and Tait, J. S. (1958). *Can. J. Zool.* **36,** 563.
Grigg, G. C. (1969). *Comp. Biochem. Physiol.* **28,** 1203.
Gomazkov, O. A. (1959). *Byul. Inst. Biol. Vodokhranilishch, Akad. Nauk SSSR* **5,** 26 (cited from Smit, 1967).
Gordon, M. S. (1968). *Science* **159,** 87.
Hart, J. S. (1952). *Univ. Toronto Studies Biol.* **60,** *Publ. Ontario Fisheries Res. Lab.* **72,** 1–79.
Hart, J. S. (1957). *Can. J. Zool.* **35,** 195.
Haschemeyer, A. E. V. (1968). *Biol. Bull.* **135,** 130.
Haschemeyer, A. E. V. (1969a). *Comp. Biochem. Physiol.* **28,** 535.
Haschemeyer, A. E. V. (1969b). *Proc. Natl. Acad. Sci. U.S.* **62,** 128.
Hebb, C., Morris, D., and Smith, M. W. (1969). *Comp. Biochem. Physiol.* **28,** 29.
Heinicke, E. A., and Houston, A. G. (1965). *J. Fisheries Res. Board Can.* **22,** 1455.
Helmreich, E., and Cori, C. F. (1964). *Proc. Natl. Acad. Sci. U.S.* **52,** 647.
Heusner, A. A., and Enright, J. T. (1966). *Science* **154,** 532.
Hoar, W. S., and Robinson, G. B. (1959). *Can. J. Zool.* **37,** 419.
Hochachka, P. W. (1965). *Arch. Biochem. Biophys.* **111,** 96.
Hochachka, P. W. (1967a). *In* "Molecular Mechanisms of Temperature Adaptation," Publ. No. 84, pp. 177–203. Am. Assoc. Advance. Sci., Washington, D.C.
Hochachka, P. W. (1967b). Unpublished data.
Hochachka, P. W. (1968). *Comp. Biochem. Physiol.* **25,** 107.
Hochachka, P. W., and Hayes, F. R. (1962). *Can. J. Zool.* **40,** 261.
Hochachka, P. W., and Somero, G. N. (1968). *Comp. Biochem. Physiol.* **27,** 659.
Hochachka, P. W., and Somero, G. N. (1970). *In* "Fish Physiology" (W. S. Hoar and D. Randall, eds.), Vol. VI. Academic Press, New York (in press).
Hoff, J. G., and Westman, J. R. (1966). *J. Marine Res.* **24,** 131.
Ingraham, J. L., and Maaløe, O. (1967). *In* "Molecular Mechanisms of Temperature Adaptation," Publ. No. 84, pp. 279–309. Am. Assoc. Advance. Sci., Washington, D.C.
Ivlev, V. S. (1960). *Zool. Zh.* **39,** 494; Transl. by W. E. Ricker, *Fisheries Res. Board Can., Transl. Ser.* **394** (1961).
Iwatsuki, N., and Okazaki, R. (1967). *J. Mol. Biol.* **29,** 155.
Jankowsky, H. D. (1964). *Zool. Anz.* **172,** 233.
Jankowsky, H. D. (1968). *Helgolaender Wiss. Meeresuntersuch.* **18,** 317.
Javaid, M. Y., and Anderson, J. M. (1967). *J. Fisheries Res. Board Can.* **24,** 1507.
Johansen, K., Franklin, D. L., and Van Citters, R. L. (1966). *Comp. Biochem. Physiol.* **19,** 151.
Johansen, P. H. (1968). *Can. J. Zool.* **46,** 805.
Johnston, P. V., and Roots, B. I. (1964). *Comp. Biochem. Physiol.* **11,** 303.
Kanungo, M. S., and Prosser, C. L. (1959). *J. Cellular Comp. Physiol.* **54,** 259.
Kaplan, N. O. (1964). *Brookhaven Symp. Biol.* **17,** 131.
Katzen, H. M., Loderman, D. D., and Cirillo, V. J. (1968). *Ann. N.Y. Acad. Sci.* **151,** 351.
Kishinouye, K. (1923). *J. Coll. Agr., Imp. Univ. Tokyo* **8,** 293.
Klicka, J. (1965). *Physiol. Zool.* **38,** 177.
Knipprath, W. G., and Mead, J. F. (1968). *Lipids* **3,** 121.
Kusakina, A. A. (1962). *Tsitologiya* **4,** 68.
Kutty, M. N. (1968). *J. Fisheries Res. Board Can.* **25,** 1689.
Lardy, H. A. (1965). *In* "Control of Energy Metabolism" (B. Chance *et al.*, eds.), pp. 245–248. Academic Press, New York.
Lardy, H. A., Foster, D. V., Young, J. W., Shrago, E., and Ray P. D. (1965). *J. Cellular Comp. Physiol.* **66,** Suppl. 1, 39.
Lowry, O. H., Schulz, D. W., and Passonneau, J. V. (1964). *J. Biol. Chem.* **239,** 1947.

McFarland, W. N. (1959). *Publ. Inst. Marine Sci.* **6**, 23.

Mantelmann, I. I. (1958). *Izv. Vses. Nauchn.-Issled. Inst. Ozern. i Rechn. Rybn. Khoz.* **47**, 1;
    Fisheries Res. Board Can., Transl. Ser. 257 (1960).

Markert, C. L. (1968). *Ann. N.Y. Acad. Sci.* **151**, 14.

Massaro, E. J., and Markert, C. L. (1968). *J. Exptl. Zool.* **168**, 223.

Meuwis, A. L., and Heuts, M. J. (1957). *Biol. Bull.* **112**, 97.

Muir, B. S., Nelson, G. J., and Bridges, K. W. (1965). *Trans. Am. Fisheries Soc.* **94**, 378.

Murray, R. W. (1965). *Cold Spring Harbor Symp. Quant. Biol.* **30**, 233.

Murray, R. W. (1967). *In* "Lateral Line Detectors" (P. Cahn, ed.), pp. 277–293. Indiana
    Univ. Press, Bloomington, Indiana.

Newell, R. C. (1966). *Nature* **212**, 426.

Newsholme, E. A., and Gevers, W. (1967). *Vitamins Hormones* **25**, 1.

Ohlenbusch, H. D., and Precht, H. (1960). *Z. Wiss. Zool.* **164**, 364.

Pegel', V. A., and Remorov, V. A. (1963). *Nauchn. Dokl. Vysshei Shkoly, Biol. Nauki* **3**,
    54.

Peterson, R. H., and Anderson, J. M. (1969). *J. Fisheries Res. Board Can.* **26**, 93.

Pitt, T. K., Garside, E. T., and Hepburn, R. L. (1956). *Can. J. Zool.* **34**, 555.

Potts, D. C., and Morris, R. W. (1968). *Marine Biol.* **1**, 269.

Precht, H. (1949). *Z. Naturforsch.* 4b, 26.

Precht, H. (1958). *In* "Physiological Adaptation" (C. L. Prosser, ed.), pp. 50–78. Am.
    Physiol. Soc., Washington, D.C.

Precht, H. (1959). *Z. Vergleich. Physiol.* **42**, 365.

Precht, H. (1961). *Z. Vergleich. Physiol.* **44**, 451.

Precht, H. (1964a). *Helgolaender Wiss. Meeresuntersuch.* **9**, 392.

Precht, H. (1964b). *Zool. Jahrb., Abt. Allgem. Zool. Physiol. Tiere* **71**, 313.

Precht, H. (1964c). *Naturw. Rundschau* **16**, 438.

Precht, H. (1968). *Helgoländer Wiss. Meeresuntersuch.* **18**, 487.

Prosser, C. L. (1958). *In* "Physiological Adaptation" (C. L. Prosser, ed.), pp. 167–180.
    Am. Physiol. Soc., Washington, D.C.

Prosser, C. L. (1967). *In* "Molecular Mechanisms of Temperature Adaptation," Publ.
    No. 84, pp. 351–376. Am. Assoc. Advance. Sci., Washington, D.C.

Prosser, C. L., and Fahri, E. (1965). *Z. Vergleich. Physiol.* **50**, 91.

Prosser, C. L., Precht, H., and Jankowsky, H. D. (1965). *Naturwissenschaften* **52**, 168.

Randall, D. J., Holeton, G. F., and Stevens, E. D. (1967). *J. Exptl. Biol.* **46**, 339.

Rao, G. M. M. (1968). *Can. J. Zool.* **46**, 781.

Rao, K. P. (1962). *Science* **137**, 682.

Roberts, J. L. (1961). *Am. Zoologist* **1**, 383.

Roberts, J. L. (1964). *Helgolaender Wiss. Meeresuntersuch.* **9**, 459.

Roberts, J. L. (1966). *Helgolaender Wiss. Meeresuntersuch.* **14**, 451.

Roots, B. I. (1968). *Comp. Biochem. Physiol.* **25**, 457.

Roots, B. I., and Prosser, C. L. (1962). *J. Exptl. Biol.* **39**, 617.

Rozin, P. N., and Mayer, J. (1961). *Science* **134**, 942.

Ruhland, M. L. (1965). *Bull. Soc. Zool. France* **90**, 347.

Sand, A. (1938). *Proc. Roy. Soc.* **B125**, 524.

Schmein-Engberding, F. (1953). *Z. Fischerei* [N.S.] **2**, 125.

Scholander, P. F., Flagg, W., Hock, R. J., and Irving, L. (1953). *J. Cell. Comp. Physiol.* **42**,
    Suppl. 1, 1.

Schultze, D. (1965a). *Naturwissenschaften* **2**, 1.

Schultze, D. (1965b). *Z. Wiss. Zool.* **172**, 104.

Smit, H. (1965). *Can. J. Zool.* **43**, 623.

Smit, H. (1967). *Comp. Biochem. Physiol.* **21**, 125.

Somero, G. N. (1969). Unpublished data.

Somero, G. N. (1969a). *Am. Naturalist* **103,** 517.

Somero, G. N. (1969b). *Biochem. J.* **114,** 237.

Somero, G. N., and De Vries, A. L. (1967). *Science* **156,** 257.

Somero, G. N., and Hochachka, P. W. (1968). *Biochem. J.* **110,** 395.

Somero, G. N., and Hochachka, P. W. (1969). *Nature* **223,** 194.

Späth, M. (1967). *Z. Vergleich. Physiol.* **56,** 431.

Spoor, W. A. (1946). *Biol. Bull.* **91,** 312.

Staib, A. H. (1962). *Acta Biol. Med. Ger.* **9,** 145.

Suhrmann, R. (1955). *Biol. Zentr.* **74,** 432.

Sullivan, C. M. (1954). *J. Fisheries Res. Board Can.* **11,** 153.

Sullivan, C. M., and Fisher, K. C. (1953). *J. Fisheries Res. Board Can.* **10,** 187.

Taketa, K., and Pogell, B. M. (1965). *J. Biol. Chem.* **240,** 651.

Thorne, C. J. R., Grossman, L. I., and Kaplan, N. O. (1963). *Biochim. Biophys. Acta* **73,** 193.

Troshin, A. S., ed. (1967). "The Cell and Environmental Temperature." Pergamon, Oxford.

Tsukuda, H. (1961). *J. Biol. Osaka City Univ.* **12,** 15.

Tyler, A. V. (1966). *Can. J. Zool.* **44,** 349.

Ushakov, B. (1964). *Physiol. Rev.* **44,** 518.

Van Handel, E. (1966). *J. Exptl. Biol.* **44,** 523.

Weatherley, A. H. (1963). *Proc. Zool. Soc. London* **141,** 527.

Wells, N. A. (1935). *Physiol. Zool.* **8,** 196.

Williamson, J. R. (1965). *J. Biol. Chem.* **240,** 2308.

Williamson, J. R., Cheung, W. Y., Coles, H. S., and Herczeg, B. E. (1967). *J. Biol. Chem.* **242,** 5112.

Wittenberger, C., and Diaciuc, I. V. (1965). *J. Fisheries Res. Board Can.* **22,** 1397.

Wohlschlag, D. E. (1957). *Ecology* **38,** 502.

Wohlschlag, D. E. (1960). *Ecology* **41,** 287.

Wohlschlag, D. E., Cameron, J. N., and Cech, J. J., Jr. (1968). *Contrib. Marine Sci.* **13,** 90.

Zahn, M. (1962). *Zool. Beitr.* [N.S.] **7,** 15.

Zahn, M. (1963). *Verhandl. Deut. Zool. Ges. Muenchen, Akad. Verlag., Leipzig* p. 562.

Chapter 4 AMPHIBIA

Bayard H. Brattstrom

I. Introduction

The Amphibia bridge the gap between their freshwater rhipidistian fish ancestors and the truly terrestrial reptiles to which they gave rise. Modern amphibians present a spectrum of this transition, with entirely aquatic forms, "typical" amphibians that return to water to breed, and many forms in many families that are essentially emancipated from aquatic lives, lay terrestrial eggs, have direct development, and forage almost entirely upon land (C. J. Goin, 1960).

However, as the skin of an amphibian is permeable to water, water loss becomes a critical problem that restricts amphibian activity and physiology. In addition, the skin is used for respiration (Whitford and Hutchison, 1963, 1965a,b). Since the skin must be kept moist for effective respiration,

135

the seeking and maintaining of water levels forces amphibians, regardless of terrestrialism, to areas of wàter, moist soil, or to special activity or physiology (Stille, 1952; Bentley, 1966; Dole, 1967; Lee, 1967). Adaptation to arid conditions requires reduction of dermal respiration and the development of water conserving mechanisms. Some of the latter may be of a sophisticated nature (Bentley, 1966), but the position of the animals is at best, perilous. In spite of this, the Amphibia have utilized a variety of behavioral, reproductive, and physiological mechanisms (C. J. Goin, 1960; O. B. Goin and Goin, 1962) to cope with the restrictions imposed by their permeable skin and carry out normal activity. This variety is also expressed in the ways amphibians solve some of the problems of their thermoregulation.

A. Ectotherms vs Poikilotherms

Classically, physiologists have used the term poikilotherm for amphibians and reptiles (Bullock, 1955). As pointed out by Cowles and others (Cowles, 1945, 1958, 1962; Cowles and Bogert, 1944; Brattstrom, 1963, 1965), the term poikilotherm implies that the body temperature of the animal is the same as ambient temperature. This may be true in some experiments, where heat conduction and radiation to the animal is absent and evaporative cooling is measured or controlled. It is also true in many entirely aquatic amphibians that the body temperature does equal water temperature. On the other hand, some amphibians bask in the sun and achieve body temperatures far above ambient temperature by directly absorbing solar radiation (Brattstrom, 1963). Others, in heat stress or in normal activity, can cool by evaporation and thereby maintain body temperatures below ambient. The best example of the latter mechanism is a frog, *Rana pipiens,* in an oven at 50°C, that maintained a body temperature of 36.8°C (Thorson, 1955). Other examples include the body temperature of a *Rana clamitans,* 17°C above ambient during basking in full sun (Brattstrom, 1963), and *Bufo canorus* with a body temperature 21.8°C *below* the substrate on which it was sitting (Cunningham, 1963). Mullally and Cunningham (1956b) give several records of active *Rana muscosa* basking in the sun, with high body temperatures, while sitting on melting ice!

That body temperature equals ambient temperature and that physiological processes closely follow changes in temperature is clearly true for most invertebrates and fish, and is perhaps equally true for some aquatic amphibians. Those amphibians and reptiles that can heat their body above ambient temperature by absorbing heat from their surroundings or the sun have been termed ectotherms (heat source from without) by Cowles (1945, 1962). The contrasting term endotherms (heat source from within) is used for birds and mammals and those large reptiles (Indian pythons, varanid lizards) that can produce some body heat that contributes to body temperature.

Since body temperature does not always equal ambient temperature in amphibians, it is imperative that in any behavioral or physiological work where temperature is a variable, the body temperature of the animals themselves, and not just that of the environment be taken. It is also often assumed that amphibians can raise their body temperatures by the heat produced as a by-product of their metabolism. The amount of heat that is thus produced is so extremely small (Fromm, 1956), that it cannot contribute significantly to the body temperature of the animal.

B. Techniques and Terms

Three instruments have markedly influenced the progress of studies of temperature regulation in amphibians and reptiles: the small bulb, rapidly registering, Schultheis thermometer made by WESCO, power- and battery-operated thermocouples and thermisters (especially those that can be taken into the field, such as the Yellow Springs Instrument Company Telethermometers), and telemetry.

Terms employed herein are as defined by Cowles and Bogert (1944), Bogert (1949), Lowe and Vance (1955), Cowles (1962), and Brattstrom (1963, 1965). Briefly, the more important terms are: *ectotherms,* major heat source from without; *endotherms,* major heat source from within, thus including heterotherms (Cowles, 1962); *heliotherms,* basking forms; *thigmotherms,* forms obtaining heat from the substrate; *voluntary minimum,* the lowest body temperature voluntarily tolerated by an animal, the temperature at which an animal emerges or retreats (in practice, usually the lowest body temperature recorded of an active individual); *voluntary maximum,* the temperature at which an animal retreats to shade, cool water, or underground retreats (in practice, the highest body temperature recorded of an active individual); *normal activity range,* the range of body temperatures of active individuals from the voluntary minimum to the voluntary maximum; *basking range,* the range of body temperatures within the normal activity range in which the animal is basking; *preferred* (also optimum, eccritic, mean), the often narrow range of temperature at which some animals carry on their normal activities, the temperature an ectotherm selects in a thermal gradient (in practice, the mean of all body temperatures recorded within the normal activity range). There is some suggestion that ectotherms may have different preferred temperatures for different activities (Hadfield, 1966; Regal, 1966, 1967), and there may be some merit in the use of the term "ecological range" for that range of body temperature where activity is primarily not thermoregulatory (i.e. feeding, courting, defending territories).

Body temperatures are usually taken cloacally, though those of extremely small frogs and salamanders are usually taken orally or in the groin with the hind leg pressed against the body. Heat conduction from the hand or thermometer is minimized by holding the animal by the toe or hind leg, preferably with gloves, and allowing the thermometer to come to rest before insertion. Air temperatures listed are those of the microclimate where the animal was obtained, usually taken 1 in. above the surface of the substrate with the bulb shaded. Soil and water temperatures are taken at a depth of 1 in., unless otherwise noted. Macroclimatic data are of little or no importance to an animal living in the microclimate within a few inches of the ground. Other techniques or terms will be explained where needed below.

II. Thermoregulation

A. ACTIVITY TEMPERATURES, PREFERENCES, AND THERMAL TOLERANCES

1. *Activity Temperatures and Preferences*

Body temperatures of active amphibians from a wide variety of taxa and habitats have recently been reviewed by Brattstrom (1963). Body temperatures range from a low of −2°C for some salamanders walking on snow, to 35.7°C for some anurans. Lethal temperatures range from critical thermal minima ($LT_{50}/24$ hr) of −4°C for some northern salamanders and frogs to critical thermal maxima (CTM = elimination of righting response, see below) as high as 42.5°C for a small Mexican tree frog, *Hyla smithi* (Brattstrom, 1968). Since tables and graphs of body temperatures have recently been given (Brattstrom, 1963), these may be summarized.

a. Salamanders. There have been no recorded body temperatures of such common and permanently aquatic salamanders as *Necturus* and *Cryptobranchus*. Their annual cycle of behavior, habits, and environmental temperatures would suggest that these forms which live in the deeper parts of large rivers and lakes have low body temperatures and that body temperature usually equals water temperature. That *Necturus* lives for much of the year at body temperature of 4°C is attested by its presence in deep dimictic lakes which have an ice cover for much of the winter. *Necturus* apparently occurs in the shallows of lakes only in spring and fall, returning to the deeper parts in midwinter and midsummer.

Most other aquatic salamanders have body temperatures that equal water temperature. Some forms, however, live only in streams, ponds, or lakes of specific temperatures, and others migrate to these habitats for breeding only when environmental and water temperatures are within specific ranges. For example, newts (*Taricha*) migrate to breeding sites following rains (and probably only rains associated with certain temperatures), and they are found in streams only when the streams reach temperatures of 12°C (*T. torosa*) or 12.5°C (*T. granulosa*). Newts, *Diemictylus viridescens,* from eastern North America enter water of a colder temperature (7.8°C). Among ambystomids, *A. maculatum* from New York will walk over snow to enter spring breeding sites before ice has left the ponds and they have low body temperatures. Other species, *A. tigrinum, jeffersonianum, opacum,* and *macrodactylum,* migrate to ponds later in the season and at higher water and body temperatures (Anderson, 1968).

While the various species of *Ambystoma* have different thermal preferences, the thermal activity found in two other ambystomid salamanders appear to be largely a function of the temperature of the habitat available. *Rhyacotriton olympicus* lives in cold, often torrential, mountain streams of northwestern North America (Stebbins, 1951). Body temperatures of these salamanders equal water temperature. The temperature of the streams in which they live, however, never reaches above 10°C, so that body temperatures of *R. olympicus* range from 5.8 to 9.6°C. The salamanders do not live in warmer streams available in their range. The young of the larger, marbled salamander, *Dicamptodon ensatus,* of the same region, lives in larger streams and rivers, while the adult in largely terrestrial in the cool, wet rain forest. Thus, body temperatures of larval *D. ensatus,* equal water temperature in these habitats and range from 12.6° to 16.2°C. The south temperate and subtropical sirens and amphiumids appear to prefer warmer temperatures, but little is known of their thermal biology. Some aquatic salamanders appear to seek out warmer parts of streams, ponds, and thermal gradients (Licht and Brown, 1967). Near-metamorphosing *Ambystoma tigrinum* larvae have been found in warmer peripheral parts of ponds, and their body temperatures were higher (26.5°C) than those of younger individuals from a later age class that were in cooler water and had body temperatures of 21.5°–22.9°C. Similar data are reported for *A. macrodactylus* by Anderson (1968). Whether salamanders in the shallow parts of ponds can absorb enough solar radiation through the water to raise their body temperatures above water temperatures, as anuran tadpoles are able to do (Brattstrom, 1962), is not yet known.

Terrestrial or aquatic salamanders, during their terrestrial stages or activities, usually have body temperatures similar to that of the wet soil on which they are found (Bogert, 1952). This is especially so on cool misty nights, under rocks or logs, or in the constant temperature of caves (Bogert,

1952; Hutchison, 1958; Brattstrom, 1963; Anderson, 1968). Activity, however, places these animals in humidities lower than those of most hiding places (Taub, 1961; Heatwole, 1962), hence allowing, as a passive function of their moist skin, evaporative cooling to lower their body temperatures. Body temperatures of such animals usually approximate that of a wet-bulb thermometer or are intermediate between soil and air temperature. The diversity of body temperatures found among terrestrial salamanders is therefore a reflection of habitats occupied, seasonal and daily activity, size (affecting rates of cooling and desiccation), and some temperature selection

TABLE I

RANGES AND MEANS OF BODY TEMPERATURES OF ACTIVE
INDIVIDUALS FOR SEVERAL FAMILIES OF SALAMANDERS
AND ANURANS[a]

Family	Range (°C)	Mean (°C)
Salamanders	−2.0–26.7	19.2
Salamandridae	7.8–26.7	13.8
Ambystomidae	5.8–26.5	17.0
Plethodontidae	−2.0–26.2	14.8
Anura	3.0–35.7	21.7
Ascaphidae	4.4–15.7	10.0
Pelobatidae	12.2–25.0	21.4
Leptodactylidae	22.0–28.2	24.7
Bufonidae	3.0–33.7	24.0
Hylidae	3.8–33.7	23.7
Ranidae	4.0–34.7	21.3
Microhylidae	15.5–35.7	26.5

[a] Data from Brattstrom (1963).

(Brattstrom, 1963; Licht and Brown, 1967). Thus, body temperatures of plethodontid salamanders range from the cryophylic *Hydromantes platy-cephalus* (body temperatures of active individuals, −2° to 11.5°C) to the more thermophylic, for plethodontid salamanders, *Manculus quadridigitatus* (26.2°C). High temperatures of 26.7°C for *Diemictylus viridescens,* 26.5°C for *Ambystoma tigrinum,* and 26.2°C for *Manculus* represent the highest temperatures known for any salamander (Table I). Licht and Brown (1967) recently recorded *Taricha rivularis* in a thermal gradient which reached between 28° and 29°C for short periods. Adverse conditions such as an increase in temperature or a decrease in humidity or water content of the substrate, serve only to drive the salamanders into deep underground retreats (Taub, 1961; Heatwole, 1962).

b. Apoda. The caecilians or gymnophiona are restricted to the tropics

(Noble, 1931). Little is known of the behavior, physiology, or ecology of these forms, except for some observations on reproduction. Only one body temperature (28.2°C) at an air temperature of 26.4° is known in a specimen of *Gymnophis multiplicata proxima* from Nicaragua. Secretive habits and slimy, slippery skin will hinder accumulation of adequate physiological and ecological information about these evolutionarily important amphibians.

c. Anura. The Anura encompasses such a diversity of forms in almost all habitats that any simple statement on thermal patterns is misleading. No studies have been performed on such permanently aquatic forms as *Xenopus* or *Pipa,* though presumedly, body temperatures equal water temperatures and the preferences are probably for warm to moderate temperatures. The cryophylic ribbed toads, *Ascaphus,* are in striking contrast to the thermophylic and largely tropical Leptodactylids (Table I). The former live almost permanently associated with cold torrential streams of the Pacific northwest (Stebbins, 1951). The frogs are nocturnal, spending the daytime in hiding, in wet moss, within or behind waterfalls and torrents. Body and water temperatures range from 4.4° to 15.7°C, and they are thus lower than any records of American Leptodactylidae (22° to 27.2°C) or most microhylid frogs (15.5°–35.7°C). The latter two families are largely tropical and subtropical (though microhylids occur in the southern portion of temperate zones), and they never encounter, or are never active, at lower temperatures. In addition, most of the members of the two families cannot survive temperatures below 5°C. Those leptodactylids that have evolved in the frog vacuum of Australia have radiated into such a variety of morphological, behavioral and physiological types, that, as expected, some forms do tolerate colder conditions, though few tolerate severe conditions (Brattstrom unpublished data).

Within the families Ranidae, Bufonidae, and Hylidae, there is a diversity of temperature types that almost matches the range of Ascaphidae and Leptodactylidae. Thus, there are cryophilic frogs found in and near cool mountain water courses (*Rana aurora* at body temperatures of 9.8°–19.°C; *R. boyli* at 8.5°–25.2°C; *R. muscosa* at 4.0°–25.6°C) and thermophylic sun-basking frogs with high body temperatures ranging up to 29.0°C for *R. clamitans,* 30.0° for *R. catesbeiana,* 30.5°C for *R. septentrionalis,* and 34.7°C for *R. pipiens.* Toads run a similar gamut, though they are usually at slightly higher temperatures than are frogs. The body temperatures during maximal activity for toads are, however, about the same as those for frogs (33.7°C). Some toads (*Bufo marinus, valliceps, mazatlanensis*) have high body temperatures largely because ambient temperatures never fall very low in their tropical–subtropical environment. Tree frogs are as diverse, with body temperatures as low as 3.8°C for *H. regilla* and as high as 34.8°C for *Acris crepitans*.

Most anurans, like most salamanders, do not seem to select any preferred temperature. Most frogs and toads are equally active at any temperature within their activity range. There may be slight preferences and advantages for certain behavior, such as calling, breeding, feeding, or hiding, at certain temperatures (Blair 1961; Martof, 1962; Savage, 1962; Brattstrom, 1963; Tester *et al.*, 1965; Hadfield, 1966; Lee, 1967; Gorman, 1968), and there may be physiological advantages in certain behavior at certain temperatures (Martof, 1962; Hadfield, 1966). Some frogs and toads and most tree frogs, however, do seem to select certain higher temperatures within their activity range, and such forms as *Smilisca baudini, Hyla cinerea, crepitans, dendroscarta, labialis, picta* have activity ranges of body temperatures of only a few degrees.

Body temperature data are conspicuously lacking for even the commonest amphibians from continents other than the Americas, and thermal characteristics of most tropical forms are poorly documented. Extensive data are available for only a few dozen of the 99 species cited by Brattstrom (1963).

d. Genetic Adaptation. Implied in the summary above is that the differences noted between species, genera, and families are genetic, i.e., represent evolutionary adaptations to diverse environments or to diverse microclimates and habitats within a single seasonally changing environment (Fry, 1947, 1958; Vernberg, 1962). That these differences are genetic (except perhaps where the environment is limited, as in the absence of cold in the tropics), is attested by the similarity in activity temperatures in different years (Fitch, 1956), in the limits of acclimation, by the results of physiological studies performed at the same temperature, and by the extensive studies, discussed below, on embryonic thermal tolerances. Population differences within the same species, implying genetic differences, have been demonstrated and discussed by Moore (1949a,b), Tashian and Ray (1957), and Jameson (1966). Species differences in the heat resistance of various tissues are summarized below and by Braun *et al.* (1963), Kusakina (1963), and Ushakov (1964). Embryos of the frog, *Rana cyanophlyctis,* with vertebral fusions (heterozygotes of a single dominant gene for the abnormality occurring with a frequency of 8–12% in natural populations) can tolerate higher temperatures during development than can the normal (recessive homozygote) individuals (Dasgupta and Grewal, 1968).

2. *Tolerances*

Beyond the activity range of an amphibian are those extremes of temperature that are limiting to the individual and the species because they are lethal.

a. Embryonic Temperature Tolerances. The extensive literature on the effect of temperature on amphibian eggs and embryonic development need not be fully elaborated here. Lillie and Knowlton (1897) supplied for first quantitative data on the effect of temperature on the growth of amphibian embryos. They showed that in *Rana pipiens* and *Ambystoma tigrinum,* the time necessary to reach a given morphological stage decreased with an increase in temperature. The extensive work in this field by Moore (1949a,b), Volpe (1953, 1957a,b), Gosner and Black (1955), Ruibal (1955, 1962), Hubbs and Armstrong (1961), Hubbs *et al.* (1963), Ballinger and McKinney (1966), Zweifel (1968), and H. A. Brown (1967, 1969) include some of the following generalizations.

1. Northern species have a lower minimal and maximal limiting temperature for normal development than do southern species.

2. Since in ectotherms, low temperatures slow down physiological processes, the embryos of northern species compensate for this by having a more rapid rate of development than southern species. This difference is most apparent at low temperatures.

3. The relative influence of different temperatures on the rate of development is less in northern than in southern species.

4. The egg size of northern species tends to be greater (more yolk) than in southern species; the egg complement is often smaller in northern than in southern species.

5. The amount of oxygen consumed in frog embryos increases with age. The oxygen carrying capacity of the water decreases with an increase in water temperature. Therefore, hatching of the embryo into the tadpole stage occurs at a later stage in the north than it does in the south.

6. The early cleavage stages have the least resistance to both low and high temperatures.

7. Embryonic characteristics of different species that appear to be adaptations to environmental temperature are for the most part constant in individuals of any one species from different latitudes.

8. There is selection for a rapid rate of development at high temperatures in frogs from lowland populations and no selection for rapid developmental rate in highland populations.

Ruibal (1962) further classifies populations of *Rana pipiens* into "Cold Races" (rapid development at low temperatures, tolerant of low temperatures, considerable hybrid inviability when crossed with warm races), characteristic of populations from Vermont, Canada, Wisconsin, New Jersey, and Colorado; "Warm Races" (rapid development at high temperatures, tolerant of high temperatures, considerable hybrid inviability when crossed with cold races), characteristic of populations from Florida, Texas, Louisiana, and Lowland Mexico; and "Slow Races" (slow development at all temperatures, narrow temperature tolerance, relatively slight hybrid inviabil-

ity when crossed with warm or cold races) characteristic of populations
from highland Mexico, intermediate Mexico, Costa Rica, and saline streams
of California.

Little information is available on thermal activity and tolerances of amphibian larvae. Brattstrom (1963) records body temperatures for *Dicamptodon, Ambystoma,* and large *Rana catesbeiana* larvae. Most were the same
temperature as the water. Licht and Brown (1967) describe thermal tolerances and preferenda for larval and adult newts (*Taricha*). Zweifel (1968)
and H. A. Brown (1969) describe thermal tolerances for some desert anuran
larvae. Orr (1955) has shown that the tadpole of *Rana pipiens* is killed
by a lower temperature and in a shorter time than is the adult. Cunningham
(1962), however, reports that newly metamorphosed toadlets of *Bufo californicus* have higher tolerances than the adult. Thermoregulatory behavior
of anuran tadpoles will be discussed below (Section II,B).

b. Tolerance to Cold. Most amphibians burrow sufficiently deep in the
soil, or remain in the mud or water of the deeper parts of ponds and
lakes (where minimum temperatures are usually 4°C), to avoid exposure
to low temperatures, and hence they generally avoid freezing (Hutchison
and Dady, 1962, 1964). Some salamanders are active on snow at body
temperatures of −2°C, while many north temperate and high montane
frogs and toads are active at near freezing temperatures (Mullally,
1952, 1953; Cunningham and Mullally, 1956; Mullally and Cunningham,
1956a,b; Brattstrom, 1963).

The ability of amphibians to survive at low water temperatures is quite
good. Hutchison and Dady (1962, 1964) studied survival rates of submerged southern toads, *Bufo terrestris,* and leopard frogs, *Rana pipiens,*
at various temperatures. The semiaquatic frog was better adapted for prolonged submersion than was the terrestrial toad, because the frogs were
able to survive submersion for longer periods (a mean of 62.1 hours at
5°C), they had a lower rate of oxygen consumption, they could use a
greater amount of the dissolved oxygen present, they had a greater surface
area per unit of weight, and because they gained less weight through water
uptake. Czopek (1962) showed that the aquatic newt can live for many
months under water and *Bombina bombina,* small *Rana esculenta,* and
R. temporaria lived for at least 30 days. While terrestrial toads, *Bufo bufo,*
lived for only 12–35 hours. There are a few records which indicate that
amphibians often do not survive cold or freezing winters (Fitch, 1956);
hence, freezing may be one of the more important environmental factors
affecting populations of amphibians.

Brattstrom (1968) presented data on cold lethal temperatures or critical
thermal minima of a variety of anurans from a range of latitudes. These

data represent the temperature at which 50% of the animals ($LT_{50}/24$ hr) did not survive (obviously dead or could not right themselves after being warmed). They show an increase in cold tolerance with an increase in latitude, and they support the suggestion (Brattstrom, 1961) that cold may be one of the more significant climatic variables restricting tropical forms to the tropics. The data are expanded and further analyzed in Figs. 1 and 2, which include determinations of $LT_{50}/24$ hr made in thermal baths or cabinets on animals acclimated to $23° \pm 2°C$ for a week. Data

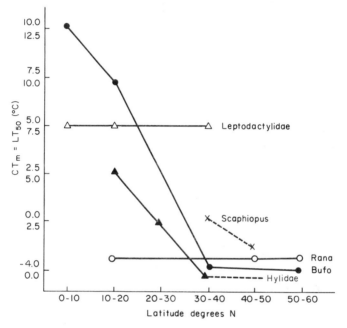

Fig. 1.   The *lowest* critical thermal minima (CTm), i.e., lowest $LT_{50}/24$ hr, for each $10°$ of latitude for several families of amphibians.

are presented for seven species of *Rana*, fifteen hylids, seven leptodacylids, fifteen bufonids, and two pelobatids as a function of the latitude of collection. The data are for forms from low elevation (below 3000 ft) only. An $LT_{50}/24$ hr of $2.5°C$ for each species for two microhylids (*Gastrophyne mazatlanensis* and *Hypopachus* sp.) from Sonora, Mexico, latitude $31°$, is not included in Figs. 1 and 2. Mean critical thermal minima and the lowest critical thermal minimum for any species for a $10°$ range of latitude are presented separately. It is clear that the leptodactylids are the least cold tolerant, and this may be a significant reason why this family is largely tropical and subtropical in distribution in the Americas. Bufonids and hylids show a change in the tolerance of cold as a function of latitude, while

most ranids from all latitudes appear to be able to tolerate temperatures
as low as —1° to —1.6°C. *Rana warschewitschi* from 5100 ft in the mountains of central Costa Rica can tolerate temperatures only as low as 4.8°C.
High alpine toads and tree frogs (not presented in Figs. 1 and 2) appear
to tolerate lower temperatures than do their equal-latitude, low elevation,

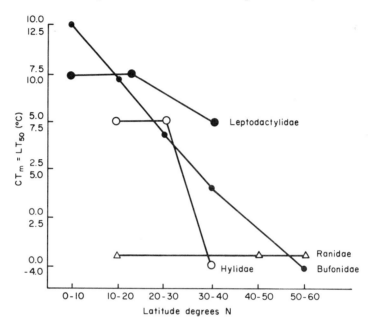

Fig. 2.   Mean critical thermal minima (CTm), i.e., mean $LT_{50}/24$ hr–10° latitude for
four families of amphibians, as a function of latitude. Data for each 10° of latitude are
grouped.

related species. These data, however, are limited and crude, and should
be considered tentative until further work is done.

  c. Tolerance to Heat. In general, amphibians are much more cryophylic
than are reptiles. Most amphibians are active with body temperatures below
30°C, though some voluntarily tolerate body temperatures as high as
35.7°C. Basking anurans may occur at higher ambient temperatures than
this, but they maintain lower body temperatures by evaporation. Temperatures of 28°C will kill some salamanders and frogs, while others can tolerate
temperatures as high as 42.5°C. As expected, the time required for death
at any temperature decreases with an increase in temperature, small individuals heat up and die before larger ones, and the death points of larval
stages may differ from those of adults. Photoperiod, time of year, hemoglobin levels, relative humidity, and acclimation also affect heat death

(Stuart, 1951; Hutchison, 1961; Brattstrom and Lawrence, 1962; Cunningham, 1962; Brattstrom, 1968).

Several criteria have been used for heat death in amphibians. Most workers have distinguished between an ecological or behavioral death point,
where recovery is possible after locomotor failure (onset of spasms, elimination of righting response), and physiological death, beyond which recovery
is impossible (lethal temperature). Hutchison and Kosh (1965), and
Hutchison *et al.* (1966) subsequently have shown that there is a species-specific and thermally variable unpredictable difference between elimination
of the righting response and onset of spasms. Cowles and Bogert (1944)
and Lowe and Vance (1955), working with reptiles, originally used the
term critical thermal maximum to mean elimination of the righting response. This definition was followed by Brattstrom and co-workers working
with frogs. However, Hutchison (1961), using salamanders, defined critical
thermal maximum as the onset of spasms. Brattstrom and Regal (1965)
used this definition for their work on salamanders. Brattstrom (1968) further noted that some salamanders do not enter a state called onset of spasms,
and suggested and used two criteria for behavioral death, CTM, the critical
thermal maximum defined as the elimination of the righting response, and
OS, the onset of spasms.

Most work on tolerance to heat has been done in relation to thermal
acclimation and will be discussed in the next section. Thermal tolerance
of eggs and larvae have been summarized above. Orr (1955) shows that
in *Rana pipiens,* different tissues died at different temperatures. Most resistant to heat were sciatic nerve and heart, while muscle death matched
whole animal death (Fig. 3).

d. Alteration of Tolerance: Acclimation, Acclimatization. Critical to any
study of thermal tolerances is an understanding of the ability of an animal
to alter these tolerances and the genetic limits of this ability. Acclimation
in amphibians, defined as short term physiological adjustment taking place
over a period of minutes, hours, or weeks, has been studied from two
points of view: metabolic studies and changes in critical thermal maxima.
Acclimatization (seasonal changes under natural conditions) studies have
been largely related to general and cellular metabolism, and to endocrinological problems.

Vernberg (1952) showed that not only was there a difference in oxygen
consumption in two species of plethodontid salamanders (*Eurycea bislineata*
consumed more oxygen per unit weight than did similarly sized individuals
of *Plethodon cinereus,* when measured at 10°C; there was no difference
when measured at 1°C), but that there were seasonal differences within
the same species when measured at 10°C. In both species, the highest

metabolic rates occurred during May–June and the lowest during October–November. Helff (1927) and Evans (1939) had earlier shown species differences in oxygen consumption in salamanders.

Tashian and Ray (1957) measured oxygen consumption in five species of tropical and four species of temperate-boreal anurans, at two temperature levels. The respiratory metabolism was higher for the northern forms than

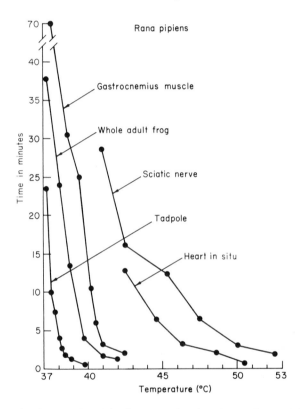

Fig. 3.   Heat death curves for adults, larvae, and various tissues of *Rana pipiens*. Modified after Orr (1955).

for tropical forms at both temperatures tested. This was expected from the general concept that activity rates are greater at given temperatures in ectotherms from northern latitudes when compared with the same or closely related southern forms (Bullock, 1955). Values for Q_{10} reported by Tashian and Ray (1957) did not significantly differ between northern and southern forms, except that *Bufo boreas* had a lower Q_{10} than had any of the other forms tested. Further, at their normal habitat temperatures, the northern species had a higher rate of respiration than had the tropical species (Tashian and Ray, 1957). Mellanby (1940) placed adult *Rana temporaria* and *Salamandra salamandra* acclimated to 10°C and 30°C in an environment of 0°C and found that the group acclimated to the higher temperature was inactive at 0°C, but the group acclimated to 10°C was active.

Seasonal effects (acclimatization) on heat production have been shown for *Rana pipiens* by Fromm (1956), and on the heat resistance of frog muscle of *Rana temporaria* by Pashkova (1963). The decrease in the heat resistance of frog muscle in the spring is in part due to hormonal changes prior to and during reproduction, and it can be modified by ground hypophyseal injections (Pashkova, 1963). Hypophyseal injections induce reproduction or modified heat resistance in winter frogs, while thyroxin injections increase, and darkness and low temperatures decrease, muscular heat resistance. The increase in heat resistance during the winter is probably related to an increase in thyroid activity, while a fall in resistance presumedly occurs because of intensification of gonadotropic function of the hypophysis during reproduction (Pashkova, 1963).

Stier and Bock (1966) found seasonal changes with temperature in the heart rate of toads. The relationship was linear in the summer, but linear only between 14°C and 23°C in the winter. Between 23° and 35°C, heart rate did not increase with body temperature in toads tested during the winter. Boral and Deb (1966) showed an increase in the oxygen and carbon dioxide content of the blood of "hibernating" (20°–22°C) over nonhibernating (28°–30°C) toads, *Bufo melanostictus,* presumedly due to the increased carrying capacity of oxygen by a higher concentration of hemoglobin and higher amounts of dissolved carbon dioxide in plasma due to hemoconcentration. King (1966) found differences in a biochemical lesion stage, characterized by increasing ^{32}P uptake in nontumor kidneys of *Rana pipiens* acclimated to 5° and 25°C. Cortelyou *et al.* (1966) further showed that there are marked effects of temperature on Parathormone-influenced phosphorus metabolism in *Rana pipiens* acclimated to different temperatures.

Blood sugar values differ for different species of amphibians and usually differ with season (Miller, 1961; Mizell, 1965). Higher values occur at the time of breeding and may be correlated with an increase in general metabolic activity and with an increase in the activity of the pituitary, interrenal, thyroid gland, and gonads (Miller, 1961). During hibernation, a decrease in blood sugar is accompanied by an increase in the liver and total-body glycogen content. Fat bodies are maximum in size and development during the fall (Miller, 1961).

McDonald *et al.* (1963) showed acclimation effects on conductance velocity in sciatic nerves of *Rana pipiens,* while Bishop (Personal communication) found only slight differences in nerve conductivity of *Rana catesbeiana*

acclimated to different temperatures, but found greater differences in
Bufo boreas.

Seasonal or acclimatization effects on the thermostability of tissues and
cells is reviewed by Zhirmunsky and Pashkova (1963) and Ushakov (1964).
Other studies have been reviewed by Fry (1947, 1958), Bullock (1955),
Precht (1958), and Precht *et al.* (1955).

Possibly the first to show acclimation effects on lethal temperatures were
Davenport and Castle (1895), who found differences in upper lethal temperatures of tadpoles of *Bufo terrestris,* depending upon the temperature
of acclimation. Groups raised at 15°C and 25°C had upper lethal temperatures of 40.3°C and 43.5°C, respectively.

McFarland (1955) showed that the lethal temperature (LT_{50}) of the
salamandrid, *Taricha torosa,* was a function of previous thermal history.
Stebbins (1954), Zweifel (1957), and Hutchison (1958) presented data
on acclimation effects on critical thermal maxima of salamanders. Hutchison
(1961) presented and summarized extensive data on the critical thermal
maxima and rates of acclimation in many species of salamanders from
the eastern United States. Brattstrom (1960, 1961) and Brattstrom and
Lawrence (1962) presented thermal acclimation data for several anurans.
These data, in addition to subsequent studies by Brattstrom and Regal
(1965), Brooks and Sassman (1965), Heatwole *et al.* (1965), Schmid
(1965b), and Brattstrom (1968), may be summarized as follows.

The critical thermal maximum (CTM) of a sample of animals acclimated to a given temperature was determined, while the remaining animals
were placed at a different temperature. Samples were removed from this
new temperature at intervals and their CTM was tested. The CTM test
was performed by heating the animals at a rate of about 1°C/min by
means of infrared lamps over vessels containing water, or by a heating
unit below the vessel. As the temperature of the animal increased, it soon
reached a temperature at which it fell on its back (or it was turned on
its back by the experimenter) and could not right itself. Its body temperature, taken at this point, was taken to be the CTM (see above). When
placed in cool water, the animal revived; if heated further, it soon began
twitching violently. Its temperature at this point was taken to be the onset
of spasms (OS). If placed in cool water it would revive. If heated further,
the animal did not revive when placed in cool water, hence it had reached
its lethal temperature.

The early studies on thermal acclimation showed that the rate of acclimation was rapid, complete in most cases in a few days; that the rate and
range of acclimation was a function of the temperature of acclimation;
and they implied that there were distributional implications in the ability
to undergo rapid acclimation. It was suggested that rapid adjustment of

the CTM would not only allow for survival under conditions of stress, especially in the rapidly changing weather of frontal westerlys, but that it also reflected physiological adjustment of metabolism to the new conditions (Vernberg, 1952, 1962; Tashian and Ray, 1957; Brattstrom, 1963). Brattstrom and Regal (1965) showed that montane plethodontid salamanders from Mexico acted, in terms of their ability to change their CTM, like most of the temperate latitude salamanders studied by Hutchison

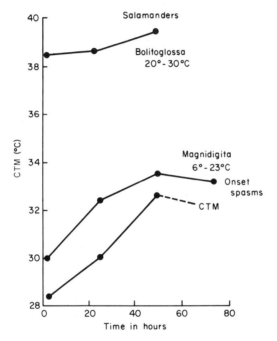

FIG. 4. Rate of acclimation in two tropical-lattitude species of plethodontid salamanders from Costa Rica transferred from the cold to heat; 20°C to 30°C (*Bolitoglossa*), or 6°C to 23°C (*Magnidigita*). *Bolitoglossa striatulata* from 1900 ft and *Magnidigita subpalmata* from over 10,000 ft. Each point represents the mean of three or more animals. CTM = critical thermal maxima.

(1961). Heatwole *et al.* (1965) showed that montane Puerto Rican frogs of the genus *Eleutherodactylus* had lower CTM than lowland forms. Tropical lowland Central American salamanders (Fig. 4), though having a high CTM, do not have much ability to change their CTM. Thus, *Bolitoglossa striatulata* from 1900 ft (Turrialba, Costa Rica) could change their CTM by only 1°C (Fig. 4). *Magnidigita subpalmatus* from over 10,000 ft (Cerro de la Muerte, Costa Rica) had both a low CTM and a low OS, and they had some ability to change these (Fig. 4). Critical thermal minima for the latter species acclimated to 20°C is at least as low as —4°C.

Based on the above considerations and experience in the tropics, Brattstrom (1968) suggested that perhaps tropical amphibians living in the uniform environment of the tropics would have little requirement for physiological adjustment and that it would be the temperate species that would show wide abilities for physiological adjustment. Data for 53 species in

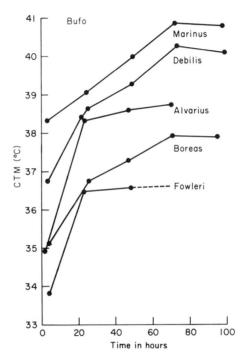

Fɪɢ. 5.   Rate of acclimation in several wide-ranging, low elevation species of toads from North and Central America transferred from 8°C to 23°C, except *B. boreas* (transferred from 5°C to 30°C) and *B. marinus* (transferred from 27°C to 38°C). Each point represents the mean of three or more animals. The range of distribution of the species is in inverse order to that on the graph; i.e., *B. marinus* is the southernmost, *B. fowleri* is the northernmost. *B. fowleri* and *boreas* are temperate forms, *alvarius* is a desert water hole and river toad, *debilis* is an arid subtropical form, and *marinus* is a subtropical and tropical form. CTM = critical thermal maxima.

anuran amphibians from a wide variety of habitats, latitudes, and altitudes in North and Central America showed that this was not the case (Brattstrom, 1968). Instead, the range of tolerance of the more southern species was higher than for the northern forms. Figure 5 shows an example of this for several wide-ranging species of toads from different latitudes.

These data (Brattstrom, 1968) further showed that there was little geographic variation in CTM within a species, except for wide-ranging forms such as *Rana pipiens, Bufo boreas,* and *Hyla regilla* (also see Jameson, 1966). Species with restricted geographic ranges, such as *Bufo exsul* and *nelsoni,* two Pleistocene relic species of *Bufo boreas* living in isolated areas of arid California and Nevada, have little or poor ability to acclimate. High altitude forms of North America acted similarly, in terms of their ability to acclimate, to low altitude forms of higher latitudes. High altitude forms in the recent mountains of Central America showed a diversity of acclimation responses. These species seem to be lowland tropical forms that had been carried or forced into a variety of restrictive thermal tolerances and poor abilities to acclimate.

Adjustment to heat was seen to be diverse, with some species overshooting and others slowly reaching full acclimation levels, and this implied that different control mechanisms might be used by different species for adjustment (Brattstrom, 1968).

B. BEHAVIORAL THERMOREGULATION

The primary means of thermoregulation in amphibians is behavioral Even this is absent in some forms, while others supplement it with a minor amount of physiological thermoregulation (see below), and all forms thus far tested have some ability to acclimate. Behavioral thermoregulation falls into two major categories; that relating to general seasonal activity and that of a specific, daily nature.

The first category includes seasonal, diurnal, and habitat-selection behavior. Many amphibians are active at specific climatic times of the year. Emergence from underground or underwater retreats, migration to breeding sites, breeding, and return to retreats is often thermally determined (Wright, 1932; Wright and Wright, 1949; Brattstrom and Warren, 1955; Blair, 1961). The more cryophylic forms, such as *Hyla crucifer* of the eastern United States, emerge early in the spring when the ice is melting and frost is on the ground at night, and they call at low air and body temperatures. As the season progresses, there are successive appearances at the breeding site of the more thermophylic amphibians. In the eastern United States, the thermophylic *Hyla versicolor* and the basking ranids are some of the last to breed. Seasonality of emergence and breeding are, however, clearly also related to water availability, humidity, barometric pressure, and internal reproductive rhythms, as well as temperature (Wright and Wright, 1949; Blair, 1961; Packard, 1966; Hock, 1967).

Owing to the stresses of daytime solar radiation, dehydration effects,

and predation pressure, most amphibians are active at night when temperatures are lower and humidities are higher (Storm, 1960; Brattstrom, 1963).
Many frogs that are active at night may also bask in the sun in the day
so that daytime body temperatures are higher than nocturnal temperatures
for the same frogs (Brattstrom, 1963).

Species-specific habitat selection in temperate regions will of course indicate what microclimatic temperatures and humidities are available to an
amphibian. For example, in a small geographic area within the Pacific
northwest, the ambystomid, *Rhyacotriton olympicus,* is found in cold, torrential streams with body temperatures of 5.8°–9.6°C; the marbled salamander, *Dicamptodon ensatus,* in larger streams or rivers or on land with
body temperatures of 9.6°C to 16.2°C; the newt, *Taricha granulosa* in
ponds with body temperatures of 12.5°–18.4°C; plethodontid salamanders
in wet areas near streams or under rocks and logs with body temperatures
as low as 7.0°–13°C (*Plethodon dunni, vehiculum, vandykei*) or as high
as 20°C (*Ensatina, Aneides*). Nearby, *Hyla regilla* or *Rana aurora* or *boyli*
may be basking with body temperatures as high as 25°C. *R. aurora* has
been recorded only as high as 19°C, though the related basking *R. cascadae*
reaches 29.0°C (Brattstrom, 1963). Habitat selection may, of course, occur
without reference to microclimates as is clearly seen in tropical rain forest
where microclimates are almost uniform throughout the rain forest, but
microhabitats are diverse (Brattstrom, 1961; Sexton, *et al.,* 1964).

Individual thermoregulatory behavior includes emergence, retreat, basking (with perhaps some orentation to and away from the sun), and microclimate selection (including shade-seeking, sun-seeking, ground contacts,
selection of water temperatures, and selection of soil temperatures). Much
of this type of behavior has been summarized above or in Brattstrom (1963).
Selection of microclimates, especially warm microclimates on cool nights,
is seen in the behavior of such forms as the hylid, *Acris crepitans. Acris*
is a basker in the daytime. At night it seeks the warmer, usually moist
soil at the edge of ponds. If the pond is sufficiently warm, the frogs will
leave the soil, hop to the pond (presumedly both for warmth and water),
and return to wet soil to sit. If the pond cools off faster than the soil,
the frogs will remain on the soil longer. Trips to the pond will decrease
in number and the time spent in the water will decrease. Should air and
soil temperatures drop faster than the pond temperature, as a result, for
example, of a strong breeze, the frogs will sit half submerged in the warmer
pond (Fitch, 1956; Brattstrom, 1963).

It was indicated above, and in Licht and Brown (1967), that some
aquatic salamanders seem to select specific or warm parts of ponds. Selection
of warm parts of ponds is most strikingly seen in the thermal aggregations
of tadpoles. On warm days, tadpoles tend to select the warmest parts of

ponds, though if the pond is shallow and the day especially hot, the very warm peripheral parts of the ponds are rejected. With individual tadpoles responding to the variety of thermal gradients within a pond, the tadpoles meet in large aggregations (from a few to thousands) in one or several parts of the pond. These aggregations are thermally related and are different from feeding, metamorphosing, and "social" aggregations (Brattstrom and Warren, 1955; Brattstrom, 1962; Bragg, 1965). In some cases, *Hyla regilla* for instance, the tadpoles may be oriented with their tails pointing to the sun, i.e., orienting away from the sun, but thus exposing their dorsal surfaces to solar radiation. As the periphery and surface of ponds cool at night, tadpoles congregate in the warmer, usually deeper, parts of ponds. Early morning warming of the edges of ponds bring the tadpoles out into patches of full sun until daily behavior begins.

These observations led Brattstrom and Warren (1955) and Brattstrom (1962) to suggest that thermal aggregations in tadpoles were adaptive and of survival value, as an increase in body temperature results in an increase in metabolism; an increase in metabolism reduces the time required before metamorphosis; hence the tadpoles might metamorphose before the ponds dried up (arid regions) or were washed out by subsequent rains (flash-flooding in arid regions, heavy rains in tropical regions). It was further suggested, and experimentally shown to be valid (Brattstrom, 1962), that an aggregation of small dark objects, such as tadpoles, in the shallow parts of ponds, could collectively absorb sufficient solar radiation, in spite of radiation lost in the top inches of water, to increase their body temperatures and further conduct this heat to the surrounding water, raising its temperature.

Lucas and Reynolds (1967) recently tested larvae of *Rana pipiens, R. catesbeiana,* and *Ambystoma tigrinum* in thermal gradients. Selection, aggregation, and seasonal differences were noted. *Rana pipiens* larvae acclimated both to cold (13°C) and warmth (25°–27°C) selected lower temperatures (20°C) than control larvae kept at 20°C, which selected 27°C. After treatment by immersion in 0.02% propylthiouracil or 10 µg/liter of L-thyroxine, *R. pipiens* larvae selected lower water temperatures in a less specific manner than untreated larvae. Hypophysectomy resulted in a random positioning in the thermal gradient, except for avoidance of the extremes of temperature.

The discrimination of temperature itself by the amphibian is poorly understood. Behavioral thermoregulation of amphibians implies that temperature detection by the animal is delicate and efficient yet temperature reception appears to be gross and usually involves detection of rapid changes in temperature of 3°C or more (Murray, 1962). Though temperature receptors in the lateral line organ of *Xenopus* have been shown to be similar to those of elasmobranch ampullae of Lorenzini, it has yet to be demonstrated that any amphibian has the sensitivity approaching many fish, which are sensitive to increases of 0.1°C (Murray, 1962).

C. Physiological Thermoregulation

As indicated above, thermoregulation in amphibians is mostly of a behavioral nature. Heat gain in amphibians is thus largely behavioral and involves the conduction and convection of heat to an animal in a favorable or selected environment, and the absorption by basking of solar and reflected radiation. Physiological heat may come from metabolic heat production, but it is too small to contribute much to body temperature.

1. *Heat Production and Metabolic Studies*

Direct calorimetric measurements of heat production of curarized frogs, *Rana pipiens,* of two acclimated groups of both fed and nonfed animals measured at a temperature of 22°–28°C, indicated an average metabolic heat production ranging from 64 to 95 cal/100 gm wet weight/hr (Fromm, 1956). There were small seasonal differences in heat production with maxima in spring and minima in fall and winter. Feeding had no effect on heat production, nor was there any correlation between oxygen consumption and heat production (Fromm, 1956). It is clear, however, that heat production is so low that it does not contribute significantly to body temperature.

Studies on gas exchange in frogs and salamanders have revealed that the role of the lungs, skin, and buccopharyngeal mucosa vary with temperature. Pulmonary and buccal respiration become more important at higher temperatures, especially for oxygen uptake. Most of the carbon dioxide produced is released through the skin. Oxygen uptake increases with the weight of the animals and with temperature. Breathing rates, buccopharyngeal movements, and tidal volumes also increase with an increase in temperature (Whitford and Hutchison, 1963, 1965a,b, 1967; Vinegar and Hutchison, 1965; Guimond and Hutchison, 1968). Body size, photoperiod, and acclimation markedly affect gas exchange (Whitford and Hutchison, 1967; Hutchison *et al.,* 1968). In the lungless plethodontid salamanders, the skin accounts for most of the oxygen uptake, but buccopharyngeal oxygen uptake becomes more important in the more terrestrial of the plethodontids (Whitford and Hutchison, 1965b). As expected, activity increases the oxygen consumption of amphibians (Johansen, 1962).

Comparative studies of metabolism and metabolic adaptation to temperature are not yet available for more than a few species. The generalities expressed by Scholander *et al.* (1953), Bullock (1955), Tashian and Ray (1957), G. W. Brown (1964), Newell (1966), Whitford and Hutchison (1967), and Hutchison *et al.* (1968) are not expected to be markedly different for other amphibians. Yet the data of Fromm (1956) and Fromm and Johnson (1955) suggest that the role of anaerobic respiration, recently found to be important in some turtles and lizards (Moberly, 1963, 1964), may play an unexpected role.

Recent studies on tissue and cellular metabolism of cryophylic (*Rana temporaria, Bufo bufo*) as opposed to thermophylic (*Rana ridibunda, Bufo viridis*) Russian amphibians have shown (Braun *et al.,* 1963) that actomyosin of skeletal muscles, hemoglobin, and surface ATP from erythrocytes of thermophylic forms had higher resistance to heat denaturation than the same proteins in cryophilic forms. Differences in heat resistance of the cholinesterase of liver homogenates between *Bufo bufo and B. viridis* were shown by Kusakina (1963). Differences in heat resistance of other tissues and cells have been shown by Rumyantsev (1963), Ushakov (1963, 1964), and Ushakov and Chernokozheva (1963). In general, the more thermophylic the species, the higher is the heat resistance of cell proteins. Thus, Vinogradova (1963) showed that the actomyosin extract of the muscle of the more thermophylic *Rana ridibunda* was maximally active at a temperature 6°C higher than that of the less thermophylic *R. temporaria.* Most of these studies have been reviewed by Ushakov (1964).

Endocrine effects on metabolism in amphibians are indicated by seasonal differences (see Section II,A,2,d). In addition, Pashkova (1963) showed that hypophysectomy in the toad, *Bufo bufo,* resulted in loss of body weight and of liver dry matter, and a fall in blood sugar. Hypophysectomy appears to impede the metabolism of fat from the fat bodies of toads during starvation, as well as reducing depletion of glycogen by the liver (Epple *et al.,* 1966). This may not be the case for salamanders, as suggested by Miller (1961). General, comparative, and cellular metabolism of amphibians has been recently reviewed by Brown (1964).

Hibernation

What is hibernation in an amphibian or reptile? Confusion exists between cold torpor (low body temperature) and hibernation (a winter period of inactivity, usually with low body temperatures and some metabolic differences). Torpor, with concomitant reduction in metabolism, can be produced at any season of the year by placing an amphibian in the cold. Cold and darkness in the winter, however, affect activity and cellular and organ metabolism (fat development, blood sugar, glycogen levels, and enzymatic changes, see above). Holzapfel (1937) presented the following criteria for hibernating, as opposed to summer frogs in cold conditions: gain of weight;

darkening of the skin; increase in muscle tonus; decrease in blood volume, number of erythrocytes, and percent of hemoglobin; increase in muscle fatigue; decrease and irregularity in the heart rate; the heart rate not increasing linearly with temperature; changes in the color of the thymus, adrenal glands, and gonads; an increase in the cell size; basiphilly; and reduction in the number of nucleoli in the cell nucleus. Holzapfel (1937) further cited some frogs, such as *Acris,* that did not seem to enter into hibernation.

Photoperiod, temperature, endocrine, and other factors need to be fully investigated and controlled in order to determine how much of the reduced metabolic activity of amphibian is the result of low body temperature (torpor) and how much is related to torpor plus inactivity (hibernation). Perhaps hibernation, in the sense in which it is used in birds and mammals, is inappropriate for use with ectotherms and poikilotherms. Perhaps Mayhew's term (1965), brumation (winter dormancy) should be used for ectotherms, where there is a depression or change in metabolism other than that simply induced by cold.

3. *Heat Loss*

Behavioral temperature regulation accounts for most of the loss of body heat; the animal seeks shade or a cool environment and it loses heat by conduction, convection, and radiation. The only known physiological control over heat loss is the regulation of evaporation of moisture from the skin. The latter, however, is related to two basic problems: water uptake and retention for long-term survival without water, and water loss for evaporative cooling in stress conditions and as a normal thermoregulatory mechanism in basking frogs.

Deyrup (1964) and Bentley (1966) have recently reviewed water regulation in amphibians, and Packer (1963), Shoemaker (1964, 1965), Schmid (1965a), Warburg (1965, 1967), Jameson (1966), McClanahan (1967), and Miller *et al.* (1967) have presented recent studies. Amphibians survive dry conditions by means of one or more of the following techniques: burrowing, microhabitat selection, huddling to reduce surface area, keratinization of the skin, water storage in the bladder, maintenance of high body water contents with low osmolarity of the body fluids, storage of urea, increased rate of water uptake, and reduced rate of water loss.

The effectiveness of evaporative cooling in emergency stress conditions has been cited above and by Brattstrom (1963). Further records include those for *Rana esculenta,* which is able to lower its body temperature by 4.6°C below an ambient temperature of 30°C (Rubner, 1924), *Plethodon glutinosus* with its body temperature 9.2°C below an ambient temperature of 20°C (Hall and Root, 1930), and the remarkable, small Australian

tree frog, *Hyla rubella,* which can survive exposure to an ambient temperature of 40°C for 8 hours, even in dry air, by evaporative cooling (Warburg,
1965). Body temperatures and observations of diurnal heliothermic ranid
frogs imply that these frogs bask, pick up water from surrounding water
or wet soil (Stille, 1952, 1958; Dole, 1967; Lee, 1967), and evaporate moisture at some constant rate to maintain their body temperature at a constant
level. There may be some control over evaporative water loss both for
more effective water retention (Warburg, 1967), and for maintenance of
a constant body temperature, provided that further water is available.
Figures 6 and 7 show the results of some preliminary studies on evaporative

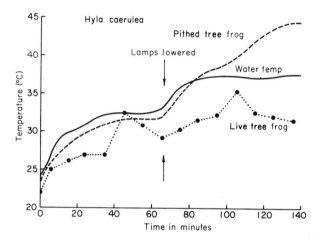

Fig. 6.   Body temperatures of live and pithed *Hyla caerulea* under heat stress, as in
Fig. 7. The live tree frog maintained body temperature by evaporative cooling even after
the heat lamps had been lowered. Data for live tree frog represent 10-minute means.

cooling in some Australian hylids exposed, with water available, to 250-W
infrared, red-bulb heat lamps over beakers with a fan blowing over the
top of the beakers. Body temperatures were monitored continuously and
the weight of the water and of the frogs was measured at the beginning
and end of the experiments. At some midpoint in the experiment, the heat
lamps were lowered from 45 to 30–31 cm. While this resulted in an additional heat input to the animal (as evidenced by the raised temperature of
the water and of the pithed tree frog) the green tree frog, *Hyla caerulea,*
appeared, by and large, to maintain the same body temperature, and at
least a body temperature far below water temperature (Fig. 6). The additional heat stress was apparently too severe for the smaller *Hyla chloris*
(Fig. 7). *Hyla caerulea* lives in much more arid regions of Australia than

does *H. chloris*. Since it is known that such things as color change (Tercofs, 1966), hormones (Alverado and Johnson, 1966), and skin lipid content (Schmid and Barden, 1965) can modify rates of water exchange through the skin, it will be interesting to see what future studies show with regard to the ability of the frog to control evaporation and hence body temperature.

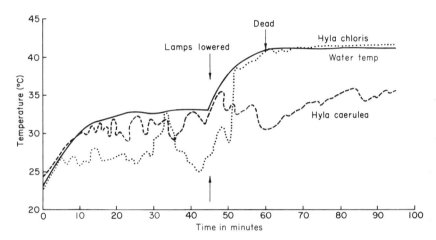

Fig. 7.   Body temperatures of two species of Australian tree frogs monitored continuously while in beakers, containing water to a depth of 10 mm, under 250-W, infrared heat lamps and with a fan blowing over them (mean wind velocity within beaker, 162 ft–min). After 45 minutes the heat lamps were lowered from 45 to 31 cm above the table. *Hyla caerulea* could continue to maintain body temperature by evaporative cooling, while *Hyla chloris* could not.

D. Implications of Temperature in Physiological Studies

Body temperature is obviously so important to an amphibian and its metabolism, that it would be expected to be a controlled or manipulated variable in all physiological studies. This is not the case. Thus, Brattstrom (1963) could cite only a few studies, other than those on metabolism per se, where temperature had been shown to have striking effects. These included the survival rate of radiated frogs, iodine-131 uptake by tadpoles, and the induction of heteroploidy.

Though most amphibian studies are conducted at "room temperature," presumedly 20°C, Stephenson (1967) had greater success with tissue cultures of amphibian cells at 30°–31° than at 20°C. Much of amphibian physiology is investigated at ecologically unimportant temperatures (Moore, 1964), or temperature has *not* been used as a variable. Thus, no studies have been done on the effect of different temperatures on rates or type of regeneration in amphibians (Rose, 1964). The role of temperature in blood and circulatory physiology, in enzyme systems (especially with the mechanisms that allow some frogs to move efficiently at low body temperatures), and in cellular metabolism is not known.

E. PROBLEMS FOR THE FUTURE

It is obvious from what has been stated above that though "the frog" has been used as a typical vertebrate animal for decades, there is still a dearth of information on the effects of temperature on the basic physiology and behavior of amphibians. Careful, coordinated field and laboratory studies of a wide variety of amphibians from diverse ecological regions are needed. Respiratory and circulatory studies are beginning, but enzyme and cellular metabolism studies are far behind. Perhaps enzyme studies and control system analysis will provide the most rewarding areas for future studies in the thermoregulation of amphibians.

III. Summary

Body temperatures of aquatic salamanders are usually identical with the water temperature in which they are found. Some aquatic salamanders appear to select specific temperatures within ponds and streams. Terrestrial salamanders are usually at the same temperature as their substrate, if the substrate is moist. Body temperatures of terrestrial salamanders away from hiding places may be as low as or lower than that of the air. As the limits of temperature and moisture tolerance are reached, terrestrial salamanders usually retreat underground. Most salamanders have no "preferred" temperatures. The salamanders usually will accept the temperatures (within the limits of tolerance) that are available. Body temperatures of active salamanders range from $-2°$ to $26.7°C$. The mean for all body temperatures is $19.2°C$.

Although body temperatures of anurans taken at night, on cloudy days, or in secretive situations may approach substrate, air, or water temperatures, many forms are heliothermic and bask in the sun. These anurans raise their body temperatures far above ambient temperatures. Heliothermism seems to be restricted to those forms or individuals near water. Some anurans never meet environmental temperatures lower than $15°$ or $20°C$; their body temperatures therefore will never drop below these temperatures. Some frogs and toads show wide ranges of thermal tolerance with no "preferred" temperature, but other toads and tree frogs have narrow activity ranges and preferences. Anurans have been taken with body temperatures ranging from $3.0°C$ to $35.7°C$, with a mean of $27.1°C$. These temperatures are higher than those for salamanders.

Thermotactic responses lead to aggregations of some tadpoles. These thermal aggregations are advantageous in raising metabolic rates and reducing the time required for larval development.

The major means of heat gain by amphibians are basking in the sun, conduction from substrate and water, and convection from air. The major means of heat loss are conduction and radiation to substrate and water, convection to air and water, and evaporative cooling. There has been no demonstration of internal heat production which would allow amphibians to raise their body temperatures. Any metabolic heat produced is so small that it has little or no effect on body temperature.

Thermal acclimation is an efficient mechanism by which amphibians can alter thermal tolerances. The rate of acclimation is rapid enough to be of survival and presumedly physiological value.

Marked seasonal changes in physiology allow some distinction of cold-, darkness-, rhythm-induced state of "hibernation" or "brumation," from low level physiological states induced simply by cold (torpor).

Thermoregulation in amphibians is mainly behavioral, but there is some evidence for physiological thermoregulation.

Amphibians as a whole present a broad spectrum of solutions to the thermal problems imposed in the transition from aquatic to terrestrial life. These solutions provided an adequate evolutionary framework for the subtleties of thermoregulatory behavior and physiology added on by the reptiles.

ACKNOWLEDGMENTS

This chapter was largely prepared during part of a National Science Foundation Senior Postdoctoral Fellowship (56017) at the Department of Zoology and Comparative Physiology, Monash University, Clayton, Virginia, Australia. I wish to thank Drs. A. J. Marshall, James W. Warren, and Anthony K. Lee for their kindness and hospitality. Previous work, some reported for the first time herein, was supported by the National Science Foundation (GB 2307) and the American Philosophical Society (G-2241, G-237J).

REFERENCES

Alverado, R. H., and Johnson, S. R. (1966). *Comp. Biochem. Physiol.* **18**, 549.
Anderson, J. D. (1968). *Herpetologica* **24**, 29.
Ballinger, R. E., and McKinney, C. O. (1966). *J. Exptl. Zool.* **161**, 21.
Bentley, P. J. (1966). *Science* **152**, 619.
Blair, W. F. (1961). *Ecology* **42**, 99.
Bogert, C. M. (1949). *Evolution* **3**, 195.
Bogert, C. M. (1952). *Ecology* **33**, 16.
Boral, M. C., and Deb, C. (1966). *Comp. Biochem. Physiol.* **18**, 653.

Bragg, A. N. (1965). "Gnomes of the Night." Univ. of Pennsylvania Press, Philadelphia, Pennsylvania.

Brattstrom, B. H. (1960). *Anat. Record* **137,** 343.

Brattstrom, B. H. (1961). *Yearbook, Am. Phil. Soc., 1960* p. 284.

Brattstrom, B. H. (1962). *Herpetologica* **18,** 38.

Brattstrom, B. H. (1963). *Ecology* **44,** 238.

Brattstrom, B. H. (1965). *Am. Midland Naturalist* **73,** 376.

Brattstrom, B. H. (1968). *Comp. Biochem. Physiol.* **24, 93.**

Brattstrom, B. H., and Lawrence, P. (1962). *Physiol. Zool.* **35,** 148.

Brattstrom, B. H., and Regal, P. (1965). *Copeia* p. 514.

Brattstrom, B. H., and Warren, J. W. (1955). *Copeia* p. 181.

Braun, A. D., Nesvetayeva, N. M., and Fizhenko, N. V. (1963). *Abstr. Intern. Symp. Cytoecol.*, Leningrad, *1963* p. 18.

Brooks, G. R., Jr., and Sassman, J. F. (1965). *Copeia* p. 251.

Brown, G. W., Jr. (1964). *In* "Physiology of the Amphibia" (J. A. Moore, ed.), pp. 1–98. Academic Press, New York.

Brown, H. A. (1967). *Evolution* **21,** 742.

Brown, H. A. (1969). *Copeia* p. 138.

Bullock, T. H. (1955). *Biol. Rev.* **30,** 311.

Cortelyou, J. R., McWhinnie, D. J., and Lehrer, L. (1966). *Am. Zoologist* **6,** 561.

Cowles, R. B. (1945). *Am. Naturalist* **79,** 561.

Cowles, R. B. (1958). *Evolution* **12,** 347.

Cowles, R. B. (1962). *Science* **135,** 670.

Cowles, R. B., and Bogert, C. M. (1944). *Bull. Am. Museum Nat. Hist.* **83,** 261.

Cunningham, J. D. (1962). *Herpetologica* **17,** 255.

Cunningham, J. D. (1963). *Herpetologica* **19,** 56.

Cunningham, J. D., and Mullally, D. P. (1956). *Herpetologica* **12,** 68.

Czopek, J. (1962). *Acta Biol. Cracov., Ser. Zool.* **5,** 241.

Dasgupta, S., and Grewal, M. S. (1968). *Evolution* **22,** 87.

Davenport, C. B., and Castle, W. E. (1895). *Arch. Entwicklungsmech. Organ.* **2,** 227.

Deyrup, I. J. (1964). *In* "Physiology of the Amphibia" (J. A. Moore, ed.), pp. 251–328. Academic Press, New York.

Dole, J. W. (1967). *Copeia* p. 141.

Epple, A., Jorgensen, C. B., and Rosenkilde, P. (1966). *Gen. Comp. Endocrinol.* **7,** 197.

Evans, G. (1939). *Ecology* **20,** 74.

Fitch, H. S. (1956). *Univ. Kansas Publ., Museum Nat. Hist.*, **18,** 417.

Fromm, P. O. (1956). *Physiol. Zool.* **29,** 234.

Fromm, P. O., and Johnson, R. E. (1955). *J. Cellular Comp. Physiol.* **45,** 343.

Fry, F. E. J. (1947). *Univ. Toronto Studies Biol.* **55,** 1.

Fry, F. E. J. (1958). *Ann. Rev. Physiol.* **20,** 207.

Goin, C. J. (1960). *Smithsonian Inst., Ann. Rept.* p. 427.

Goin, O. B., and Goin, C. J. (1962). *Evolution* **16,** 364.

Gorman, J. (1968). *Copeia* p. 167.

Gosner, K. L., and Black, I. H. (1955). *Am. Midland Naturalist* **54,** 102.

Guimond, R. W., and Hutchison, V. H. (1968). *Comp. Biochem. Physiol.* **27,** 171.

Hadfield, S. (1966). *Copeia* p. 581.

Hall, F. G., and Root, R. W. (1930). *Biol. Bull.* **58,** 52.

Heatwole, H. (1962). *Ecology* **43,** 460.

Heatwole, H., Mercado, N., and Ortiz, E. (1965). *Physiol. Zool.* **38,** 1.

Helff, O. M. (1927). *J. Exptl. Zool.* **49,** 353.

Hock, R. J. (1967). *Copeia* p. 227.

Holzapfel, R. A. (1937). *Quart. Rev. Biol.* **12,** 65.

Hubbs, C., and Armstrong, N. E. (1961). *Texas J. Sci.* **13,** 358.

Hubbs, C., Wright, T., and Cuellar, O. (1963). *Southern Naturalist* **8,** 142.

Hutchison, V. H. (1958). *Ecol. Monographs* **28,** 1.

Hutchison, V. H. (1961). *Physiol. Zool.* **34,** 92.

Hutchison, V. H., and Dady, J. (1962). *Am. Zoologist* **2,** 341.

Hutchison, V. H., and Dady, J. (1964). *Herpetologica* **20,** 149.

Hutchison, V. H., and Kosh, R. J. (1965). *Herpetologica* **20,** 233.

Hutchison, V. H., Vinegar, A., and Kosh, R. J. (1966). *Herpetologica* **22,** 32.

Hutchison, V. H., Whitford, W. G., and Kohl, M. (1968). *Physiol. Zool.* **41,** 65.

Jameson, D. L. (1966). *Ecology* **47,** 605.

Johansen, K. (1962). *Ecology* **43,** 146.

King, G. S. (1966). *Am. Zoologist* **6,** 532.

Kusakina, A. A. (1963). *Abstr. Intern. Symp. Cytoecol.*, Leningrad, *1963* p. 35.

Lee, A. K. (1967). *Australian J. Zool.* **15,** 367.

Licht, P., and Brown, A. G. (1967). *Ecology* **48,** 597.

Lillie, F. R., and Knowlton, F. P. (1897). *Zool. Bull.* **1,** 179.

Lowe, C. H., and Vance, V. J. (1955). *Science* **122,** 73.

Lucas, E. A., and Reynolds, W. A. (1967). *Physiol. Zool.* **40,** 159.

McClanahan, L. (1967). *Comp. Biochem. Physiol.* **20,** 73.

McDonald, H. S., Chiramonte, G., and Tarnowski, L. E. (1963). *Am. Zoologist* **3,** 547.

McFarland, W. N. (1955). *Copeia* p. 191.

Martof, B. S. (1962). *Physiol. Zool.* **35,** 38.

Mayhew, W. W. (1965). *Comp. Biochem. Physiol.* **16,** 103.

Mellanby, K. (1940). *J. Physiol. (London)* **98,** 27.

Miller, D. A., Standish, M. L., and Thurman, A. E. (1967). *Physiol. Zool.* **40,** 500.

Miller, M. R. (1961). *In* "Comparative Physiology of Carbohydrate Metabolism in Heterothermic Animals" (A. W. Martin, ed.), pp. 125–147. Univ. of Washington Press, Seattle, Washington.

Mizell, S. (1965). *J. Cellular Comp. Physiol.* **66,** 251.

Moberley, W. R. (1963). *Physiol. Zool.* **36,** 152.

Moberley, W. R. (1964). *Am. Zoologist* **4,** 391.

Moore, J. A. (1949a). *Evolution* **3,** 1.

Moore, J. A. (1949b). *In* "Genetics, Paleontology and Evolution" (G. Jepsen *et al.*, eds.), pp. 315–338. Princeton Univ. Press, Princeton, New Jersey.

Moore, J. A., ed. (1964). "Physiology of the Amphibia," pp. xii–654. Academic Press, New York.

Mullally, D. P. (1952). *Copeia* p. 274.

Mullally, D. P. (1953). *Copeia* p. 182.

Mullally, D. P., and Cunningham, J. D. (1956a). *Herpetologica* **12,** 57.

Mullally, D. P., and Cunningham, J. D. (1956b). *Herpetologica* **12,** 189.

Murray, R. W. (1962). *Advan. Comp. Physiol. Biochem.* **1,** 117.

Newell, R. C. (1966). *Nature* **212,** 426.

Noble, G. K. (1931). "The Biology of the Amphibia," pp. 1–577. McGraw-Hill, New York.

Orr, P. R. (1955). *Physiol. Zool.* **28,** 294.

Packard, G. G. (1966). *Am. Naturalist* **100,** 667.

Packer, W. C. (1963). *Ecology* **44,** 643.

Pashkova, I. M. (1963). *Abstr. Intern. Symp. Cytoecol.*, Leningrad, *1963* p. 45.

Precht, H. (1958). *In* "Physiological Adaptation" (C. L. Prosser, ed.), pp. 50–78. Am. Physiol. Soc., Washington, D.C.

Precht, H., Christopherson, J., and Hensel, H. (1955). "Temperatur und Leben." Springer, Berlin.

Regal, P. J. (1966). *Copeia* p. 588.

Regal, P. J. (1967). *Science* **155**, 1551.

Rose, S. M. (1964). *In* "Physiology of the Amphibia" (J. A. Moore, ed.), pp. 545–622. Academic Press, New York.

Rubner, M. (1924). *Biochem. Z.* **148**, 268.

Ruibal, R. (1955). *Evolution* **9**, 322.

Ruibal, R. (1962). *Copeia* p. 189.

Rumyantsev, P. P. (1963). *Abstr. Intern. Symp. Cytoecol.*, Leningrad, *1963* p. 52.

Savage, R. M. (1962). "The Ecology and Life History of the Common Frog (*Rana temporaria temporaria.*" Hafner, New York.

Schmid, W. D. (1965a). *Ecology* **46**, 261.

Schmid, W. D. (1956b). *Ecology* **46**, 559.

Schmid, W. D., and Barden, R. E. (1965). *Comp. Biochem. Physiol.* **15**, 423.

Scholander, P. F., Flagg, W., Walters, V., and Irving, L. (1953). *Physiol. Zool.* **26**, 67.

Sexton, O. J., Heatwole, H., and Knight, D. (1964). *Caribean J. Sci.* **4**, 261.

Shoemaker, V. H. (1964). *Comp. Biochem. Physiol.* **13**, 261.

Shoemaker, V. H. (1965). *Comp. Biochem. Physiol.* **15**, 81.

Stebbins, R. C. (1951). "Amphibians of Western North America." Univ. of California Press, Berkeley, California.

Stebbins, R. C. (1954). *Univ. Calif. (Berkeley) Publ. Zool.* **54**, 47.

Stephenson, E. M. (1967). *J. Embryol. Exptl. Morphol.* **17**, 147.

Stier, T. J. B., and Bock, H. C., Jr. (1966). *Proc. Soc. Exptl. Biol. Med.* **123**, 149.

Stille, W. T. (1952). *Ecology* **33**, 149.

Stille, W. T. (1958). *Copeia* p. 217.

Storm, R. B. (1960). *Herpetologica* **16**, 251.

Stuart, L. C. (1951). *Copeia* p. 220.

Tashian, R. E., and Ray, C. (1957). *Zoologica* **42**, 63.

Taub, F. B. (1961). *Ecology* **42**, 682.

Tercofs, R. R. (1966). *Comp. Biochem. Physiol.* **17**, 937.

Tester, J. R., Parker, A., and Siniff, D. B. (1965). *J. Minnesota Acad. Sci.* **33**, 27.

Thorson, T. B. (1955). *Ecology* **36**, 100.

Ushakov, B. P. (1963). *Abstr. Intern. Symp. Cytoecol.*, Leningrad, *1963* p. 73.

Ushakov, B. P. (1964). *Physiol. Rev.* **44**, 518.

Ushakov, B. P., and Chernokozheva, I. S. (1963). *Abstr. Intern. Symp. Cytoecol.*, Leningrad, *1963* p. 75.

Vernberg, F. J. (1952). *Physiol. Zool.* **25**, 245.

Vernberg, F. J. (1962). *Ann. Rev. Physiol.* **24**, 517.

Vinegar, A., and Hutchison, V. H. (1965). *Zoologica* **50**, 47.

Vinogradova, A. N. (1963). *Abstr. Intern. Symp. Cytoecol.*, Leningrad, *1963* p. 78.

Volpe, E. P. (1953). *Physiol. Zool.* **26**, 344.

Volpe, E. P. (1957a). *Physiol. Zool.* **30**, 164.

Volpe, E. P. (1957b). *Am. Naturalist* **41**, 303.

Warburg, M. R. (1965). *Australian J. Zool.* **13**, 317.

Warburg, M. R. (1967). *Comp. Biochem. Physiol.* **20**, 27.

Whitford, W. G., and Hutchison, V. H. (1963). *Biol. Bull.* **124**, 344.

Whitford, W. G., and Hutchison, V. H. (1965a). *Copeia* p. 53.

Whitford, W. G., and Hutchinson, V. H. (1965b). *Physiol. Zool.* **38,** 228.

Whitford, W. G., and Hutchison, V. H. (1967). *Physiol. Zool.* **40,** 127.

Wright, A. H. (1932). "Life Histories of the Frogs of the Okefinokee Swamp, Georgia." Macmillan, New York.

Wright, A. H., and Wright, A. A. (1949). "Handbook of Frogs and Toads of the United States and Canada." Cornell Univ. Press (Comstock). Ithaca, New York.

Zhirmunsky, A. V., and Pashkova, I. M. (1963). *Abstr. Intern. Symp. Cytoecol.*, Leningrad, *1963* p. 85.

Zweifel, R. G. (1957). *Ecology* **38,** 64.

Zweifel, R. G. (1968). *Bull. Am. Museum Nat. Hist.* **140,** 1.

Chapter 5 REPTILES

James R. Templeton

I. Introduction

Reptiles have been quite properly classified as ectothermic, poikilothermic, and cold-blooded. These definitions hold because all reptiles must secure a great part of their body heat from outside the body, most have appreciable daily and seasonal changes in body temperature, and during the troughs of these changes, their blood is much colder than that of mammals and birds, which are termed, antithetically, endothermic, homeothermic, and warm-blooded. These latter terms suggest an ability to regulate body temperature, whereas, unfortunately, the former terms do not (see

Chapter 4). Only certain marine turtles do not appear to thermoregulate. These creatures are found in such stable thermal environments that their body temperatures probably fluctuate less than do those of many homeother-mic, warm-blooded animals. The remainder of the reptiles studied do effectively thermoregulate, albeit primarily by behavior, and this ability has been extensively studied and discussed (Weese, 1919; Sergeyev, 1939; Cowles, 1940; Cowles and Bogert, 1944; Strel'nikov, 1944; Bogert, 1949a, 1959; Curry-Lindahl, 1956; St. Girons and St. Girons, 1956; Soulé, 1963; Schmidt-Nielsen and Dawson, 1964; Heath, 1965; Brattstrom, 1965).

Often cited as a convincing demonstration of such behavioral thermoregulation are the observations of Strel'nikov (1944) and Pearson (1954), showing that certain lizards at high altitudes possessed body temperatures approximately 30°C higher than the temperature of the air, as a result of solar radiation. Less dramatic in terms of temperature differences, but equally convincing in terms of temperature sense, are the observations that nocturnal snakes accumulate and remain on roads having temperatures only a few degrees higher than those of the surrounding soil (Brattstrom, 1965).

Reptiles not only produce relatively less metabolic heat than do birds and mammals, but they lack effective surface insulation and subdermal fat, as well. These inadequacies prevent reptiles from being appreciably independent of environmental temperatures. Even so, they possess many physiological and structural attributes correlated with thermoregulation. In addition, the lack of surface insulation allows very rapid exchange of heat with the thermal environment, and, by behaviorally selecting or avoiding certain thermal parameters, reptiles are able to regulate body temperature during periods of activity as well as are many homeotherms, in all but the most extreme of climates.

II. Body Temperatures

As Prosser and Brown (1961) remarked, temperature can be measured so easily that the literature is wealthy with such data. Unfortunately, many of the early data have been either inaccurately taken or are suspected of being so. The use of black-bulb thermometers has minimized inaccuracy of air temperature measurements during the day, but temperatures of the substrate are still marginally accurate (Soulé, 1963; Schmidt-Nielsen and Dawson, 1964), and require special instruments for greatest accuracy. Quick-recording mercury thermometers minimize inaccuracies in mercury lag and heat exchange when the temperature is taken of small reptiles held in the hand. The body temperatures of relatively unrestrained lizards have recently been measured by Lee and Badham (1963) and DeWitt

(1967), and of totally unrestrained lizards by radiotelemetry (Mackay, 1964; Warburg, 1965a,b; McGinnis and Brown, 1966; McGinnis, 1967; Stebbins and Barwick, 1968) in both the field and the laboratory. Sometimes, additional information that would make the thermal data more meaningful and interpretable are not given. Such information might include other thermal parameters, the kind of thermal environment, and the immediate past history and biological state of the animal.

Cowles and Bogert (1944) categorized data on body temperatures into terms that allow useful comparisons to be made between reptile groups. These terms have generally been accepted by workers in both the field and the laboratory, but the means by which the data are collected, although sophisticated, is still to be adequately standardized (see Chapter 4). Although this terminology is widely used, comparison and interpretation of data is often made difficult because different workers secure data and define terms by different means. For example, Hutchison *et al.* (1966a) suggested that the onset of muscle spasms in turtles was a better criterion by which to judge loss of locomotor ability and therefore to determine the critical thermal maximum (CTM) than was the loss of the righting response used by previous workers (Brattstrom and Lawrence, 1962; Brattstrom, 1963, 1965; Brooks and Sassman, 1965), because, not only is this onset more sharply and easily observed, but turtles, as well as other reptiles and amphibians, can swim coordinatedly after they have lost the righting response. Licht *et al.* (1966b) rejected the onset of muscle spasms in lizards as a standard for CTM and chose measurement of survival time at high temperatures instead. They found that many lizards, especially geckos, soon recovered from the spasms and paralysis, even if maintained at that apparent CTM.

The use of the term *preferred temperature,* when calculated from field data, has been recently questioned, not on anthropomorphic grounds, as it has been in the past (Gunn and Cosway, 1938), but because animals are often found to be active in such adverse thermal environments that behavioral thermoregulation around a preferred temperature is either impossible or is abandoned while defending a territory or avoiding a predator (Licht *et al.,* 1966a,b; DeWitt, 1967). To determine preferred temperature, they used broad temperature gradients unlike the steep temperature gradients used by Herter (1940), and criticized by Bogert (1949a), as causing ontogenetic differences in body temperatures. Lizards placed therein chose body temperatures whose means often differed from those of the same population recorded in the field (Table I). These findings provoke reconsideration of the generally accepted concept advanced by Cowles and Bogert (1944) and Bogert (1949a, 1959), that a reptile while active maintains a body temperature within a preferred range. Field records may indicate the activity range of body temperatures, but these need not be the preferred range nor their mean the preferred body temperature. The reptile may be active at a particular time at nonpreferred temperatures, or it may appear to prefer a body temperature that is optimal for one particular stage of body activity or function. The desert iguana, *Dipsosaurus dorsalis,* may abandon normal behavioral thermoregulation (see Section IV) while defending a territory or avoiding a predator (DeWitt, 1967). The snake, *Natrix natrix,* of Europe, is often found, after a rain, hunting hydrophilic

TABLE I

COMPARISON OF BODY TEMPERATURE REGULATION OF LIZARDS IN THE FIELD
AND IN LABORATORY THERMAL GRADIENTS[a]

| | Body temperatures (°C) | | | |
| | Field | | Laboratory | |
Species	Mean	Range	Mean	Range
Amphibolurus barbatus barbatus	34.8	30.0–40.0	35.7	32.4–38.1
A. b. minimus	32.8	28.4–36.7	36.3	33.4–39.2
A. b. minor	35.0	31.8–38.4	35.8	32.0–37.8
A. caudicinctus	39.0	34.8–41.0	37.7	33.9–40.3
A. inermis	39.3	34.5–43.0	36.4	33.7–38.7
A. ornatus	36.6	28.8–39.6	36.6	34.1–38.1
A. reticulatus	37.0	35.0–40.6	37.0	34.4–39.2
Moloch horridus	34.1	31.5–39.9	36.7	32.5–39.0
Physignathus longirostris	37.0	34.2–39.0	37.1	33.3–39.3
Tiliqua occipitalis	33.7	30.5–35.5	32.9	29.1–35.2
T. rugosa	32.7	25.0–37.0	33.8	31.2–36.0

[a] From Licht *et al.* (1966a).

prey when the temperature is far from optimal (St. Girons and St. Girons, 1956). Body temperatures that are not optimal may limit certain body functions, such as digestive efficiency, but these temperatures need not be maintained during all phases of daily activity. The nocturnal gecko, *Gehyra,* remains active until midnight on warm nights, but retires earlier on cold nights. During the day, they actively thermoregulate under sunlit bark shelter (Section IV, 3,b) to achieve maximal heat gain (Bustard, 1967). Bustard suggested that digestion virtually ceases after midnight, but maximal digestive efficiency is maintained during the day. Mackay (1968) found that peristaltic contractions of the guts of two large, recently fed, lizards, *Varanus and Ctenosaura,* measured telemetrically, showed a distinct daily rhythm which generally matched the cycle of body temperature and gross activity. Regal (1966) found that captive lizards (*Lygosoma, Gerrhonotus,* and *Xantusia*) were only rarely observed to use the warm areas of their cages. After feeding, however, they sought out these heated areas. In addition, a captive snake, *Constrictor constrictor,* avoided basking before feeding. Upon being fed, it basked under the existing heat lamp at first, keeping that portion of the body containing the bolus under the lamp. Later, it coiled its body near the edge of the heated area. Regal concluded that digestive efficiency of these reptiles is not passive, and the digestive state may be only one determinant in thermoregulatory activities; other variables besides digestion doubtlessly influence thermophilic orientations in ectotherms.

III. Thermal Preferences and Tolerances

Nocturnal reptiles tolerate, and are found active, at lower body temperatures than are diurnal forms (Sergeyev, 1939; Cowles and Bogert, 1944). The abundant thermal data of Brattstrom (1965) show that burrowing, nocturnal, and nonbasking thigmotherms, which gain body heat by conduction, are generally less thermophilic and tolerate lower body temperatures than do heliotherms, which primarily gain body heat from solar radiation (Fig. 1). However, tropical species possess activity temperatures similar to

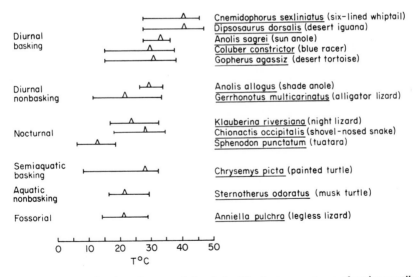

FIG. 1. Range (bars) and means (triangles) of body temperatures of active reptiles representing different behavioral aspects of thermoregulation. Ranges extend from the lowest temperature voluntarily tolerated to the highest. (Data from Brattstrom, 1965.)

temperate forms; yet they cannot tolerate cold temperatures as well as can the temperate species. Also, some reptiles have narrow ranges of body temperature (e.g. *Sceloporus*), whereas others, such as *Gerrhonotus* and *Ctenosaura,* possess wide ranges (Soulé, 1963; Brattstrom, 1965). Aquatic turtles generally have a significantly lower CTM than do terrestrial species, with semiaquatic forms possessing intermediate resistance to heat (Hutchison *et al.,* 1966a). Among North American lizards, the iguanids and teids appear more thermophilic than other saurian families (Brattstrom, 1965), yet Fitch (1968) found considerable interspecific variation in body temperatures of active teids of equatorial South America. Among Australian lizard families, the agamids are more heat tolerant than the skinks. The geckos vary considerably; some genera are less heat resistant than the skinks, whereas others resist heat death better than do the agamids (Licht *et al.,* 1966b). Similarly, Cloudsley-Thompson (1965), in tropical Africa, found the nocturnal gecko, *Tarentola,* to resist heat death as well as did the diurnal skink, *Mabuya.*

For a discussion of heat resistance and heat damage to proteins and to tissues such as muscle, nerve, and germ cells of lizards and other poikilotherms, see the reviews by Ushakov (1964) and by Dawson (1967).

Bogert (1949a,b), after measuring the body temperatures of many species of fence lizards, *Sceloporus*, and whiptails, *Cnemidophorus*, living in diverse thermal habitats, found the former genus to be less thermophilic than the latter and concluded that thermal preferences of congeners were similar, regardless of dissimilar habitats. Brattstrom (1965), however, using Bogert's own data (1949b) showed graphically that the mean body temperature of sceloporine species did vary inversely with elevation and therefore coolness of habitat. The iguanid genus, *Anolis* of the neotropics, also has many species, both thigmothermic and heliothermic which inhabit a wide variety of thermal habitats. The appreciable differences in thermal preferences found between these species correlate well with the thermal habitat of each species (Ruibal, 1961).

Sceloporus occidentalis and *Sceloporus graciosus,* in favorable situations in California, can maintain, behaviorally, a body temperature within 2° or 3°C of the mean of the activity range. However, if each species must compete keenly, either intraspecifically or interspecifically, for cool retreats and relatively cool foraging areas, precise behavioral control of thermoregulation may be abandoned, and body temperatures are forced up several degrees higher than the normal mean (Rodgers, 1953).

Body temperatures preferred by some species within the Australian agamid genus, *Amphibolurus*, in a temperature gradient, differed by small but significant amounts. However, the mean body temperature of amphibolurine congeners, taken in nature, differed not only between species but between subspecies as well (Licht *et al.*, 1966a). Significant differences in resistance to heat death also occur among these congeners and also among the congeneric skinks of Australia (Licht *et al.*, 1966b). Hutchison *et al.* (1966a) found no significant differences in physiological tolerance to high temperature, as measured by the onset of muscle spasms in subspecies of the box turtle, *Terropena carolina,* nor in the stinkpot, *Sternotherus odoratus,* but these authors did find such differences to be significant in various subspecies of *Chrysemys picta,* which apparently correlate with their particular zoogeography.

Thermal tolerances characteristic of a particular species can often be lowered by acclimating them to lower temperatures. Lizards, *Urosaurus ornatus,* exposed for 7–10 days at 15°C suffered locomotor impairment at a body temperature 1.5°C lower than that of animals kept at 35°C (Lowe and Vance, 1955). Similarly, the CTM of *Sceloporus occidentalis* kept at 7°C for 34 days was 0.5°C lower than that of lizards maintained at room temperature. These lizards captured in summer also had a significantly higher CTM than did spring animals taken from the same habitat (Larson, 1961). In the painted turtle, such acclimation can be enhanced by shortening the photoperiod. Turtles acclimated to 30°, 20°, and 10°C had progressively lower critical thermal maxima with decreasing temperature. Decreasing photoperiod from 16 hours light and 8 hours dark to 8 hours light and 16 hours dark also depressed the CTM (Hutchison and Kosh, 1965).

Kosh and Hutchison (1968) have shown that sensitivity to high temperatures (CTM) in eastern painted turtles, *Chrysemys picta,* follows a circadian rhythm (Fig. 2). Turtles acclimated to long days (16 hours) and moderate temperatures (20°C) showed, in most cases, significantly, and in all cases appreciably, more tolerance to temperature if CTM's are taken at late morning (0930 hours), at early afternoon (1330 hours), at later afternoon (1730 hours), or at evening (2130 hours) than if they are measured at night (0130 hours) or at early morning (0530 hours). Turtles acclimated to short days (8 hours) and cool temperatures (10°C) showed significantly greater tolerance to temperature when measured in the early afternoon than at any other measuring period except late morning. These two groups were considered "naturally" acclimated, since their regimes are not unlike similar environmental conditions to which they would normally be exposed. A third group exposed to long days and cool temperatures were considered "unnaturally" acclimated. They were most tolerant to high temperatures in evening and at night than at any other time. A fourth group "unnaturally" acclimated to short days and moderate temperatures showed a trend to be more temperature tolerant at late morning than at any other time. The CTM's of the "naturally" acclimated groups fluctuated in phase (Fig. 2) whereas the third and fourth groups were each out of phase with the other twc by —8 hours and +4 hours, respectively. Kosh and Hutchison consider the acclimation to long days and moderate temperatures to be the only one that might be adaptive, since the greatest temperature tolerance occurred at the time of the day when temperatures would be highest in summer. This interesting phenomenon deserves further

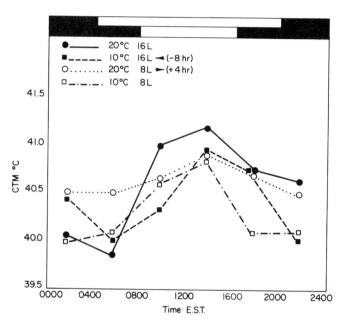

Fig. 2.   Variations plotted with time of day of the critical thermal maxima of turtles acclimated to different temperatures and photoperiods. The two curves represented by closed circles and open squares are considered "natural" acclimations (see text), and are plotted directly from the data. The other two curves (open circles and closed squares) if so plotted would have peaks at 0930 and 2130 hours, respectively, and would thereby be out of phase. Instead, these two have been shifted in direction (see arrows) a certain amount of time (see figures in parentheses) so that all curves are in phase and the similarity in patterns can be noted (Kosh and Hutchison, 1968).

study not only to clarify whether physiological processes are being moniteted in phase and periodicity with set phases of rhythmical environment, but also to see if it occurs in other animals. If so, the time of day at which animals are tested for thermal sensitivity would be important, and those previous data showing no daily testing times would have to be reexamined.

The effect of thermal acclimation or acclimatization on preferred body temperatures has not been so nicely demonstrated. *Sceloporus occidentalis* acclimated to either 12° or 25°C prefer to maintain body temperatures

of 33°C or 34°C, when placed in a laboratory thermal gradient, the same
temperatures they maintain while active in the field, but if acclimated
to 35°C they surprisingly have average body temperatures, in the gradient,
of only 30°C (Wilhoft and Anderson, 1960). DeWitt (1967) found body
temperatures preferred by desert iguanas in a temperature gradient to be
about 38.5°C. Yet the body temperature of desert iguanas measured in
the field in summer by DeWitt and also by Norris (1953) were often
near 42°C. Apparently they were unable to thermoregulate at preferred
levels due to high thermal levels everywhere in the habitat. However, animals freshly exposed to this hot mid-August habitat still preferred body
temperatures of 38.5°C when placed in a temperature gradient. Such acclimatization apparently does not affect preferred temperatures in the desert
iguana, but its effect on the temperature preferred by other reptiles in
a thermal gradient remains to be determined.

It is generally agreed that interspecific similarities and variations in thermal preferences and tolerances are genetically determined adaptations to
the thermal environment (Cowles and Bogert, 1944; Bogert, 1949a, 1959;
St. Girons and St. Girons, 1956; Schmidt-Nielsen and Dawson, 1964; Licht
et al., 1966a,b). Whether these adaptations are mainly behavioral or physiological, or to what extent phenotypic variations such as acclimation modify
them, is still unknown (Licht *et al.*, 1966a,b).

IV. Behavioral Thermoregulation

Except for certain marine and fossorial forms which live in an environment consisting of essentially one thermal parameter, most reptiles are able
to gain or lose heat within their environment by conduction, convection,
and radiation, and thereby maintain activity body temperatures characteristic of the species.

A. DESCRIPTIVE APPROACH

1. *Aquatic Reptiles*

Little is known concerning behavioral thermoregulation in the sea snakes
(Hydrophidae) and the sea turtles (Dermochelidae and Chelonidae). Some
species of sea snakes are reported to bask upon the surface of the sea
and may be seen by the hundreds during the day when the sea is calm.
Those sea snakes of the genus *Laticauda* are often found on land, albeit
near the shore (M. Smith, 1964). Both Pope (1949) and Carr (1952)
have mentioned members of both families of sea turtles floating and apparently sleeping at the sea's surface, but neither author referred to this

as basking. The green turtle, *Chelonia*, was reported by Grant (1927) to emerge and bask on uninhabited Hawaiian beaches and rocky shores. The other sea snakes and sea turtles apparently never leave the water, except that female turtles haul out to deposit eggs. The body temperature of these completely aquatic forms would most likely be that of the tropical and semitropical seas in which they swim. Boyer (1965) suggested that the body temperatures of sea turtles are probably more constant than those in other reptile groups.

Only a few fresh water turtles approach being as aquatic, and therefore as limited in opportunities to thermoregulate behaviorally, as the marine forms. The alligator snapping turtle, *Macrochelys,* is highly aquatic (Pope, 1949). The common snapping turtle, *Chelydra,* and the musk turtle, *Sternotherus odoratus,* seldom leave the water and the basking habit is either poorly developed or absent (Pope, 1949; Boyer, 1965; Brattstrom, 1965). They apparently thermoregulate, however, by selecting water with the most optimal temperature, either floating near or on the warmed surface, or submerging in warm shallow parts of ponds. The soft-shelled turtles (Trionychidae) are also highly aquatic but they do leave the water occasionally to bask (Pope, 1949), and they are therefore intermediate in thermoregulatory behavior between the aquatic and semiaquatic forms.

2. Semiaquatic Reptiles

Although semiaquatic turtles probably select an optimal water temperature and thereby regulate body temperatures within the limits of the thermal levels available, because of their well-developed basking habits, they have many avenues of behavioral thermoregulation open to them. According to Boyer (1965), the emydid turtles have the most highly developed basking behavior of the Chelonia, and it is on this group that many of the quantitative studies of thermoregulatory behavior in turtles have been carried out. Sexton (1959) found basking, painted turtles, *Chrysemys,* in the springtime in Michigan to have body temperatures 10°–17°C above that of the air. Brattstrom (1965) found the body temperatures of basking painted turtles to average 27.8°C, whereas body temperatures of active swimming turtles measured only 14.0°C. In his report on the basking habits in turtles of the coast of Louisiana, Boyer (1965) suggested that the higher body temperatures due to basking may be more nearly optimal for physiological processes than the lower body temperatures in the water. He found that light intensity played an important role in thermoregulation and that turtles oriented on basking sites so as to increase or decrease the angle of incidence of striking solar rays. However, as occupied sunny sites became shaded, only rarely did the turtles there shift about or cease their basking. Turtles appeared to select basking sites according to size, availability, and field of view; but no evidence was shown that they selected a site in terms of its thermal conductivity. Air temperatures, especially in summer, were often sufficient to raise the body temperature above that of the water and the substrate regardless of solar intensity. The spiny soft-shelled turtle, *Trionyx ferox*, does not bask on cool, windy days (Brattstrom, 1965). Erb (1965) also has found that wind velocity, air and water temperatures, solar radiation, and basking position are critical factors that affect basking and rate of heat gain in turtles.

Behavioral thermoregulation appears well developed in the Crocodilia. The nile crocodile, *Crocodilus niloticus,* of Uganda and Rhodesia typically hauls out to bask in the hour before dawn and before air temperatures rise above those of the water (Cott, 1961). After basking for a couple of hours and with body temperatures supposedly near the upper limit for normal activity, they either retreat to the shade, return to the water, or lie on the bank partly submerged in the water. They appear to thermoregulate while partly submerged, positioning themselves so that the heat absorbed from solar radiation is lost by conduction to the water. By midday, generally, most have returned to the water, whereupon they reemerge on land to bask in the afternoon. About 30 minutes before sunset, and before the air temperatures fall below that of the water, the crocodiles return to the water where most remain throughout the night. This cycle can be delayed or interrupted wholly or in part by cloudy days or cold weather. Cloudsley-Thompson (1964) reported that over a 5-day period captive nile crocodiles of Khartoum exhibited a weak diurnal rhythm of activity more marked in cooler weather than in hot, and more activity was shown in early evening than at other times. They also tended to leave the water, to bask, more frequently when the air temperature was about 24°C than at other temperatures.

3. *Terrestrial Reptiles*

a. Burrowing Reptiles. Like aquatic reptiles, these forms live in an environment consisting basically of one thermal parameter. *Anniella* inhabits soil with temperature near or at its optimal body temperature and this legless lizard follows temperature changes in the soil accordingly (Brattstrom, 1965). Body temperatures measured in a laboratory temperature gradient closely approximate the mean body temperatures of animals collected in the field (Fig. 1). Little is known about the thermoregulation of other burrowers such as the amphisbaenids, but they probably follow temperature gradients in the soil also.

b. Nocturnal Reptiles. Nocturnal reptiles as a group remain under shelter usually underground during the day; but unlike strictly burrowing forms, they roam abroad at night when proper thermal conditions exist at the surface. While underground they probably select appropriate thermal levels in the soil and follow these levels as they shift in response to the daily or seasonal thermal changes occurring at the surface (Klauber, 1939, 1951). Upon emergence at the surface at night, these reptiles can probably also select those substrates having temperatures which will allow body temperatures to approach or be maintained at the optimal level, even though the temperatures of the air and of the various substrates are within a degree or two of each other. Evidence for this selection can be seen in the number of reptiles recorded on blacktop highways, at night, which are only slightly warmer than the soil or air (Brattstrom, 1965). Some nocturnal reptiles have patterns of behavioral thermoregulation in addition to those described above. The tuatara, *Sphaenodon punctatum,* has nocturnal body temperatures during activity lower than those of most amphibians (Brattstrom, 1963), yet it basks in the sun like a heliotherm (Bogert, 1953). The ring snake in Kansas, *Diadophis punctata,* considered to be primarily nocturnal, has also been reported to bask in full sunlight in autumn or under sun-heated flat rocks in the spring (Fitch, 1956b). Still others like the geckos, *Coleonyx* and *Phyllodactylus,* and the night lizard, *Xantusia,* while mainly nocturnal, are suggested to bask in the direct sunlight entering through the cracks in the rocks in which they hide (Brattstrom, 1965). The nocturnal Australian gecko, *Gehyra,* presses against the inner surface of sunlit tree bark during the day. If the day becomes overly warm it moves to shaded bark, and presses against the tree trunk rather than against the bark (Bustard, 1967). Finally, certain snakes such as the crotalids are nocturnal during the hot season only and are considered diurnal, occasional baskers at other seasons (Fitch, 1956b).

c. Diurnal Thigmothermic Reptiles. Of the great number and variety of diurnal reptiles only a very few species are known not to bask. The Bornean skink, *Sphenomorphus sabanus,* a diurnal inhabitant of the floor stratum of the lowland rain forest apparently has access to sunlight but has never been observed to remain stationary therein. This thigmotherm ranges throughout the forest and appears able to maintain its relatively low activity body temperature (24°–28.4°C) without solar radiation (Inger, 1959). The shade anoles, *Anolis allogus* and *A. lucius,* live near the floor of dense Cuban jungles where the sun's rays rarely penetrate. Therefore, basking sites are unavailable (Ruibal, 1961). Because captive *A. allogus* definitely avoided sunlight, Ruibal suggested that this species may be an obligatory nonheliotherm, but the possibility was not precluded that both species could well be facultative if sunlight were available. Facultative non-heliotherms also occur outside of the tropics. The Great Plains skink,

Eumeces obsoletus, emerges late during the day, when thermal environments are high enough to allow it to achieve and maintain its low activity temperature without basking (Fitch, 1955, 1956b). However, both this skink and the alligator lizard, *Gerrhonotus multicarinatus,* another facultative non-heliotherm, are known to bask if environmental temperatures are lower than usual, but they usually receive most of their heat from the air, from ventral contact with the substrate, or from dorsal contact with the underside of sun-heated rocks (Fitch, 1956b; Cunningham, 1966).

d. Heliothermic Reptiles. With the possible exception of the Crocodilia and some of the semiaquatic turtles, the reptiles previously described have been essentially thigmothermic and primarily utilize heat conduction to thermoregulate behaviorally. Heliotherms may exchange heat by conduction and convection, but they gain heat primarily from solar radiation. Heliotherms include the land tortoises, diurnal snakes, and lizards. Because much work has been carried out on desert lizards, much of the ensuing discussion will concern the complex thermoregulatory behavior of these heliotherms. Generally, activity temperatures are reached by basking. When these temperatures are attained, the animal shuttles between different thermal levels, such as in sun and shade, at the same time performing its daily activities. If all aspects of the thermal environment become too hot, the animal retreats to cooler areas, usually underground, until conditions abroad are more favorable. Much of the literature relates this behavior to temperature, and Heath (1965), working with *Phrynosoma,* has not only described the thermal behavior but has accurately measured the thermal parameters involved as well.

Before heliotherms become active in the morning they usually bask to raise body temperatures to levels that provide alertness and celerity of movements. The collared lizard, *Crotaphytus* (Fitch, 1956a) may emerge from its overnight shelter into the sunlight in several stages of several minutes each. The snout, the head, the shoulders, the forebody and finally the entire body, are successively exposed to the sun. The chuckwalla, *Sauromalus,* hidden in a crevice (Cowles and Bogert, 1944) and the eared lizard, *Holbrookia,* buried in the sand (Bogert, 1959), may expose just the head to the sun, thereby absorbing sufficient heat to attain activity temperature. The sidewinder, *Crotalus* (Cowles and Bogert, 1944), and the glass snake, *Ophisaurus* (Fitch, 1956b), reach and maintain activity temperatures by submitting only part of their buried bodies to the sun. Similarly, the tropical green iguana, *Iguana iguana,* apparently does not bask in full sun but exposes only part of its body to the sun in its sun–shade mosiac arboreal environment (McGinnis and Brown, 1966).

A fully emerged animal basking on a level surface, especially if the air

or substrate is cool and the sun is low, may increase the surface area exposed
to the sun, or cause the sun's rays to strike the surface perpendicularly
(Fig. 3), either by pointing its head away from the sun, allowing the rays
to strike the dorsum, or by pointing its head perpendicularly to the sun's
rays allowing dorsolateral solar impact (Cowles and Bogert, 1944; Bogert,
1959; Heath, 1965). Absorption of solar radiation may also be increased
by tipping the respective surfaces toward the sun. If in the "dorsolateral"
position, the legs on the opposite or shady side extend. If the head is
pointed away from the sun, the front legs extend and the animal may
also raise the forebody higher by placing its front legs on pebbles or other

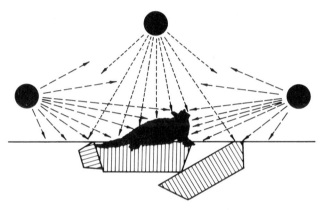

FIG. 3.   A diagrammatic representation of orientation behavior in *Phrynosoma*. Large
differences in the amount of radiation impinging on the body result when the animal
shifts its position. Facing into the sun on the right results in exposure of the body to a
radiant heat load proportional to the shadow on the left. Facing away from the sun on the
left results in the shadow to the right. The shadow immediately below the animal results
from positive normal orientation. (This diagram is reproduced through the courtesy of
Professor Raymond B. Cowles and Dr. J. E. Heath, 1965.)

objects (Heath, 1965). The exposed surface can be further increased in
area by changes in body contour (St. Girons and St. Girons, 1956; Heath,
1965). In the horned lizard, Heath found the surface area exposed to radiation to remain maximal at body temperatures below 30°C. However, as
temperatures rise above this point the ribs move backward, slimming and
deepening the animal and the exposed surface area thereby decreases. Many
heliotherms position themselves on inclined surfaces to allow the sun's rays
to strike more perpendicularly. The horned lizard (Heath, 1965), the marine iguana, *Amblyrhynchus cristatus* (Bartholomew, 1966), and the
bearded dragon, *Amphibolurus barbatus* (Lee and Badham,1963), all may
bask with heads upward, whereas the granite spiny lizard, *Sceloporus orcutti*
basks head downwards on rocks (Mayhew, 1963). During this preactivity

basking period, if the substrate is warm (Fig. 4), the heliotherm will behave thigmotactically by flattening out on it (Bartholomew, 1966). If the substrate is cold, the body will be raised above it or it is avoided completely in favor of insulated basking spots such as mats of grass (Pearson, 1954).

Fɪɢ. 4. (a) The "prostrate basking posture" of marine iguanas. (b) The "elevated basking posture." Courtesy of Dr. G. A. Bartholomew.

Once activity temperature is reached, the heliotherm maintains it, within relatively narrow limits, by moving in and out of sun and shade (Sergeyev, 1939; Cowles and Bogert, 1944; Bogert 1949a,b; Johnson, 1965). Heath (1965) calls these shuttling movements. He found, as would be expected, that as the day becomes warmer, horned lizards spend less and less time

in the sun and more in the shade, until at midday all activity was confined
to the shade. Although Heath quantified sun–shade times, as did Mayhew
(1963) for the granite spiny lizard, useful comparison with other species
abroad on other days can be made only after all thermal parameters are
known. Nevertheless, shuttling undoubtedly allows heliotherms to pursue
their daily activities while maintaining body temperatures within the activity
range.

As environmental temperatures rise, heliotherms may remain longer in
the sun by orienting negatively to sun and heat. The elevated basking
posture of the Galapagos marine iguana excellently exemplifies such negative orientation. Whole groups of these animals, all facing uphill with fore-
bodies raised and parallel to the sun's rays were described by Bartholomew
(1966), "to be mechanically aimed at the sun" (Fig. 4). This posture,
Bartholomew contended, minimizes heat gain from the sun and substrate
and maximizes heat loss by convection to the relatively cool trade winds
that blow regularly across the Galapagos. Quite possibly, heat may also
be lost by radiation from the abdomen to the shaded substrate beneath.
Similar postures have been noted in other heliotherms. Frequently, the
tails and toes are lifted up, the animal contacting the substrate only with
the heels of the feet (Cowles and Bogert, 1944; Fitch, 1956a). Al-
ternatively, the desert iguana and the racerunner, *Cnemidophorus,* may
slightly bury the abdomen in the sand, rather then elevating it. In such
a position the tail, and sometimes the front feet, are lifted off the substrate
(Norris, 1953). Norris also described how the desert iguana removes the
hot surface layer of sand to expose the cooler strata beneath. Stopping
on hot sand the animal drops the abdomen and wriggles the whole body
and tail from side to side. If the sand is unusually hot it pushes the sand
ahead with shoveling movements of the front feet and drives the body
forward into the resulting excavation with the hind feet. Schmidt-Nielsen
and Dawson (1964) commented that, although this behavior reduces contact with the hot surface, it does appear to bring about maximal exposure
to the heat.

Generally, diurnal reptiles can move more rapidly than less thermophilic
forms (Mosauer, 1936). Some species of lizards can run bipedally, and
by so lifting the body above the hot substratum and its adjoining hot layer
of air, reduce heat abosrption. The desert iguana, the sand lizard *Uma,*
and the collared lizard are all able to run bipedally (Stebbins, 1954).
Similarly, the sidewinding movement of *Crotalus ceraster* is not only a
rapid form of locomotion for a crotalid, but it also reduces contact of
the body with the substrate at any one time, by about one half. This
nocturnal snake, if forced to move over hot substrates, would thereby

absorb comparatively less heat than if it moved like other crotalids (Cowles, 1956).

When all thermal parameters at ground level become unbearably hot, the reptile must retreat underground. However, the desert iguana has one last resort before it also must enter underground burrows. It climbs large creosote bushes, *Larrea divaricata*, where the air is somewhat cooler than nearer the ground. If the bush is in flower, *Dipsosaurus* may continue its foraging and eat the blossoms (Cowles, 1946), but the arboreal sorties continue into the summer, when the bush is no longer in bloom (Norris, 1953) indicating that the behavior is thermoregulatory in nature.

B. Experimental Approach

Initiation, duration, and cessation of activity in reptiles appear to be related to temperature and light. When these factors are manipulated in laboratory temperature gradients, interesting rhythms result. Evans (1966) showed that the diurnal lizard *Uta,* exposed to a 12-hour photoperiod, with temperature fluctuating between $22°–27°C$, was most active in the light, warm phase, whereas the nocturnal lizard *Coleonyx*, exposed to the same conditions, was most active in the dark, cool phase. The light and temperature $(33°–23°C)$ cycles were then changed so that the cycles became out of phase. The activity of *Uta* appeared dependent upon the temperature but not the light cycle. The activity of *Coleonyx* seemed not to depend upon either but upon an interaction of the two. Evans suggested that the activity of *Coleonyx* is closely coupled to a biological clock mechanism but that that of *Uta* is not. Because the activity of *Uta* follows a temperature cycle rather than the light cycle, regulation of that activity in a natural environment may occur by synchronizing activity with daily emergence, which in turn is coupled to the biological clock mechanism.

The morning emergence of *Phrynosoma* in the laboratory appears independent of temperature and suggests involvement of an endogenous rhythm. Heath (1962) kept these horned lizards under a 12-hour photoperiod at low, but constant, ambient temperatures. Radiant heat sufficient to warm them to activity temperatures was provided for 8 hours daily, beginning with the onset of light. Within 2 hours after the radiant heat was removed, the animals had buried themselves at least 2 cm deep in the sand and remained there through the night. Fifteen minutes before light and heat were provided in the morning, 70% of the animals had emerged and were active. Such a circadian rhythm, according to Heath, would allow this ectotherm to secure a safe, nocturnal shelter without losing activity time in the morning.

The activity of the nocturnal shovel-nosed snake, *Chionactis*, prior to its emergence from the sand each evening, also appears to be spontaneous. Norris and Kavanau (1966) observed the activity of this snake placed in a box of loose sand having a vertical temperature gradient. They concluded that *Chionactis* became active spontaneously 24 hours or less from the time it last emerged. The snake than either emerged if the temperature of sand above it had dropped to a habitable level or waited until it had. Upon emergence, its biological clock is presumably reset in some fashion, thus allowing the snake to become active again, often somewhat less than 24 hours later. Because the cycle is often shorter than 24 hours, the snake could thereby take advantage of daily and seasonal variations in the surface temperature. This cycle would also account for its emergence at different hours in the spring, summer, and fall, and in areas having well-defined thermal levels.

Because most diurnal reptiles are inactive at night, their body temperatures most likely fall to that of the environment. Low nocturnal body temperatures may not be simply tolerated by the animal but may be preferred, since some lizards at least, voluntarily seek out a cold environment in which to spend the night, even though a warmer area may be available. Regal (1967) studies several species of lizards in temperature gradients provided with a photoperiod of 10 hours light and 14 hours dark. Each lizard maintained its characteristic activity temperature during the day but became inactive at night at the cooler part of the gradient. The body temperature fell below the minimal level which was voluntarily tolerated during the day. Such a change in temperature preference, Regal suggested, would be ecologically advantageous for it causes the lizard to retreat to cooler areas as environmental temperatures fall in the evening, rather than to attempt thermoregulation abroad under suboptimal conditions or to be led into warmer open areas where it would be more vulnerable to predation.

V. Physiological Thermoregulation

A. Production of Heat

1. Standard Metabolism

a. Effect of Body Size. Oxygen consumption measured under standard or resting conditions varies with body size in reptiles, as it does in all animals (Zeuthen, 1953), except possibly in turtles (Benedict, 1932; Hutton et al., 1960). Dawson and Bartholomew (1956) collected metabolic data measured at 30°C from four families and six genera of lizards weighing from 2 to 1300 gm, and they derived the equation: ml O_2/hr = $1.26W^{0.54}$, where W equals body weight in grams. Bartholomew and Tucker (1964) included recent data and replotted this relationship using five families and eleven genera of lizards, measured at 30°C and weighing from 2 to 4410 gm (Fig. 5), and they put forward the following revised equation: ml O_2/hr = $0.82W^{0.62}$, which is equivalent to ml O_2/gm/hr = $0.82W^{-0.38}$. The 95% confidence limits calculated for the exponent −0.38 by Bartholomew and Tucker are rather wide (0.304–0.462), but they considered such width not surprising in view of the limited data and the different methods used by the different workers who acquired the data. They also noted that metabolism in lizards changes much more rapidly with size than it does in

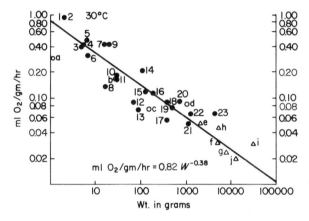

Fig. 5.   Relation between oxygen consumption at 30°C and body weight in lizards and snakes. The data for lizards (1–23 only), fitted by the method of least squares, yield the equation and the line (Bartholomew and Tucker, 1964). Points (a–j) represent data for both lizards and snakes not used by these authors. See Table II for species and source of data.

mammals, even though lizards are ectothermic. The standard metabolism of four additional lizard species reported since 1964, and of snakes, has been included in Fig. 5 and Table II.

It is of interest to compare the metabolism of reptiles at 37°C with that of homeotherms. Benedict (1932), though he did not actually study very large reptiles at that temperature, predicted from his extrapolated data that men of comparable size produced about 5, 3.5, and 3 times, respectively, more heat than did pythons, alligators, and Galapagos tortoises. Dawson and Bartholomew (1956) showed that hummingbirds (Pearson, 1950) and shrews (Morrison *et al.,* 1953) produced about ten times more heat than did their small lizards of comparable weight. Again, Dawson and Bartholomew (1958) reported that the desert iguana at 37°C produces

TABLE II

Oxygen Consumption (at 30°C) and Body Size in Lizards*

Code No.	Species	Weight (gm)	ml O₂/ gm/hr	Reference
1	*Sceloporus occidentalis*	2	0.910	Dawson and Bartholomew (1956)
7	*Sceloporus occidentalis*	16	0.431	Dawson and Bartholomew (1956)
2	*Uta stansburiana*	2	0.900	Dawson and Bartholomew (1956)
5	*Uta stansburiana*	6.5	0.480	Dawson and Bartholomew (1956)
10	*Crotaphytus collaris*	30	0.185	Dawson and Templeton (1963)
12	*Dipsosaurus dorsalis*	69	0.090	Dawson and Bartholomew (1958)
21	*Iguana tuberculata*	1120	0.050	Benedict (1932)
18	*Amphibolurus barbatus*	373	0.088	Bartholomew and Tucker (1963)
22	*Uromastix* sp.	1250	0.066	Krehl and Soetbeer (1899)
11	*Eumeces obsoletus*	30	0.166	Dawson (1960)
17	*Cyclodus gigas* (= *T. scincoides*)	374	0.055	Martin (1903)
19	*Tiliqua scincoides*	493	0.077	Bartholomew *et al.* (1965)
3	*Lacerta muralis*	5	0.408	Gelineo and Gelineo (1955)
4	*Lacerta sicula*	5.5	0.425	Gelineo and Gelineo (1955)
6	*Lacerta melisellensis*	6.8	0.323	Gelineo and Gelineo (1955)
9	*Lacerta viridis*	19.2	0.436	Gelineo and Gelineo (1955)
14	*Lacerta* sp.	110	0.220	Krehl and Soetbeer (1899)
8	*Varanus acanthurus*	16.9	0.139	Bartholomew and Tucker (1964)
13	*Varanus gouldii*	89	0.074	Bartholomew and Tucker (1964)
15	*Varanus gouldii*	127	0.119	Bartholomew and Tucker (1964)
16	*Varanus punctatus*	185	0.113	Bartholomew and Tucker (1964)
20	*Varanus gouldii*	714	0.092	Bartholomew and Tucker (1964)
23	*Varanus varius*	4410	0.050	Bartholomew and Tucker (1964)
a	*Lygosoma laterale*	1.1	0.303	Hudson and Bertram (1966)
b	*Gerrhonotus multicarinatus*	29.4	0.170	Dawson and Templeton (1966)
c	*Sauromalus obesus*	152.0	0.073	Boyer (1967)
d	*Iguana iguana*	1054	0.085	Tucker (1966)
e	*Drymarchon corais*	2040	0.052	Benedict (1932)
f	*Crotalus atrox*	4920	0.032	Benedict (1932)
g	*Constrictor constrictor*	7680	0.023	Benedict (1932)
h	*Python molurus*	5200	0.045	Benedict (1932)
i	*Python reticulatus*	30,200	0.029	Benedict (1932)
j	*Python molurus*	12,370	0.02	Hutchison *et al.* (1966b)

* See legend of Fig. 5.

about one-seventh the metabolic heat of that of the kangaroo rat, *Dipodomys panamintinus,* and the antelope ground squirrel, *Citellus leucurus* (Dawson, 1955). More recently, Bartholomew and Tucker (1963) reported that a guinea pig (Brody, 1945) produces almost six times more heat per gram, measured at 37°C, than does *Amphibolurus* of similar size.

Sufficient metabolic data now exists to allow calculation of a metabolism

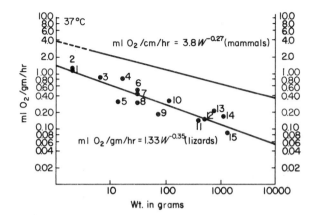

Fig. 6.   Relation of oxygen consumption at 37°C to body weight in lizards, compared with a similar curve derived for mammals. The data fitted by the method of least squares yield the equation and the line. See Table III for species and source of data.

weight curve of lizards measured at 37°C (Fig. 6, Table III) and to compare these data with a similar curve for mammals (Brody, 1945).

Fifteen metabolic measurements of lizards weighing from 2 to 1250 gm give, by the method of least squares, the equation: ml O_2/hr = $1.33W^{0.65}$, which is equivalent to ml O_2/gm/hr = $1.33W^{-0.35}$. The 95% confidence limits for the exponent -0.35 are also rather wide, extending from -0.44 to

TABLE III

RESTING METABOLISM OF LIZARDS AND MAMMALS AT A BODY TEMPERATURE OF 37°C

Code No.	Lizard	Weight (gm)	(a) Lizard	(b) Theoretical mammal	a/b	Reference
			\multicolumn{2}{c} ml O_2/gm/hr		
1	*Uta stansburiana*	2.0	1.1	—	—	Dawson and Bartholomew (1956)
2	*Sceloporus occidentalis*	2.0	1.20	—	—	Dawson and Bartholomew (1956)
3	*Uta stansburiana*	6.5	0.85	2.3	2.5	Dawson and Bartholomew (1956)
4	*Sceloporus occidentalis*	16.0	0.78	1.8	2.3	Dawson and Bartholomew (1956)
5	*Uta mearnsii*	13.7	0.30	1.85	6.2	Murrish and Vance (1968)
6	*Gerrhonotus multicarinatus*	29.4	0.50	1.5	3.0	Dawson and Templeton (1966)
7	*Eumeces obsoletus*	30.0	0.43	1.5	3.5	Dawson (1960)
8	*Crotaphytus collaris*	30.0	0.30	1.5	5.0	Dawson and Templeton (1963)
9	*Dipsosaurus dorsalis*	69	0.18	1.2	6.7	Dawson and Bartholomew (1958)
10	*Lacerta* sp.	110	0.32	1.05	3.3	Krehl and Soetbeer (1899)
11	*Amphibolurus barbatus*	373	0.14	0.77	5.6	Bartholomew and Tucker (1963)
12	*Tiliqua scincoides*	493	0.15	0.70	4.7	Bartholomew et al. (1965)
13	*Varanus gouldii*	714	0.21	0.64	3.0	Bartholomew and Tucker (1964)
14	*Iguana iguana*	1054	0.167	0.56	3.3	Tucker (1966)
15	*Uromastix* sp.	1250	0.085	0.56	6.6	Krehl and Soetbeer (1899)

—0.26, but again these data come from different authors using different techniques. Also, metabolism of lizards at 37°C, as at 30°C, changes more rapidly with size than it does in mammals. A theoretical 10-gm mammal would produce 3.5 times more heat than a theoretical lizard of that weight, but a 10-kg mammal would theoretically produce almost seven times more heat than a similarly sized lizard, at 37°C.

b. Effects of Temperature. The rate of resting oxygen consumption in reptiles increases with temperature, and, like many biological processes, obeys the law of van't Hoff. The expression for the rate of change, the

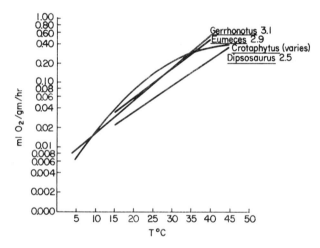

FIG. 7.   Relation of oxygen consumption to body temperature in cold resistant lizards *Gerrhonotus* (Dawson and Templeton, 1966), *Eumeces* (Dawson, 1960), and in heat resistant lizards, *Crotaphytus*, (Dawson and Templeton, 1963), and *Dipsosaurus* (Dawson and Bartholomew, 1958). In all species the average weight was 30 gm except *Dipsosaurus*, which averaged 70 gm. Numbers following names refer to the Q_{10} corresponding to the slope of the respective line.

Q_{10}, has been calculated for much of the early reptilian metabolic data by Benedict (1932). The Q_{10} ranges from 1.3 in the alligators to 3.9 in the rattlesnake, *Crotalus atrox*. More recent studies have been carried out, mostly on lizards, giving a Q_{10} that varies from 2.5 to 3.3.

When the logarithm of the metabolism of reptiles is plotted against temperature, the resultant curve generally follows one of three patterns. It may be linear throughout the temperature range with a constant Q_{10}, e.g., *Gerrhonotus* (Fig. 7); the curve may be linear within the lower temperature range, giving a constant Q_{10}, but it breaks at an intermediate temperature and then remains linear throughout the upper range, with a reduced but constant Q_{10} (e.g. *Amphibolurus*); or, the relationship may be curvilinear throughout the temperature range, with a constantly decreasing Q_{10}, as exemplified by *Crotalus atrox* (Benedict, 1932) and by *Crotaphytus collaris* (Fig. 7). If the Q_{10} changes as the temperature increases, the change is always in the direction of a decrease.

A comparative and intensive study of the variation of resting metabolism with temperature, on four species of lizard of differing thermal sensitivity and preference, has been carried out by Dawson and co-workers (1966) (Fig. 7). The validity of their data is enhanced by the similarity in weight of the lizards and by the uniformity in techniques and procedures. The desert iguana and collared lizard are the most thermophilic, the skink less so, and the alligator lizard least of all. The latter two species consume about 0.5 ml O_2/gm/hr at 39°C or 40°C, whereas the thermophilic desert iguana and collared lizard do not consume that much oxygen until they reach body temperatures of about 45°C. The lowered metabolism of the thermophilic species at high temperatures, brought about either by a lateral displacement of the curve toward the temperature axis or by the lower Q_{10} at high temperatures, may partly account for their decreased sensitivity to heat. On the other hand, both the collared lizard and the desert iguana are quite lethargic at body temperatures at which the alligator lizard is still coordinated. The metabolism of the alligator lizard is relatively insensitive to low temperatures, possessing a constant Q_{10} of 3.1 even at 5°C, whereas the metabolism of the collared lizard shows a Q_{10} of 7.7 at that temperature. Therefore, in view of these data, possession of high resting metabolic rates at both high and low temperatures contribute to increased resistance to the cold but at the expense of being sensitive to heat.

c. Effects of Thermal Acclimation. The metabolic rate of some lizards can be altered by exposing them to constant but different temperatures. One group of *Urosaurus ornatus* was maintained by Vance (1953) at 35°C, another at 8°C. When both were measured at 15°C, the group acclimated at the high temperature had a significantly lower oxygen consumption than that of the other group. Murrish and Vance (1968) maintained one group of *Uta mearnsi* at 35°C for 7–10 days, and another group at 15°C, before measuring metabolism at body temperatures between 15° and 40°C. At body temperatures below 30°C, the metabolism temperature curve for animals acclimated at 35°C was displaced 5°C toward the high end of the temperature scale from the curve of the group acclimated to 15°C. At body temperatures above 30°C, the curves were displaced about 10°C from each other (Fig. 8). Thus, heat-acclimated animals measured at 40°C had about the same metabolism as cold-acclimated animals measured at 30°C. Gelineo and Gelineo (1955) kept *Lacerta m. melisellensis* and *L. m. galvagnii* first for several weeks at 20°–24°C, then for several weeks at

11°–12°C, and finally at 20°–22°C. After each period of time they measured metabolism at 13°, 19°, 25°, and 30°C. The metabolism temperature curve measured after acclimation to 11°–12°C was shifted downward on the temperature scale about 10°C from the other two curves. Schmidt-Nielsen and Dawson (1964) found this translation to be not only remarkable, but an example of perfect thermal acclimation, since the lizards acclimated to

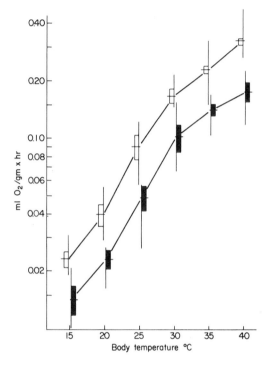

FIG. 8.   Relation of oxygen consumption to body temperature in thermally acclimated lizards, *Uta mearnsi*. Solid black rectangles represent lizards acclimated at 35°C, open rectangles, at 15°C. Horizontal lines equal the mean; vertical lines, the range; and the rectangles on either side of the mean, two standard errors of the mean (Murrish and Vance, 1968).

and measured at 13°C had about the same metabolism as they had when acclimated to and measured at 24°C. Most animals do not acclimate so perfectly. Dawson and Bartholomew (1956) found only partially effective compensation to temperature in *Sceloporus occidentalis*. One group kept at 16°C for 3 weeks and measured at 33°C had significantly higher metabolic rates than those kept and measured at 33°C, but the displacement of the metabolism temperature curve was only 3°C.

d. Effects of Hibernation. Little is known concerning the metabolism of hibernating reptiles. Potter and Glass (1931) reported that hibernating lizards have a low metabolism. Metabolism apparently does not change during hibernation in *Anolis carolinesis* but this neotropical lizard does not have long periods of winter inactivity and may be active on any warm winter day (Dessauer, 1953). The desert iguana, *Dipsosaurus*, however, hibernates without interruption from October to March in shallow self-constructed burrows in the desert sand (Cowles, 1941; Norris, 1953). Moberly (1963) found that desert iguanas freshly removed from their hibernacula metabolize similarly to active control animals at body temperatures between 15°C and 20°C. At temperatures between 30°C and 40°C, however, the hibernators consumed significantly less oxygen than did the controls. Hibernators also breathed significantly slower at the higher temperatures than did the controls.

2. *Active Metabolism*

Benedict (1932) showed that a 6-kg Boa, *Constrictus constrictus*, made active by agitation, increased its metabolism and thereby its body temperature 6°C above room temperature. A 6-kg python, *P. molurus*, measured after agitation during periods devoid of muscular activity, maintained an increased metabolism which was sometimes four- to sixfold greater than standard rates, for about 5 hours before settling down. A 5-kg tortoise, *Testudo denticulata*, also in Benedict's laboratory, increased its metabolism at 30°C by typical "cage activity" from a standard of 80 cal to as high as 272 cal/kg/24 hr, a 3.5-fold increase. The muscle activity of 110–130-kg female green sea turtles, *Chelonia mydas*, caused body temperatures to rise 2°–3°C above those of the sea, sand, and air when these females were on land to deposit eggs (Hirth, 1962). Such rises in body temperatures during activity occur in large reptiles apparently because of the slow loss of heat from their great bulk. Kirk and Hogben (1946) showed that 4-kg alligators cooled very slowly. From this Cott (1961) suggested that the much larger nile crocodile, *Crocodilus niloticus*, would lose heat, acquired by basking during the day, to the water very slowly during its long nocturnal submergence. The muscular exertion of swimming in search of prey would also counter heat loss, and body temperatures might remain above that of the water, far into the night.

Probably the most interesting of all reports of such elevated body temperatures in reptiles are those of large incubating female pythons. The early history of thermoregulatory studies in these animals has been amply reviewed by Benedict (1932) and sketched recently by Hutchison *et al.* (1966b). These latter investigators presented convincing evidence that the India python, *Python moluris*, can raise its metabolism and thereby its body temperature while incubating eggs. Whereas metabolism of the non-brooding pythons (12.37 kg) is characteristic of other reptiles, the oxygen consumption of the same animal while brooding (14.25 kg) is essentially endothermic. Hutchison and his group showed that at an ambient temperature of 33°C both brooding and nonbrooding pythons consume similar quantities of oxygen; but as the temperature dropped to 25.5°C, the brooding snake appreciably increased metabolism by spasmodic muscular contractions

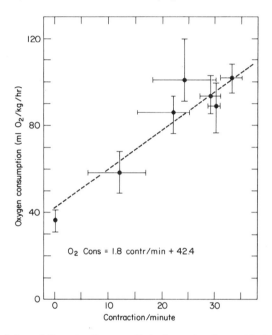

Fig. 9.   Correlation of the rate of spasmodic body contractions with the rate of oxygen consumption in a brooding Indian python. Dashed line and regression equation calculated by method of least squares. Vertical lines, range of oxygen consumption; horizontal lines, range of contraction rate; circles, means. (From Hutchison *et al.*, 1966b.)

(Fig. 9). The temperature of 33°C was likened to the lower critical temperatures of birds and mammals, which precipitate shivering. However, the python appeared neither able to increase nor maintain this elevated metabolism as temperatures fell below 25.5°C. The muscular contractions correlate directly with oxygen consumed according to the equation,

$$\text{ml } O_2/\text{kg/hr} = 1.8 \text{ (No. of contractions/min)} + 42.4$$

and the increase in body temperature over that of the environment by the temperature differential,

$$°C = 0.1 \text{ (No. of contractions/min)} + 1.3.$$

The brooding python at 25.5°C can consume 9.3 times more oxygen than
when it is not brooding. Temperature differentials as high as 4.7°C were
recorded.

3. *Metabolic Scope for Activity*

A recent concept, metabolic scope for activity (Fry, 1947), is the difference between maximal and minimal metabolic rates and signifies the
amount of energy available for release above that simply needed for body
maintenance. Moberly (1968a) stated that this concept is true only if the

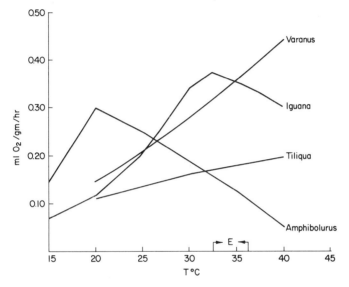

FIG. 10.   Relation of metabolic scope for activity in $O_2/gm/hr$, to body temperature
in *Varanus* sp. (Bartholomew and Tucker, 1964); *Iguana* (Moberly, 1968a); *Tiliqua* (Bartholomew *et al.*, 1965); and *Amphibolurus* (Bartholomew and Tucker, 1963). E refers to
range in which the eccritic temperatures of the four genera fall.

animal during muscular activity does not temporarily abandon some maintenance process, and if it does not metabolize anaerobically to any extent.
Maximal and minimal rates so far obtained from lizards are the highest
and lowest rates the investigators are able to obtain during the study. Fortu-
nately, lizards are often extremely quiet and, conversely, struggle violently
against their retaining bonds. Bartholomew and Tucker (1964) noted that
maximal rates obtained by subdermally shocking *Varanus* (2.5 V, 4
shocks/sec) were no higher than those obtained during these spontaneous
violent struggles.

Metabolic scope for activity of four lizards from four different families
vary considerably when plotted against temperature (Fig. 10). No lizard

has the greatest scope for activity near its preferred temperature (33°–36°C). The scope does not appear to correlate with the size of the species but perhaps if extended size ranges within a species were measured for their scope, such correlations could be shown, as they have been in fishes (Job, 1955). Bartholomew and Tucker (1963) interpreted the high metabolic scope at 20°C in *Amphibolurus* as beneficial in helping the agamid to avoid enemies or to seek areas in which it could reach its eccritic temperatures of about 30°C.

Moberly (1968a,b) has extensively measured metabolic scope and associated parameters in *Iguana iguana*. Metabolic scope in restrained animals is greatest at a body temperature of 32°C, the maximum being only fourfold greater than the minimum oxygen consumption. Vigorous bursts of activity therefore cannot be supported entirely by aerobic metabolism. For example, one restrained iguana at 35°C, struggling vigorously for 5 minutes supplied only one-fourth of the required energy by aerobic metabolism; the remainder came from muscle glycogen stores via anaerobic pathways. Removal of the oxygen debt is temperature dependent and occurs maximally at 35°C (Moberly, 1968a). The energetic cost to an iguana walking in a treadmill at any given rate of speed is temperature independent. Although the animal uses more oxygen when it walks faster, the rate of oxygen increase per unit increase in speed actually decreases, thereby improving efficiency of locomotion. A lizard therefore would require almost twice the oxygen to travel 1 km walking at 2.8 m/min as it would traveling at 6.2 m/min. The capacity for activity without accumulating any oxygen debt is highly temperature dependent. At 30°C an iguana can walk 6.2 m/min sustained by aerobic metabolism alone, but at 20°C it can walk no faster than 2.2 m/min without acquiring an oxygen debt (Moberly, 1968b).

B. Transport of Heat and Oxygen

The increased requirements for oxygen brought about by rises in temperature or activity are met by concomitant changes in the cardiovascular system. The transport of oxygen can be expressed by,

$$O_2 \text{ uptake} = \text{Cardiac output} \times AV\ O_2 \text{ difference}$$

where cardiac output is the amount of blood ejected from the heart each beat multiplied by the number of beats per unit time, and the AV difference is the difference in oxygen content of arterial and venous blood, which is actually the amount of oxygen delivered to the tissues. The role of the cardiovascular system in oxygen and heat transport and in thermoregulation in lizards has recently been reviewed by Tucker (1967).

1. *Heart Rates During Inactivity*

The resting heart rate of reptiles increases with decrease in body size (Table IV). At 30°C, and within 1 minute, the heart of the 1-gm ground skink will beat 100 times (Hudson and Bertram, 1966), whereas the heart rate of the 4.4-kg monitor lizard is less than 20/min.

Like metabolism, heart rate increases with temperature; but heart rate and oxygen uptake are not always uniformly related, nor need they necessarily be, since stroke volume and AV difference must also be considered. Unlike the Q_{10} for metabolism, the Q_{10} for heart rate of more than ten species of lizards, comprising five families, varies only from 2.0 to 2.5, between temperatures of 20° and 40°C (Table IV). Except for two species (*Lygosoma* and *Crotaphytus*), the Q_{10} for each species within that temperature range is constant. Heart rates available for body temperatures below 20° usually show a larger Q_{10}. As the animal is cooled, the low body temperature at which the heart markedly slows (increased Q_{10}) marks the point at which sensitivity to cold is manifested. Two cold-resistant species, the Great Plains skink (Dawson, 1960) and the alligator lizard (Dawson and Templeton, 1966), maintain a constant Q_{10} until they are cooled to 10°C, whereupon Q_{10} increases. However, the desert iguana, (Dawson and Bartholomew, 1958) and the collared lizard (Dawson and Templeton, 1963) show such an increased Q_{10} at temperatures about 10°C higher. The quantitative effect of temperature on heart rate has been impressively illustrated by Dawson (1960) in *Eumeces*. The heart rate of this skink is only 2.5/min at 0°C, but it is 300/min at body temperatures between 40° and 43°C. In certain iguanid lizards, the heart rate diminishes at high temperatures (Licht, 1965; Bartholomew and Lasiewski, 1965). The latter authors interpret this diminution as a mechanism for decreasing the rate at which the lizard's heart is beating after its body temperature has reached an optimal level.

2. *Heart Rates During Activity*

Licht (1965) found heart rates of lizards to increase abruptly with the activity induced by a mechanical stimulus and, when maximal, to be double or triple the resting rates. Maximal heart rates had a higher Q_{10} below 25°–30°C than had resting rates (3.5 as opposed to 2.5), but as temperatures increased, the Q_{10} for maximal heart rates progressively decreased until it became less (1.1) than that of the resting rates (2.0). The differences, in beats/min, between maximal and minimal heart rates, which Licht termed heart rate increments, increased with temperature, reaching a maximum at a level near the upper limits of the preferred temperature range of the particular species (as measured in a thermal gradient), whereupon

TABLE IV

Effects of Temperature and Body Weight on Heart Rate and Oxygen Pulse of Lizards

Genus	Weight (gm)	Heart rate				Oxygen pulse ml O_2/gm/hr $\times 10^{-5}$			References
		Q_{10} lower curve	Thermal point[a] (T°C)	Q_{10} upper curve	Beats/min (30°C)	20°C	30°C	40°C	
Lygosoma	1	2.61	26	2.15	100	—	4.55	3.61[b]	Hudson and Bertram (1966)
Sceloporus	7.4	2.5	30	2.0	85	—	—	—	Licht (1965)
Uma	19.2	2.5	30	2.0	80	—	—	—	Licht (1965)
Eumeces	30.0	6.5	16	2.2	76	2.73	3.63	4.77	Dawson (1960)
Gerrhonotus	29.4	6.9–2.3[c]	10	2.3	90	2.43	3.13	3.79[d]	Dawson and Templeton (1966)
Crotaphytus	30.0	8.8–2.5[c]	22	2.5–1.8[c]	80	3.93	3.85	3.34	Dawson and Templeton (1963)
Dipsosaurus	69.2	4.8	18	2.5	48	3.0	3.1	3.1	Dawson and Bartholomew (1958)
Sauromalus	150	4.9	20	2.0	60	—	—	—	Templeton (1964b)
Sauromalus	153	—	20	2.0	41	3.5	2.8	1.8[e]	Boyer (1967)
Amphibolurus	373	3.6	20	2.34	41	4.43	3.67	3.05	Bartholomew and Tucker (1963)
Tiliqua	493	—	20	2.25	45	2.25	3.22	3.11	Bartholomew et al. (1965)
Varanus spp.	714	—	20	2.5	33	3.31	3.1	3.1	Bartholomew and Tucker (1964)
Iguana	1054	—	20	2.19	50	3.21	3.30	3.79	Tucker (1966)
Iguana		—		2.02	44	3.05	3.15	3.25	Moberly (1968a)
Amblyrhynchus	1360	—	15	—	23	—	—	—	Bartholomew and Lasiewski (1965)

[a] The point at which the lower heart rate curve plotted with temperature breaks to form the upper curve, or if no Q_{10} is given for the lower curve, that point at which the upper curve begins.

[b] Measured at 36°C.

[c] Q_{10} decreases as temperature increases.

[d] Measured at 35°C.

[e] Low value may be due to effects of previous hypoxia.

it decreased with higher temperatures. Conversely, Bartholomew and Tucker (1963, 1964) and Bartholomew *et al.* (1965) found the Q_{10} for maximal heart rates of their lizards to be lower than that for minimal heart rates, and the Q_{10} for each remained constant. Also, increments were maximal at levels somewhat below the preferred temperature of each species. The difference between these data and those of Licht, as Licht suggests, may be due to differences in methods. Actually, because ectotherms can usually be found abroad and active at any particular body temperature within a broad range, maximal physiological responses or maximal potential for such responses need not necessarily occur at the thermal preferendum. A cold or an extremely warm animal may need physiological reserves as much as, or more than, one which is at its preferred temperature. For example, the desert iguana has its maximal increment for heart rate at 42°C (Licht, 1965) which correlates with its activity temperature in summer; yet its preferred temperature is more than 4°C lower (DeWitt, 1967). Furthermore, the excised ventricles of this lizard are impressively heat resistant and respond to stimulation after exposure to temperatures between 45°–50°C, yet maximal tension was greatest between 25° and 35°C and declined faster with higher temperatures than with lower (Dawson and Bartholomew, 1958).

3. *Oxygen Pulse, Stroke Volume, and AV O₂ Difference*

Metabolism and heart rate can be related through the term "oxygen pulse," which is usually expressed as milliliters of O_2 consumed per heart beat per gram of body weight, or

Oxygen pulse $=$ metabolism/heart rate

$$= \text{stroke volume} \times \text{AV } O_2 \text{ difference}$$

Heart rate and metabolism (oxygen uptake) have been measured simultaneously and the oxygen pulse calculated therefrom in many lizards (Table IV). The values for oxygen pulse in these lizards are remarkably uniform, varying at 30°C from 2.5 to only 4.55 ml O_2/mg/hr $\times$ 10^{-5}. The oxygen pulse does not correlate with either body size or taxonomic position; but it may vary with temperature even if not always directly.

As metabolism increases with a rise in body temperature, the increased demand for oxygen transport is always met by an increased heart rate, and sometimes by an increased oxygen pulse as well. When lizards are warmed, *Amphibolurus, Sauromalus,* and *Lygosoma* (Table IV) decrease oxygen pulse, the varanids and *Dipsosaurus* do not change oxygen pulse, and *Iguana, Gerrhonotus,* and *Eumeces* increase it. Finally, oxygen pulse remains constant in *Crotaphytus* or rises in *Tiliqua* until an intermediate body temperature is reached, whereupon it falls in both species as body temperatures continue to rise. The significance of this diversity from the standpoint of thermal adjustment is not, at present, clear.

Until recently (Tucker, 1966), the oxygen pulse was computed from simultaneously measured metabolic and heart rate data, and the respective roles of stroke volume and AV O_2 differences were only surmised. Tucker simultaneously measured heart rate, oxygen consumption, and oxygen content of the dorsal aorta and sinus venosus of the iguana, *Iguana iguana*, and therefrom calculated AV O_2 difference and stroke volume by the Fick principle. Extreme values of stroke volume in these large lizards ranged from 0.38 to 2.5 ml/kg, but average values decreased with rising body temperature from 1.9 ml/kg at 20°C to 0.97 ml/kg at 38°C. Meanwhile, the mean values for the AV O_2 difference increased from 1.9 at 20° to 4.1 ml O_2/100 ml blood at 38°C. These increases in the AV O_2 difference were accomplished by the tissues extracting more oxygen from the blood rather than the blood carrying more oxygen. Even though stroke volume dropped with temperature, the rise in heart rate caused cardiac output to increase. When two iguanas were stimulated to activity by electric shocks, AV O_2 difference and heart rate were augmented in both, but stroke volume increased in the one but decreased in the other.

4. *Oxygen Capacity of the Blood*

Tucker (1966) has compared the cardiovascular data of *Iguana* at body temperatures of 38°C with that of mammals of comparable size. Metabolism and heart rate were about one-third the values of basal mammalian rates, stroke volumes (over 2 ml/kg) were double, AV O_2 differences were similar, but cardiac output was roughly one-half that of mammalian values. Oxygen capacity of the blood (8.4 ml O_2/100 ml blood) and hemoglobin content (19 gm/100 ml blood) were below those of other lizards and snakes, which range from 6 to 16 ml O_2/100 ml blood (Dawson and Poulson, 1962) and 26–31 gm/100 ml red blood cells (Dill *et al.*, 1935; Edwards and Dill, 1935; Dittmer, 1961), respectively. These values for lizards and snakes are similar to those of homeotherms. Dawson and Poulson (1962) measured the oxygen capacities of lizard blood and reviewed similar data for other reptiles and found the higher values in reptiles to overlap those for some homeotherms. They suggested that the higher requirements for oxygen transport in homeotherms were not met in a major way by increasing oxygen transport capacity of the blood but by other means such as increasing cardiac output.

5. *Oxygen Saturation of the Blood*

The capacity of reptilian blood, under experimental conditions, to carry oxygen may approximate that for mammals, but the transport of oxygen per unit volume of blood to the tissues also depends upon the extent to which hemoglobin combines with O_2 in the lungs. Blood in the dorsal aorta of the iguana averaged 72% saturation (Tucker, 1966), and White (1959) found the blood in the systemic arches and pulmonary vein of this animal to be only 63% saturated with oxygen. Blood returning from the artificially ventilated lung of the snapping turtle, *Chelydra,* was never more than 85% saturated (Steggerda and Essex, 1957). These values are considerably lower than those (93–98%) for mammals.

6. *Admixing of Aerated and Nonaerated Blood*

The transport of oxygen is complicated by possible mixing of aerated and nonaerated blood. In crocodilians, the ventricular and auricular septa are complete, but the left aorta arises from the right ventricle which pumps only venous blood. Also the aerated blood of the right aorta can feasibly enter the left aorta through their intimate posterior union and through the Foramen of Pinizza. Noncrocodilian reptiles, which possess an incomplete ventricular septum, can, from anatomical evidence, feasibly send venous blood into the left aorta or send oxygenated blood into the pulmonary artery, hence inefficiently recirculating it in the lung. Recent evidence, collected by radiography and blood sampling, in part supports the view that the anatomy and dynamics of the reptilian heart can prevent mixing of venous and pulmonary blood. White (1956) and Greenfield and Morrow (1961) reported that the left aorta of crocodilians receives blood not from the right ventricle but from the right aorta and hence is oxygenated. Steggerda and Essex (1957) found the blood of the left aorta to be only about 10% contaminated with the nonaerated blood from the right ventricle, but that the nonaerated blood in the pulmonary artery going to the lung was greatly admixed with pulmonary venous blood coming from the lung. White (1959) found neither kind of mixing in the hearts of the iguana or the snake, *Coluber*. Foxon *et al.* (1956), by radiography, noted that some venous blood from the right ventricle entered the left arch of *Lacerta,* but aerated blood from the lungs enters only the right arch and the carotid arteries. Khalil and Zaki (1964) found the left arch of snakes, a tortoise, and a crocodile carried blood with less oxygen than did the right arch. The blood of the pulmonary artery of the monitor lizard was more oxygenated than was the sinus venosus blood, suggesting a contribution of aerated blood from the pulmonary vein to the artery via the ventricle. Tucker (1966) measured the blood oxygen content of the systemic arches in iguana. Interestingly, in half the lizards, the two arches had blood of equal oxygen content, but in the other half, blood from the left arch had a lower mean saturation percentage. He calculated that 56% of the blood entering the left aorta was venous in origin.

7. *Possible Functions of the Aortic Arches*

Ewer (1950) suggested that the lungs of lizards cannot handle the entire cardiac output. The left arch then functions to shunt off the excess venous blood while the right arch sends oxygenated blood to the head and anterior body. Tucker (1966) agreed that the right arch functions to supply the brain and major sense organs with well-oxygenated blood but questioned the proposed function for the left arch because often the heart apparently sends all venous blood to the lungs. Tucker proposed that the left arch plays a thermoregulatory role. When the lizard is cooling, venous blood is sent through the lungs; but when it is heating, large quantities of venous blood bypass the lung and enter the left arch. As the left arch offers less resistance to blood flow than does the lung, this would thereby reduce the energy required for any increased cardiac output, presumably associated with heat transport, during heating (Bartholomew and Tucker, 1963, 1964). For a further discussion of the comparative functional morphology of the reptilian heart and its associated blood vessels, see the recent review by White (1968).

8. *Jugular Shunts and Head-Body Temperatures*

Another type of shunt has been noted in lizards that are being heated. Horned lizards, *Phrynosoma,* while basking under a heat lamp possess head temperatures as high as 5°C above that of the body. This temperature differential diminishes as the lizard further warms between 30°C and 37°C, and during this time the animals swell their eyes at frequent intervals (Heath, 1964, 1966). Such puffiness of the eyelids and protrusion of the eyes in lizards was postulated by Bruner (1907) to result from blood engorgement of the cranial sinuses by contracture of the internal jugular constrictor muscle surrounding the internal jugular vein which drains the sinuses. Bruner suggested that such swelling aids ecdysis of the skin surrounding the eye. Stebbins (1954) suggested it to be part of a mechanism to remove sand particles from the eye. Templeton (1964a) found that the occasional eye swelling of the chuckwalla, *Sauromalus,* during pulmonary inflation, was not due to impaired venous return into the visibly expanded thorax because intrathoracic pressures never rose appreciably during such lung distension.

Heath (1964, 1966) suggested that, as the horned lizard basks, the head warms faster than the body, but heat exchange between head and body is reduced by the close proximity of the internal jugular veins, which drain the head, and the internal carotid artery, which supplies the head with blood (Fig. 11). The warmer venous blood loses heat to the cooler arterial blood by countercurrent exchange; but some heat exchange may also occur between blood and surrounding tissues. When rising body temperatures reach about 30°C, the internal jugular constrictor muscle contracts, shunting the warmer venous blood into the external jugular and vertebral veins, where no countercurrent mechanism exists. Simultaneously, the arterial blood entering the head from the cooler body is deprived of heat exchange and therefore has a lower temperature than before. Heat exchange between

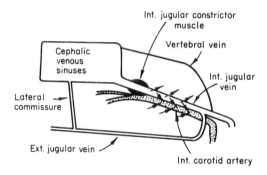

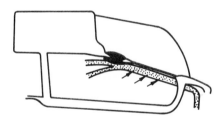

FIG. 11.   Diagram showing the relations of the major vessels in the head of the horned lizard. The cephalic venous sinuses of the head are shown for the sake of simplicity as a single space. *Top:* The internal jugular vein is open. Arrows indicate heat exchange between internal jugular vein, internal carotid artery, and tissues of neck. *Bottom:* Closure of the internal jugular constrictor muscle causes the collapse of the internal jugular vein. Venous return is through shunt to external jugular vein. Cool blood warmed only by neck tissues enters head, while warm blood flows through external jugular vein to body. (From Heath, 1966.)

head and body now occurs, and the temperature differential between the two is thereby reduced. Pressures in the cephalic sinuses during unimpeded flow of the internal jugular vein range from -5 to 5 mm H_2O (Heath, 1966), but within 3–20 sec after flow was occluded by bilaterally closing off the veins with hemostats, the pressure rose to 60–70 mm H_2O. The cephalic sinus venous pressure increased also with rising temperatures during unimpeded venous flow, but decreased with increasing temperature when the internal jugular vein was occluded.

Templeton (1960) heated the desert iguana, *Dipsosaurus,* in a chamber immersed in a circulating-water bath but found no such great temperature differences between the head and body, nor did DeWitt (1967), who measured the head and body temperatures in this species when placed either in a temperature gradient provided with a substrate source of heat, or when tethered in the desert. However, this lizard often has swollen and blinking eyes when its head is heated, and when it emerges from its desert burrow in the morning, it often exposes only its head. DeWitt suggested that, like the horned lizard, the desert iguana may preferentially keep head temperatures high during emergence, then later equalize head–body temperatures by shunting venous blood.

9. *Blood Pressure and Associated Cardiovascular Changes*

Arterial pressures in turtles and alligators are considerably lower than those for snakes and lizards. Systolic and diastolic pressures in the snapping turtle, *Chelydra,* were 30/20 mm Hg (Steggerda and Essex, 1957); in *Pseudemys,* 40/34 mm Hg (Rodbard and Feldman, 1946); and in *Alligator mississippiensis* 28/17 mm Hg (Andersen, 1961). Mean arterial pressure in the ring snake *Coluber natrix* was 89 mm Hg (Lehmann, 1925), and both the snakes, *Tripodonstus* and *Viperus,* had systolic and diastolic pressures of 60/50 mm Hg (Johansen, 1959). Templeton (1964b) found the highest resting arterial pressures in the chuckwalla, *Sauromalus,* to be 100/90 mm Hg. Arterial pressures in squamatenes, therefore, are similar to those of homeotherms.

Arterial pressures rise steadily with body temperature in turtles (Woodbury, 1941; Rodbard and Feldman, 1946), but fall precipitously as temperatures rise above 40°C (Rodbard and Feldman, 1946). As body temperatures of *Chelydra* rise, the rate of diastolic descent of the blood pressure also increases, apparently caused by a vasodilatation. In spite of the vasodilatation, blood pressure also rises, thereby indicating an increase in cardiac output (Woodbury, 1941). Arterial pressures also rise with temperatures in the chuckwalla, *Sauromalus,* but with rising temperatures above 25°C, pressures remain constant (Fig. 12). At low body temperatures, diastolic runoff is less steep, suggesting constriction of the vascular bed, and, simultaneously, the jugular vein is usually engorged with blood, indicating that the slowly beating heart is unable to handle the venous return. Because cardiac output increases with high temperatures, yet blood pressure remains constant, the peripheral resistance of the vascular bed must be correspondingly reduced (Templeton, 1964b).

10. *Dermovascular Changes with Temperature*

Cowles (1958) reported that small quantities of water (0.2–0.5 ml) injected subdermally and dorsolaterally into the desert iguana were dissipated more rapidly when the blob of water was heated than when it was cooled. Also, the thermal gradient directly across the skin, as measured by small thermocouples, was much greater when the skin was cooled than when it was heated. When a chilled animal was heated, the thermal gradient decreased. Cowles suggested that these phenomena were due to changes in dermovascular flow. Dermal heating increases the flow of blood to the skin and subdermal temperatures tend to approach those of the cloaca. Conversely, dermal cooling reduces blood flow from the body, and subdermal temperatures tend to approach those of the cooled surface. Such a

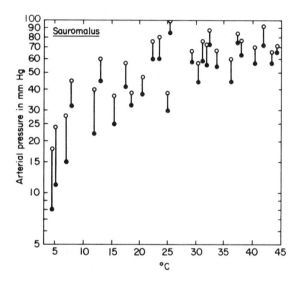

Fig. 12.   Relation of carotid pressure to body temperature in nine adult *Sauromalus obesus.* Open circles refer to systolic pressure, closed circles to diastolic pressure, and the extent of each vertical connecting bar to the respective pulse pressure. (From Templeton, 1964b.)

system would collect heat when the skin was hot, and disperse it to the body, and would reduce loss of body heat when the skin was cool. Furthermore, increased dermovascular flow may also serve to protect the skin from uncomfortably high or damaging insolation, especially if the skin surface is not heavily cornified or if the animal inhabits arid regions.

C. Exchange of Heat

1. *Heating and Cooling Rates in Lizards*

Lizards from four different families measured under carefully controlled conditions warm faster than they cool, which signifies physiological capacity for thermoregulation. The bearded dragon, *Amphibolurus,* cools about 75%

as fast as it warms (Bartholomew and Tucker, 1963), varanid lizards cool about 88% as fast as they warm (Bartholomew and Tucker, 1964), the blue-tongued skink, *Tiliqua*, 80 to 90% as fast (Bartholomew *et al.*, 1965), and the marine iguana, *Amblyrhynchus*, measured in both air and water (Fig. 13), cools only half as fast as it warms (Bartholomew and Lasiewski, 1965). Therefore, by augmenting the rate of heat gain and diminishing the rate of heat loss, heliothermic lizards can increase the amount of time they can remain active at preferred temperatures. This ability would be especially advantageous to the marine iguana, which forages in the cold sea and then must heat up rapidly upon its return to land.

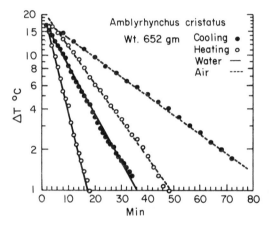

Fig. 13.   Heating and cooling rates of the marine iguana in water and in air. ΔT is the difference between T_A and T_B. Rate of air flow, 113 cm/sec. During heating, $T_A = 40°C$; during cooling, $T_A = 20°C$. (From Bartholomew and Lasiewski, 1965.)

Changes in body shape, pulmonary ventilation, water evaporation, and radiative properties were eliminated as possible factors contributing to differences in these heating and cooling rates, which left only metabolism and circulatory changes involving heat transport to be considered (Bartholomew and Tucker, 1963). Obviously, if a lizard consumes oxygen maximally during both heating and cooling, the rate of heating would be increased and the rate of cooling would be correspondingly decreased. Metabolism was not measured at all in *Amblyrhynchus* and was measured only at constant temperatures in *Amphibolurus*, *Varanus*, and *Tiliqua*, but heart rates were measured during both heating and cooling. Assuming that maximal heart rates indicate maximal metabolism and that minimal heart rates indicate minimal metabolism, these investigators estimated metabolism during heating and cooling. Both *Tiliqua* and *Varanus* metabolized maximally during both heating and cooling, but *Amphibolurus* metabolized maximally during heating but minimally during cooling.

Using available data and making certain assumptions, Bartholomew and Tucker (1963) derived a formula for thermal conductance with which a measure of the heat transfer through the body of a lizard can be obtained:

$$C = C^1 - M/(T_B - T_A)$$

Where C is thermal conductance; M, oxygen consumption; $T_B - T_A$, the difference between ambient and body temperature; and C^1, the apparent thermal conductance calculated directly from the slope of the heating or cooling curve. Thermal conductance expressed in ml O_2 (gm hr $°C)^{-1}$ is higher during heating than during cooling in both *Amphibolurus* and *Varanus* but remains constant in *Tiliqua* (Table V).

TABLE V
THERMAL CONDUCTANCE[a] CORRECTED FOR METABOLISM AT 30°C

Species	No. of animals	Mean weight (gms)	Air flow (cm/sec)	Heating	Cooling	Cooling / Heating
Amphibolurus	5	497	240	0.740	0.613	0.829
Varanus	1	1060	270	0.374	0.327	0.87
Tiliqua	2	466	146	0.37	0.37	1.0

[a] Values expressed as ml O_2 (gm hr $°C)^{-1}$. See text for references.

Metabolism, therefore, in *Amphibolurus* was calculated to contribute about 25% of the difference between the rate of heating and cooling; whereas circulatory factors contributed the remaining 75%. Endogenous heat production in varanid lizards appears to be more important than circulatory changes in controlling the rates of heating and cooling. The metabolism of *Tiliqua* apparently accounts completely for the differences observed between heating and cooling.

The thermal conductance of lizards, as would be expected, is much higher than that of mammals of comparable size. Guinea pigs have only 17% the thermal conductance of *Amphibolurus* and the pocket mouse, *Perognathus,* has the same thermal conductance as that lizard but weighs only 6% as much. Lizards are thus characterized by low metabolism and high conductance; whereas mammals are characterized by high metabolism and low conductance (Bartholomew and Tucker, 1963).

2. *Evaporative Water Loss*

Reptiles exchange heat with the environment primarily by conduction, convection, and radiation; but they also dissipate heat by the evaporation

of water from body surfaces. Such evaporative cooling appears more obligatory than thermoregulatory since it occurs at all body temperatures. Cutaneous water loss at temperatures of approximately 20°C may account
for 70% of the evaporative water loss in certain lizards (Dawson *et al.,*
1966) and more than that amount for other lizards, turtles, and crocodiles
(Bentley and Schmidt-Nielsen, 1966). Both respiratory and cutaneous water
loss increases with temperature, but water lost from the respiratory tract
increases proportionately more than that from the skin. The increase in
cutaneous water loss appears to be due primarily to the increased capacity
of warmed air to hold more water vapor; whereas the increase in respiratory
water loss with temperature is due to the concomitant increase in ventilation
as well.

Reptiles from arid regions evaporate relatively less water from the skin
and respiratory tract than do those from more moist habitats (Bogert and
Cowles, 1947; Bentley and Schmidt-Nielsen, 1966; Dawson *et al.,* 1966;
Claussen, 1967). Because animals from hot arid habitats can ill afford
loss of water, evaporative cooling should be considered as an expensive
thermoregulatory mechanism to dissipate heat and is primarily used only
during emergencies.

All reptilian groups exhibit changes associated with augmenting water
loss when they become heated. Crocodiles when hot, gape widely and thus
expose the moist mucosa to the air (Cott, 1961). Turtles froth at the
mouth when hot (Langlois, 1902; Baldwin, 1925). Horned lizards, when
maintained at elevated temperatures, produce a copious flow of clear cloacal
fluid which moistens the vent and base of the tail and possibly acts to
cool the animal (Heath, 1965). Certain cold resistant lizards and snakes
open their mouths widely, as if gasping, when body temperatures approach
lethal limits (Cowles and Bogert, 1944; Dawson, 1960; Dawson and Templeton, 1966). Perhaps, the most hightly developed response is seen in heliothermic lizards which pant, not unlike dogs. As body temperatures approach
the upper limits of tolerance, these lizards open their mouths widely and
partially extrude a vascularized tongue (Langlois, 1902; Cowles and Bogert,
1944; Curry-Lindahl, 1956; Dawson and Bartholomew, 1958; Dawson and
Templeton, 1963; Templeton, 1967). Sometimes, the tongue, lower jaw, and
gular pouch (e.g. *Dipsosaurus*) vibrate rapidly and continuously (Templeton,
1960).

The respiratory rate, which is temperature dependent in all reptiles
measured (Fig. 14), increases markedly in some lizards when the panting
threshold is reached, e.g., *Uromastix* and *Varanus* (Langlois, 1902), and
Crotaphytus (Dawson and Templeton, 1963). The panting collared lizard
generally decreases its tidal volume (Fig. 15), causing breathing to be quite
rapid and shallow yet allowing ventilation to remain constant (Templeton

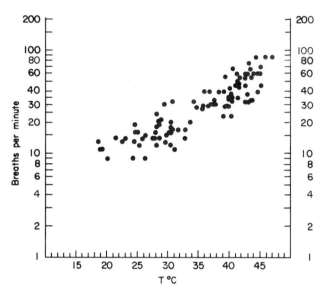

FIG. 14. Relation of breathing rate to body temperature in ten adult desert iguanas. All data shown were taken during periods preceded by at least 5 minutes of inactivity. The Q_{10} is approximately 2.5. (After Dawson and Bartholomew, 1958.)

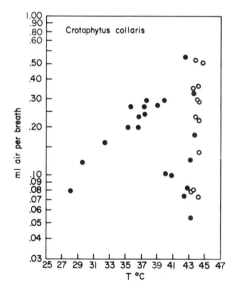

FIG. 15. Tidal volume of collared lizards in relation to temperature. Solid circles represent values at various temperatures for nonpanting animals, and open circles, values for panting individuals whose mouths were agape. Q_{10} for tidal volume between 27° and 39°C, approximately 1.7. (From Templeton and Dawson, 1963.)

and Dawson, 1963). The abdomen may be strongly compressed in the panting desert iguana (Cowles and Bogert, 1944) or it may expand and contract at the same rate as that of the thorax but at alternate times (Templeton, 1960).

3. *Evaporative Cooling and Metabolic Heat Production*

Data are too limited to assess properly the role of evaporative cooling in dissipating metabolic heat in all reptilian groups. Like most homeotherms,

TABLE VI

EVAPORATIVE COOLING IN RELATION TO METABOLISM

Temperature (°C)	Evaporative water loss (mg/gm/hr)	(a) Evaporative cooling (cal/gm/hr)	Oxygen consumption (ml/gm/hr)	(b) Heat production (cal/gm/hr)	a/b (%)
Dipsosaurus (Templeton, 1960); (Dawson and Bartholomew, 1958)					
32	0.86	0.50	0.10	0.48	104
36	1.16	0.67	0.18	0.86	78
40	2.08	1.21	0.24	1.15	105
44	3.64	2.11	0.35	1.68	126
Crotaphytus (Dawson and Templeton, 1963)					
32	0.46	0.26	0.21	1.01	26
36	0.58	0.33	0.26	1.25	26
40	0.73	0.42	0.32	1.54	27
44	4.70	2.58	0.40	1.92	134
Gerrhonotus (Dawson and Templeton, 1966)					
25	0.43	0.25	0.11	0.53	47
30	0.53	0.31	0.19	0.91	34
35	1.15	0.66	0.34	1.63	40
38	2.43	1.40	0.44	2.12	66

lizards and snakes can dissipate, at the most, a slight excess of their resting heat production. Benedict (1932) found that evaporative cooling in pythons often dissipated all heat produced by metabolism. Dawson and Templeton (1966) reported that the cold-resistant alligator lizard (Table VI), which apparently does not pant, dissipated only two-thirds of its body heat by evaporative cooling, even at temperatures near its critical thermal maximum of 39°C (Licht, 1964). Templeton (1960) measured water loss in the desert iguana, *Dipsosaurus,* and compared these results with metabolic data on this species collected by Dawson and Bartholomew (1958). Both the desert iguana and the collared lizard, *Crotaphytus* (Dawson and Templeton,

1963), while panting, can dissipate about 1.3 times the metabolic heat produced by evaporative cooling (Table VI).

4. *Thermal Effects of Evaporative Cooling*

Many authors have reported that reptiles can lower their body temperature below that of the environment by evaporative cooling (Langlois, 1902; Martin, 1903; Benedict, 1932; Lueth, 1941). Unfortunately, a lot of the data has not been measured under controlled conditions. Since reptiles readily exchange heat with all parameters of the thermal environment, the animal must be measured in a controlled temperature chamber for valid results. Templeton (1960) found the desert iguana, which possesses a highly developed panting response, to remain essentially at the temperature of the chamber while panting. Conversely, Warburg (1965a) reported that the large agamid lizard, *Amphibolurus barbatus,* and to a lesser extent the skink, *Tiliqua rugosa,* can lower its body temperature several degrees below that of the chamber. The smaller agamid, *Amphibolurus reticularis* (Warburg, 1965b), however, was like *Dipsosaurus,* being unable to lower its body temperature to any great extent by evaporative cooling.

Placing reptiles in humid air, of course, reduces or prevents evaporative cooling. Cole (1943) showed that *Sceloporus,* under a mercury-vapor lamp in humid air (relative humidity, 100%), reached lethal temperatures in 4.5 minutes, whereas a similar lizard identically heated in relatively dry air (relative humidity, 30%) reached lethal temperatures in 26 minutes. Under more carefully controlled conditions, Warburg (1965a,b) heated various species of Australian lizards in a constant temperature chamber. At high ambient temperatures, the lizards survived only a few hours; but survival time was markedly shortened when the air was humid rather than dry. Although these lizards often maintained body temperatures below high ambient temperatures in dry air, body temperatures sometimes rose to 2° to 3°C above ambient if placed in humid air. Templeton (1960) obtained similar results under similar experimental conditions, in the desert iguana. In addition, when this lizard was both wrapped in insulative batting and placed in humid air at 46°C, metabolic heat could not be adequately lost by conduction, radiation, or by evaporation of water. Body temperatures rose to lethal levels. Animals in such experimental conditions were essentially killed by their own metabolic heat.

D. RADIATION AND THERMOREGULATION

1. *Radiation within the Visible Spectrum*

Exchange of body heat by radiation is extremely important to reptiles. The ability to lighten or darken the skin gives the animal control over the reflection and absorption, respectively, of that radiation in the visible spectrum that strikes its body. However, it must be emphasized that skin color may also be important in concealing the animal from predators, but has little to do with the exchange of infrared radiation which is outside the visible spectrum.

Primitive lizards, the geckonids, iguanids, chameleonids, and xantusids, can quickly change color, but other lizards and reptiles cannot. The melanophores in the skin are apparently under both nervous and hormonal control in chameleons (Zoond and Eyre, 1934; Sand, 1935; Zoond and Bokenham, 1935) and in the horned lizard, *Phrynosoma* (Redfield, 1918; Parker, 1938), under at least hormonal control in the gecko, *Hemodactylus* (Noble and Bradley, 1933) and apparently under only hormonal control in *Anolis* (Kleinholz, 1938). Changes in the physical and excitatory states of the lizard, as well as light and temperature, can effect changes in skin color. Presumably, melanophores are directly affected by temperature without nervous or hormonal intervention (H. M. Smith, 1946). Atsatt (1939) found iguanids and geckos to be dark at low temperatures; but at a specifically higher temperature, they become light. Conversely, the night lizard, *Xantusia,* changes from light to dark as temperature increases. The specific temperature which induces the color change correlates well with the thermal properties of the lizards' habitat. Lizards from the desert require a higher critical temperature to become light than do nondesert forms. Illumination does not cause color change in these lizards if temperatures are either high or low, but may induce blanching in some forms if temperatures are moderate.

Experimentally, dark lizards absorb more heat and thereby warm faster than do light-colored forms (Cole, 1943; Bogert, 1959). Attainment of optimal body temperatures would therefore be enhanced by lizards in the dark phase; but when these temperatures are reached, the change to the light phase would reduce further absorption of heat and thereby lessen the danger of overheating (Cole, 1943). The dark phase, by expediting heat absorption when soil and air temperatures are low, as in spring or fall or at dawn or dusk, would increase the number of minutes each day that the lizard could remain abroad at activity temperatures; yet when solar radiation is maximal and ambient temperatures are high, the light phase would also extend such activity time by reducing the absorption of radiant heat (Cowles and Bogert, 1944). Unlike most iguanids, the sand lizard *Uma,* blanches only slightly with rising temperatures (Atsatt, 1939; Norris, 1958). It probably has little need for such a thermoregulatory mechanism, however, since it emerges completely from the sun-warmed desert sand in the morning only after it has reached its activity temperature (Norris, 1958). Cowles (1940) suggested that *Xantusia* is light at low temperatures and dark at high temperatures because it is primarily concerned with getting warm enough, not with getting too warm. Its nocturnal secretive habits support this premise (H. M. Smith, 1946).

Atsatt (1939) used colored guides and photography to analyze color changes. Norris (1958) measured, spectrophotometrically, the intact skin of *Uma* through the visible spectrum, and found that it matched that of the sand upon which it lives. Hutchison and Larimer (1960) measured the reflectivity of the excised skins of seventeen species of lizards from five families over a spectral range from the far ultraviolet (320 mμ) to the near infrared (1100 mμ). The average heat gained by the dorsal integument calculated from reflectivity data clearly correlated with temperature and humidity of the habitat being highest in tropical rain forest species and decreasing progressively in species from the temperate forest, plains, semidesert, and desert habitats. The species within one habitat group have similar reflectivities even though color, texture, and scale size are rather different, which indicates that the human eye would have difficulty judging reflectivity using these parameters.

The ability of certain lizards at very high altitudes to reach body temperatures 30°C above that of the air, as mentioned in Section IV, suggests that such animals might possess an unusual capacity to darken the integument. Norris (1967) studied these color relationships spectrophotometrically in those species of *Sceloporus* which live at high altitudes above 9000 ft in the mountains of Arizona and California. His data suggest that, whereas high altitude forms can become very dark, their low altitude counterparts can darken as much or even slightly more so. Norris concluded that the unique capability of these lizards to invade high altitudes lies either in behavioral traits, which allow them to use either the warm microclimates of blackish sandstone outcroppings or to be active at unusually low air and body temperatures.

2. *Radiation Outside the Visible Spectrum*

Whereas color changes play important roles in both concealment from predation and in thermoregulation, changes in reflectivity of infrared radiation play only a thermoregulatory role. Norris (1967) exemplified the relationship between the color and texture of the integument and the exchange of infrared radiation. A visibly white reptile reflects light from the visible spectrum while simultaneously it may absorb that part of the long-wave, infrared (800–1000 mμ) impinging upon it. Furthermore, surface texture seems to be the one useful indicator to the investigator. Smooth or polished surfaces such as the enamellike belly surfaces of certain desert reptiles reflect long-wave, infrared, whereas rough or matte surfaces characteristic of the dorsum tend to absorb. The belly of such a reptile would therefore tend to reflect infrared radiation coming from the hot sand upon which it stands. Although Hutchison and Larimer (1960) considered the effects of infrared radiation on thermal exchange, Norris (1967), using spectrophotometric techniques, was the first to measure the reflectivity of the reptilian integument through the infrared part of the spectrum. Interestingly, and perhaps surprisingly, Norris found that iguanid lizards weighing less than 30 gm absorb in both the ultraviolet and infrared, whereas, larger lizards and snakes reflect in the infrared. Small lizards, including juveniles of large lizards, which, because of their size, heat up quickly anyway would in addition tend to absorb infrared radiation and thereby warm even faster. Norris suggested that a small heliothermic lizard may profit by being as absorptive as possible. The small lizard would lose more heat by forced convection than a larger one. Its larger surface–mass ratio reduces thermal lag as it moves in and out of different thermal levels during activity and it could come to a thermal equlibrium within its eccritic range even while maximally absorptive. Conversely, the large lizard with a greater thermal lag would tend to heat continuously while active until rising body temperatures forced it to retreat. High reflectivity in the infrared would slow the heating process and extend the activity period a little longer.

Many diurnal reptiles as well as some fish and amphibians have the peritoneum lined with melanin. This black pigment may also occur in the skin and muscles. Bodenheimer *et al.* (1953) and Hunsaker and Johnson (1959) failed to detect the transmission of ultraviolet light through the excised skin of lizards. The latter authors suggested that the black peritoneum did not serve to absorb such harmful radiation but to regulate body temperature. Porter (1967), however, using perhaps more sensitive detecting equipment, did show that the black peritoneum of iguanid lizards kept harmful ultraviolet and visual light of short wavelength from reaching the body cavity. Diurnal lizards, such as *Cnemidophorus* and *Eumeces,* which lack the black peritoneum, possess heavy melanin desposits in the skin which totally absorb such radiation. Interestingly, the gecko, *Coleonyx* and the leaf nosed snake *Phyllorynchus,* both nocturnal forms, allow the shorter wavelengths of light to enter the body cavity. Porter concluded that the black peritoneum functions as a radiation shield rather than as a significant thermoregulatory device.

3. *Concealment and Thermoregulation*

Because color and color changes are obviously involved in both concealment and thermoregulation, the relative importance of each has been discussed at length in the literature. The mutuality or exclusiveness of the relationship is usually complex and may change with the activity cycle of the animal. The desert iguana can be used again as an example citing the observations of Norris (1967). This lizard is dark only for a brief period in the morning while basking. While it is still cold, energy absorption is predominant over color matching. During the activity period, color matching may play the predominant role. However, as desert heat becomes intense, less thermophilic forms, including predators, retreat. At this time, the lizard remains abroad shining white and conspicuous against the sand. This "superlight" coloration may allow the animal to extend its activity period in a thermal environment vacant of predators, at which time thermoregulation can play the predominant role. Other cases have been reported with seemingly support permanent predominance of concealment. Lizards such as *Uta* and *Sauromalus* dwelling in black lava beds are permanently darkened (Cowles, 1958; Norris, 1958, 1967), and a nearly white subspecies of *Sceloporus undulatus* from White Sands in New Mexico is unable to change color (Lowe and Norris, 1956). *Uta* living on light colored substrates retain color lability, whereas hatchlings living on dark lava flows are at first color labile, but after the first few weeks of life they darken permanently (Norris, 1967).

4. *Calculation of Thermal Flux*

Norris (1967) has calculated the effects of color changes on heating rates of several iguanids and of the snake, *Crotalus cerastes,* using his reflectivity data. To do this, he chose a hypothetical yet realistic environment which simplified the calculation of heat exchange. He also made certain fairly reasonable assumptions such as the shape and homogeneity of the body. His resultant calculations are interesting and correlate with the ecology of each species. For example, a quiescent desert iguana near sea level in Riverside County, with a body temperature of 36°C, is assumed to be standing on flat sand having a surface temperature of 40°C. The sky is clear, the air temperature is 30°C, and no wind is blowing. The toes are penetrated into the isothermal layer of the sand. His body is assumed to be cylindrical, 3 cm in diameter, and is homogeneous throughout. In the lightest color phase, this 62-gm lizard was calculated to gain a net energy load of 71.2 cal/min vs 92.4 cal/min in its darkest phase. This results in a temperature increase of 1.40°C/min, which is certainly an appreciable amount considering the fact that the heat load in this arbitrary environment is relatively high. If the animal should be exposed to an extremely high heat load such as when desert sands are scorching, color change would probably have a minimal effect on body temperature change, but if the animal is otherwise in thermal equilibrium with his environment, Norris suggests that color change could account for the animal's entire temperature change.

E. Parietal Eye

The reptilian parietal eye found only in certain lizards and in the tuatara, *Sphenodon,* apparently plays a role in thermoregulation. The structure and physiology of the pineal apparatus has been briefly surveyed by Stebbins and Eakin (1958). In reptiles, the "third eye" situated postorbitally on the top of the head appears specialized for light and heat reception. The yellow cornea and the lens are transparent, and the heavily pigmented retina, which is backed by a reflective guanine tapetum, possesses rodlike cells, but the "eye" lacks lids and an iris mechanism for controlling the amount of entering rays. A nerve leads from the end vesicle to the habernula apparatus in *Sphenodon* and some lizards, but is entirely lacking in others. The retina of the parietal eye of both *Sceloporus* and *Xantusia* appears to possess secretory activity (Stebbins and Eakin, 1958). These investigators either removed the parietal eye of four species of diurnal iguanid lizards or covered it with aluminum foil. The experimental animals both in the field and in captivity increased locomotor activity and daily exposure to light. They also became more restless, less viable, and were less inclined to retreat when approached. The thyroid gland also showed a higher epithelium and less colloid than those of sham operated lizards. The nocturnal lizard *Xantusia* also increased motor activity when its parietal eye was shielded (Glaser, 1958); but *Sphenodon* (only one specimen was tested) did not respond in these ways, even when its parietal eye was shielded for as long as months (Stebbins, 1958). Stebbins suggested that, in view of the low metabolism of *Sphenodon,* 2 months was perhaps not long enough for such results to be manifested. Stebbins and Eakin (1958) and Glaser (1958) concluded that the parietal eye may function as a photothermal dosimeter which acts to inhibit further activity after the lizard has been exposed to a proper amount of sunlight. By preventing metabolic excesses and insuring maintenance of energy reserves, the lizard may live a less intense but longer life.

F. Neural Control of Body Temperature

1. *Temperature Sense and Control*

The variety of temperature-dependent activities in reptiles suggests precise temperature sense and control. For example, many behavioral activities in lizards such as shuttling between sun and shade and orienting positively or negatively to the sun's rays occur at characteristic body temperatures, each having boundary limits of only a few degrees. Physiological responses such as panting and changes in coloration also occur at predictable body temperature levels. In addition, many reptiles are active at body temperatures only a few degrees below the level maximally tolerated, which in turn may be only another few degrees below the lethal level. The margin of safety is therefore small, making precise temperature sense and control almost mandatory.

2. *Application of Reptilian Thermoregulation to Thermoregulatory Models*

The industrial temperature regulators used as models by Hardy (1961) to illustrate mechanisms of thermoregulation in mammals are also applicable to such regulation in reptiles.

a. "On-off" regulators. The on–off system contains a thermostat which turns the effector (heater or cooler) on or off in an all-or-nothing fashion. The onset and duration of panting with mouth agape in both mammals (Hardy, 1961) and reptiles (Heath, 1965) exemplify this type of control. Although the duration of panting can vary under this system, the activity or magnitude of the effector cannot.

The bipartite type of on–off regulator possesses two thermostats each having different temperature settings, one acting to cool, the other to heat. It is exemplified by the behavior of reptiles shuttling between sun and shade. Entry into sunlight occurs when the body temperature falls to a particular level, and when the temperature rises to a characteristic level, the animal seeks shade. Other such coupled systems may be positive and negative solar orientation, and burrowing and emergence at high temperatures in horned lizards (Heath, 1965).

b. Proportional Controllers. The proportional control system does not have the large oscillations in temperature characteristic of the on–off regulator. The output of the effector corresponds continuously to the deviation of temperature from the controlled level. Horned lizards exposed to direct sunlight increase apparent body area with decreases in body temperature. This change in body area acts as a proportional controller. The temperature-dependent changes in albedo seen in certain lizards (see Section V, D) may also act a proportional control system (Heath, 1965). The extent of submergence of basking nile crocodiles in water may also be similarly controlled (see Section IV,A,2). Although certain iguanid lizards such as *Crotaphytus* and *Dipsosaurus* may pant fully yet intermittently suggesting on–off control, they also may increase the magnitude of panting as body temperatures rise. The mouth will at first open slightly, the development of the full panting response is gradual, and by the time the animals is panting fully, it is doing so continuously. This response suggests involvement of a proportional controller.

c. Rate Controller. This model causes the effector output to vary according to the rate of temperature change. It therefore "quickens" the response of the system as it recognizes at once the magnitude of the imposed thermal load. Heath (1965) cited the phenomenon of faster heating than cooling in lizards (see Section V,C,1) as weak evidence of such a mechanism, since the animal attempts to increase or maintain his body temperature, and presumably, vasomotor mechanisms of an anticipatory nature are involved. Possibly, the following phenomenon acts through a rate control mechanism. When *Dipsosaurus* is warmed rapidly by intense heat it begins to pant at a lower body temperature (39°–40°C) than when it is heated slowly (about 43°C). This suggests that peripheral thermoreceptors are responding to a temperature threshold, or to the rate of temperature change, or to both, which, if so, would qualify the system as a rate controller. In any case, the body temperature must reach the lower level before panting ensues, regardless of skin temperature or the change in skin temperature.

3. Thermoregulatory Sites

Rodbard *et al.* (1950) initially demonstrated the existence of a thermosensitive area in the brain of reptiles, specifically in the turtle, *Pseudemys*. When a thermode, implanted inside the midline near the midportion of the cerebrum at the level of the third ventricle, was heated, blood pressure began to rise almost immediately. Conversely, when the thermode was cooled, blood pressure dropped. Heath *et al.* (1968), using more sophisticated techniques and without damaging brain tissue, have localized this thermosensitive area specifically in the anterior hypothalamus of *Pseudemys*. Although blood pressure rises in response to elevating body temperatures (see Section V,B,9), it is not yet clear if such rises that occur when the hypothalamus is heated result from thermoregulatory responses. Furthermore, there is still no experimental evidence that the hypothalmus is involved in the physiological thermoregulation of reptiles.

However, recently, Hammel *et al.* (1967) implicated the reptilian preoptic region in behavioral thermoregulation. They implanted a pair of thermodes astraddle the brain stem near the preoptic region of the blue-tongued lizard, *Tiliqua scincoides*. Three weeks, or more, later the animals were allowed to oscillate only between a cold area (15°C) and a hot box (45°C). Normal values of colonic, skin, and brain temperature were taken. When the brain stem was subsequently heated to about 41°C, the lizard left the hot environment earlier than usual or when its colonic and skin temperatures were still lower than normal (Fig. 16). Conversely, when the animal in the hot box had its brain stem cooled, it left the hot box later than usual or after its colonic and skin temperatures had risen to above normal levels. Lizards in the cold area did not respond so predictably when brain stem temperatures were altered. When the brain stem was heated, only one animal of three tested left the cold box while skin and colonic temperatures were still below the usual values. When the brain stem was cooled, two of the three left the cold box before skin and colonic temperatures had fallen to normal exiting levels. However, colonic, or skin temperatures, or both must be at appropriate levels before any of these responses will occur and therefore not only the hypothalamus is involved. It is of interest that heating the preoptic region of one animal had no effect on heating or cooling rates which agrees with the results of Bartholomew *et al.* (1965) that any circulatory adjustments associated with changes in body temperature of *T. scincoides* (see Section V,C,1) are not of thermoregulatory significance.

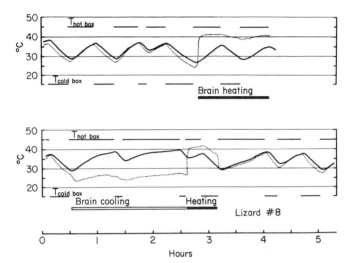

FIG. 16. Colonic (solid line) and brain stem (dashed line) temperatures of a lizard, *Tiliqua*, while it oscillated between a hot and cold environment. The brain temperature was normal except where heating or cooling of the brain with thermodes is indicated. (From Hammel *et al.*, 1967.)

Cabanac *et al.* (1967), working in the same laboratory, juxtaposed a microelectrode with the implanted thermode and thermocouple in the hypothalamus of *Tiliqua* and recorded extracellular action potentials over a temperature range of approximately 20°–36°C. When the area was heated, warm-sensitive neurons increased their spontaneous activity. Conversely, local cooling caused cold-sensitive neurons to increase spontaneous activity by firing in bursts synchronous with breathing movements. The warm neurons were about 10% as sensitive to temperature as were corresponding units previously studied in laboratory mammals, but the cold units of *Tiliqua* and of mammals seem comparable in sensitivity to temperature. These authors preferred not to conclude firmly that these neurons are involved in thermoregulation, yet they suggested that one may imagine that in *Tiliqua* exist the roots of the later-evolved physiological hypothalamic thermostat.

REFERENCES

Andersen, H. T. (1961). *Acta Physiol. Scand.* **53**, 23.
Atsatt, S. R. (1939). *Publ. Univ. Calif. Los Angeles Biol. Sci.* **1**, 237.
Baldwin, F. M. (1925). *Biol. Bull.* **48**, 432.
Bartholomew, G. A. (1966). *Copeia* p. 241.
Bartholomew, G. A., and Lasiewski, R. C. (1965). *Comp. Biochem. Physiol.* **16**, 573.
Bartholomew, G. A., and Tucker, V. A. (1963). *Physiol. Zool.* **36**, 199.
Bartholomew, G. A., and Tucker, V. A. (1964). *Physiol. Zool.* **37**, 341.
Bartholomew, G. A., Tucker, V. A., and Lee, A. K. (1965). *Copeia* p. 169.
Benedict, F. G. (1932). *Carnegie Inst. Wash. Publ.* **425**, 529.
Bentley, P. J., and Schmidt-Nielsen, K. (1966). *Science* **151**, 1547.
Bodenheimer, F. S., Halperin, A., and Swirski, E. (1953). *Bull. Res. Council Israel B2*, 436.
Bogert, C. M. (1949a). *Evolution* **3**, 195.
Bogert, C. M. (1949b). *Anales Inst. Biol. (Univ. Nacl. Mex.)* **20**, 415.
Bogert, C. M. (1953). *Zoologica* **38**, 63.
Bogert, C. M. (1959). *Sci. Am.* **200**, 105.
Bogert, C. M., and Cowles, R. B. (1947). *Am. Museum Novitates* **1358**, 1.
Boyer, D. R. (1965). *Ecology* **46**, 99.
Boyer, D. R. (1967). *Comp. Biochem. Physiol.* **20**, 437.
Brattstrom, B. H. (1963). *Ecology* **44**, 238.
Brattstrom, B. H. (1965). *Am. Midland Naturalist* **73**, 376.
Brattstrom, B. H., and Lawrence, P. (1962). *Physiol. Zool.* **35**, 148.
Brody, S. (1945). "Bioenergetics and Growth." Reinhold, New York.
Brooks, G. R., Jr., and Sassman, J. F. (1965). *Copeia* p. 251.
Bruner, H. L. (1907). *Am. J. Anat.* **7**, 1.
Bustard, H. R. (1967). *Copeia* p. 753.
Cabanac, M., Hammel T., and Hardy, J. D. (1967). *Science* **158**, 1050.
Carr, A. (1952). "Handbook of Turtles of the United States, Canada, and Baja California."
    Cornell Univ. Press, Ithaca, New York.
Claussen, D. L. (1967). *Comp. Biochem. Physiol.* **20**, 115.
Cloudsley-Thompson, J. L. (1964). *Animal Behaviour* **12**, 98.
Cloudsley-Thompson, J. L. (1965). *J. Zool.* **146**, 55.
Cole, L. C. (1943). *Ecology* **24**, 94.
Cott, H. B. (1961). *Trans. Zool. Soc. London* **29**, 211.
Cowles, R. B. (1940). *Am. Naturalist* **79**, 160.
Cowles, R. B. (1941). *Ecology* **22**, 125.
Cowles, R. B. (1946). *Copeia* p. 172.
Cowles, R. B. (1956). *Copeia* p. 211.
Cowles, R. B. (1958). *Evolution* **7**, 347.
Cowles, R. B., and Bogert, C. M. (1944). *Bull Am. Museum Nat. Hist.* **83**, 265.
Cunningham, J. D. (1966). *Herpetologica* **22**, 1.
Curry-Lindahl, K. (1956). *Soc Roy. Zool. Belg.* **87**, 45.
Dawson, W. R. (1955). *J. Mammal.* **36**, 543.
Dawson, W. R. (1960). *Physiol. Zool.* **33**, 87.
Dawson, W. R. (1967). *In* "Lizard Ecology: A Symposium" (W. W. Milstead, ed.),
    p. 230. Univ. of Missouri Press, Columbia, Missouri.

Dawson, W. R., and Bartholomew, G. A. (1956). *Physiol. Zool.* **29,** 40.

Dawson, W. R., and Bartholomew, G. A. (1958). *Physiol. Zool.* **31,** 100.

Dawson, W. R., and Poulson, T. L. (1962). *Am. Midland Naturalist* **68,** 154.

Dawson, W. R., and Templeton, J. R. (1963). *Physiol. Zool.* **36,** 219.

Dawson, W. R., and Templeton, J. R. (1966). *Ecology* **47,** 759.

Dawson, W. R., Shoemaker, V. H., and Licht, P. (1966). *Ecology* **47,** 589.

Dessauer, H. C. (1953). *Proc. Soc. Exptl. Biol. Med.* **82,** 351.

DeWitt, C. T. (1967). *Physiol Zool.* **40,** 49.

Dill, D. B., Edwards, H. T., Bock, A. V., and Talbot, J. H. (1935). *J. Cellular Comp. Physiol.* **6,** 37.

Dittmer, D. S., ed. (1961). "Blood and Other Body Fluids." Fed. Am. Soc. Exptl. Biol., Washington, D.C.

Edwards, H. T., and Dill, D. B. (1935). *J. Cellular Comp. Physiol.* **6,** 21.

Erb, J. (1965). Personal communication (see Brattstrom, 1965).

Evans, K. J. (1966). *Comp. Biochem. Physiol.* **19,** 91.

Ewer, R. F. (1950). *Am. Naturalist* **84,** 215.

Fitch, H. S. (1955). *Ecol. Monographs* **25,** 59.

Fitch, H. S. (1956a). *Univ. Kansas Publ., Museum Nat. Hist.* **8,** 213.

Fitch, H. S. (1956b). *Univ. Kansas Publ., Museum Nat. Hist.* **8,** 417.

Fitch, H. S. (1968). *Herpetologica* **24,** 35.

Foxon, G. E. H., Griffith, J., and Price, M. (1956). *Proc. Zool. Soc. London* **126,** 145.

Fry, F. E. J. (1947). *Publ. Ontario Fisheries Res. Lab.* **68,** 1–62.

Gelineo, S., and Gelineo, A. (1955). *Compt. Rend. Soc. Biol.* **149,** 387.

Glaser, R. (1958). *Science* **128,** 1577.

Grant, C. (1927). *Copeia* **164,** 69.

Greenfield, L. J., and Morrow, A. G. (1961). *J. Surg. Res.* **1,** 97.

Gunn, D. L., and Cosway, C. A. (1938). *J. Exptl. Biol.* **15,** 555.

Hammel, H. T., Caldwell, F. T., Jr., and Abrams, R. M. (1967). *Science* **156,** 1260.

Hardy, J. D. (1961). *Physiol. Rev.* **41,** 521.

Heath, J. E. (1962). *Science* **138,** 891.

Heath, J. E. (1964). *Physiol. Zool.* **37,** 273.

Heath, J. E. (1965). *Univ. Calif. (Berkeley) Publ. Zool.* **64,** 97.

Heath, J. E. (1966). *Physiol. Zool.* **39,** 30.

Heath, J. E., Gasdorf, E., and Northcutt, R. G. (1968). *Comp. Biochem. Physiol.* **26,** 509.

Herter, K. (1940). *Z. Vergleich. Physiol.* **28,** 105.

Hirth, H. F. (1962). *Copeia* p. 647.

Hudson, J. W., and Bertram, F. W. (1966). *Physiol. Zool.* **39,** 21.

Hunsaker, D., and Johnson, C. (1959). *Copeia* p. 311.

Hutchison, V. H., and Kosh, R. J. (1965). *Herpetologica* **20,** 233.

Hutchison, V. H., and Larimer, J. L. (1960). *Ecology* **41,** 199.

Hutchison, V. H., Vinegar, A., and Kosh, R. J. (1966a). *Herpetologica* **22,** 32.

Hutchison, V. H., Dowling, H. G., and Vinegar, A. (1966b). *Science* **151,** 694.

Hutton, K. E., Boyer, D. R., Williams, J. C., and Campbell, P. M. (1960). *J. Cellular Comp. Physiol.* **55,** 87.

Inger, R. F. (1959). *Ecology* **40,** 127.

Job, S. V. (1955). *Univ. Toronto Studies Biol. ser. no.* **61,** *Publ. Ontario Fisheries Res. Lab.* **73,** 39 pp.

Johansen, K. (1959). *Circulation Res.* **7,** 828.

Johnson, S. R. (1965). *Am. Midland Naturalist* **73,** 1.

Khalil, F., and Zaki, K. (1964). *Z. Vergleich. Physiol.* **48,** 663.

Kirk, R. L., and Hogben, L. (1946). *J. Exptl. Biol.* **48,** 213.

Klauber, L. M. (1939). *Bull. Zool. Soc. San Diego* **14,** 1.
Klauber, L. M. (1951). *Trans. San Diego Soc. Nat. Hist.* **11,** 141.
Kleinholz, L. H. (1938). *J. Exptl. Biol.* **15,** 474.
Kosh, R. J., and Hutchison, V. H. (1968). *Copeia* p. 244.
Krehl, L., and Soetbeer, F. (1899) *Arch. Ges. Physiol.* **77,** 611.
Langlois, J. P. (1902). *J. Physiol. Pathol. Gen.* **4,** 249.
Larson, M. W. (1961). *Herpetologica* **17,** 113.
Lee, A. K., and Badham, J. A. (1963). *Copeia* p. 387.
Lehmann, F. (1925). *Tabulae Biol. (Berlin)* **1,** 142.
Licht, P. (1964). *Comp. Biochem. Physiol.* **13,** 27.
Licht, P. (1965). *Physiol. Zool.* **38,** 129.
Licht, P., Dawson, W. R., Shoemaker, V. H., and Main, A. R. (1966a). *Copeia* p. 97
Licht, P., Dawson, W. R., and Shoemaker, V. H. (1966b). *Copeia* p. 162.
Lowe, C. H., Jr., and Norris, K. S. (1956). *Herpetologica* **12,** 125.
Lowe, C. H., Jr., and Vance, V. J. (1955). *Science* **122,** 73.
Lueth, F. X. (1941). *Copeia* p. 125.
McGinnis, S. M. (1967). *Copeia* p. 472.
McGinnis, S. M., and Brown, C. W. (1966). *Herpetologica* **22,** 189.
Mackay, R. S. (1964). *Nature* **204,** 355.
Mackay, R. S. (1968). *Copeia* p. 252.
Martin, C. J. (1903). *Phil. Trans. Roy. Soc. London* **195,** 1.
Mayhew, W. M. (1963). *Herpetologica* **18,** 217.
Moberly, W. R. (1963). *Physiol. Zool.* **36,** 152.
Moberly, W. R. (1968a). *Comp. Biochem. Physiol.* **27,** 1.
Moberly, W. R. (1968b). *Comp. Biochem. Physiol.* **27,** 21.
Morrison, P. R., Ryser, F. A., and Dawe, A. R. (1953). *Federation Proc.* **12,** Abstr. No. 325.
Mosauer, W. (1936). *Ecology* **17,** 56.
Murrish, D. E., and Vance, V. J. (1968). *Comp. Biochem. Physiol.* **27,** 329.
Noble, G. K., and Bradley, H. T. (1933). *Biol Bull.* **64,** 289.
Norris, K. S. (1953). *Ecology* **34,** 265.
Norris, K. S. (1958). *Bull. Am. Museum Nat. Hist.* **114,** 253.
Norris, K. S. (1967). *In* "Lizard Ecology: A Symposium (W. W. Milstead, ed.), p. 162.
    Univ. of Missouri Press, Columbia, Missouri.
Norris, K. S., and Kavanau, J. L. (1966). *Copeia* p. 650.
Parker, G. H. (1938). *J. Exptl. Biol.* **15,** 48.
Pearson, O. P. (1950). *Condor* **52,** 145.
Pearson, O. P. (1954). *Copeia* p. 111.
Pope, C. H. (1949). "Turtles of the United States and Canada." Alfred A. Knopf, New
    York.
Porter, W. P. (1967). *Ecol. Monographs* **37,** 273.
Potter, G. E., and Glass, H. B. (1931). *Copeia* p. 128.
Prosser, C. L., and Brown, F. A., Jr. (1961). "Comparative Animal Physiology."
    Saunders, Philadelphia, Pennsylvania.
Redfield, A. C. (1918). *J. Exptl. Zool.* **26,** 275.
Regal, P. J. (1966). *Copeia* p. 588.
Regal, P. J. (1967). *Science* **155,** 1551.
Rodbard, S., and Feldman, D. (1946). *Am. J. Physiol.* **190,** 320.
Rodbard, S., Samson, F., and Ferguson, D. (1950). *Am. J. Physiol.* **160,** 402.
Rodgers, T. L. (1953). Unpublished PhD. Thesis, University of California Microfilm
    U.C. 488, 1.
Ruibal, R. (1961). *Evolution* **15,** 98.

St. Girons, H., and St. Girons, M. C. (1956). *Vie Milieu* **7**, 133.
Sand, A. (1935). *Biol. Rev.* **10**, 361.
Schmidt-Nielsen, K., and Dawson, W. R. (1964). *In* "Handbook of Physiology" (Am. Physiol. Soc., J. Field, ed.), Sect. 4, p. 467. Williams and Wilkins, Baltimore, Maryland.
Sergeyev, A. (1939). *Compt. Rend. Acad. Sci. URSS* **22**, 49.
Sexton, O. J. (1959). *Ecol. Monographs* **29**, 112.
Smith, H. M. (1946). "Handbook of Lizards." Univ. of Cornell Press (Comstock), Ithaca, New York.
Smith, M. (1964). "Monograph of the Sea Snakes (Hydrophiidae)." Verlag J. Cramer, Weinheim.
Soulé, M. (1963). *Copeia* p. 107.
Stebbins, R. C. (1954). "Amphibians and Reptiles of Western North America." McGraw Hill, New York.
Stebbins, R. C. (1958). *Copeia* p. 183.
Stebbins, R. C., and Barwick, R. E. (1968). *Copeia* p. 541.
Stebbins, R. C., and Eakin, R. M. (1958). *Am. Museum Novitates* **1870**, 1.
Steggerda, F. R., and Essex, H. E. (1957). *Am. J. Physiol.* **190**, 320.
Strel'nikov, I. D. (1944). *Zool. J. USSR* **23**, 250.
Templeton, J. R. (1960). *Physiol. Zool.* **33**, 136.
Templeton, J. R. (1964a). *Comp. Biochem. Physiol.* **11**, 31.
Templeton, J. R. (1964b). *Physiol. Zool.* **37**, 300.
Templeton, J. R. (1967). *Copeia* p. 224.
Templeton, J. R., and Dawson, W. R. (1963). *Physiol. Zool.* **36**, 104.
Tucker, V. A. (1966). *J. Exptl. Biol.* **44**, 77.
Tucker, V. A. (1967). *In* "Lizard Ecology: A Symposium" (W. W. Milstead, ed.), p. 258. Univ. of Missouri Press, Columbia, Missouri.
Ushakov, B. P. (1964). *Physiol. Rev.* **44**, 518.
Vance, V. J. (1953). M.Sc. Thesis, University of Arizona, Tuscon, Arizona.
Warburg, M. R. (1965a). *Australian J. Zool.* **13**, 331.
Warburg, M. R. (1965b). *Australian J. Zool.* **13**, 563.
Weese, A. O. (1919). *Am. Naturalist* **53**, 33.
White, F. N. (1956). *Anat. Record* **125**, 417.
White, F. N. (1959). *Anat. Record* **135**, 129.
White, F. N. (1968). *Am. Zoologist* **8**, 211.
Wilhoft, D. C., and Anderson, J. D. (1960). *Science* **131**, 610.
Woodbury, R. A. (1941). *Am. J. Physiol.* **132**, 725.
Zeuthen, E. (1953). *Quart. Rev. Biol.* **28**, 1.
Zoond, A., and Bokenham, N. A. H. (1935). *J. Exptl. Biol.* **12**, 39.
Zoond, A., and Eyre, J. (1934). *Phil. Trans. Roy. Soc. London* **B223**, 27.

Chapter 6　**BIRDS**

William R. Dawson and Jack W. Hudson

I. Introduction

Birds have originated from a reptilian stock quite distinct from that giving rise to the mammals, and homeothermy must have developed independently in the two evolutionary lines. This may be reflected in the small but significant disparity between the general levels at which body temperature is maintained under comparable conditions in the two classes. Most of the thermoregulatory processes of birds appear at least superficially similar to those of mammals. However, representatives of the two groups differ in certain details of their mechanisms for heat and cold defense. Insufficient information is available concerning the neural mechanisms governing temperature regulation in birds to permit meaningful comparisons with mammals.

Some special considerations apply to avian temperature regulation. Physiological control of body temperature has evolved in conjunction with a nearly universal capacity for flight among birds. The commitment of most species to this mode of locomotion has had a number of consequences of thermoregulatory significance. With the exception of a few flightless forms, notably the ostrich (100–125 kg) and some of the extinct elephant birds (approximately 450 kg), adult birds weigh no more than a few kilograms, with perhaps 95% of the species falling in the range of 2–1000 gm. Such a size distribution, with all its implications concerning intensity of metabolism and insulative capacity, contrasts markedly with that for mammals, many species of which fall between 5 and 500 kg, with a few reaching immense size, e.g., the elephant on land (approximately 5×10^3 kg) and the blue whale in the sea (approximately 1.5×10^5 kg).

The requirements of flight have had a profound influence on the physiology as well as the size of birds. The large scale energetic demands characteristic of vigorous flight must have imposed stringent requirements upon the respiratory and circulatory systems from a thermolytic as well as a metabolic standpoint. The system of air sacs, constituting such a distinctive feature of the avian respiratory system, is a conspicuous manifestation of such demands. Flight must also impose aerodynamic requirements for streamlining of the plumage that may not always be congruent with insulative needs.

Avian thermoregulation is interesting not only because of the constraints and demands imposed upon most birds by flight, but also because of behavioral considerations. Although many species utilize underground burrows, cavities in trees, and elaborately structured nests during the breeding season, relatively few avail themselves of such shelter at other stages in their life history. Moreover, certain species actually increase their thermoregulatory problems by depositing their eggs in exposed situations which would be injurious without parental protection. For example, goatsuckers, such as the poor-will (*Phalaenoptilus nuttallii*) and the lesser nighthawk (*Chordeiles acutipennis*), lay their eggs on the sparsely shaded desert floor (Grinnell and Miller, 1944), and the emperor penguin (*Aptenodytes foresteri*) breeds on antarctic sea ice during the darkness of midwinter (Stonehouse, 1967). All these avian traits of behavior cause evasion of temperature extremes to play a less significant role in the lives of most birds than in those of their counterparts among small mammals.

Avian thermoregulation has been discussed from a variety of standpoints over the past 16 years (see, for example, Hutchinson, 1954; Sturkie, 1954; Hart, 1957, 1961, 1964; King and Farner, 1961, 1964; Dawson, 1962; Irving, 1962; West, 1962; Bartholomew and Cade, 1963; Dawson and Schmidt-Nielsen, 1964; Whittow, 1965a,b; Hammel, 1968; Dawson and Bartholomew, 1968). During the period since the last comprehensive review (King and Farner, 1961), a particularly large amount of information has accumulated. The present review of the temperature regulation of birds attempts to consider this process in the light of this newer material, drawing heavily on many of the papers cited above.

II. Avian Levels of Body Temperature in the Absence of Thermal Stress

It is of limited utility to specify a single, characteristic body temperature for a bird, since thermal level is strongly influenced by such factors as time of day, activity, and ambient temperature. Birds of many orders, when inactive at moderate ambient temperatures in the waking phase of their daily cycle, have body temperatures falling between 40°C and 43°C (Table I), a higher range than the 36°C to 39°C or 40°C commonly associated with higher eutherian mammals (see Eisentraut, 1961). However, species representing the orders Sphenisciformes (penguins), Struthioniformes (ostrich), Casuariiformes (emu and casuaries), Apterygiformes (kiwis), Gaviiformes (loons), Podicipediformes (grebes), and Procellariiformes (albatrosses, shearwaters, petrels, and allies) virtually all show body temperatures in this mammalian range (Table I). In addition, certain members of the orders Caprimulgiformes (goatsuckers and allies) and Apodiformes (hummingbirds and swifts) have body temperatures of less than 40°C under the conditions previously specified. McNab (1966) suggests that the relatively low body temperatures of the penguins, ratites (ostrich, emu, and casuaries), kiwis, and procellariiform birds are reflections of large size; he interprets his compilation of data on an extensive array of birds to indicate, with certain exceptions, the existence of a loose, inverse correlation

TABLE I

Body Temperatures for Birds of Various Orders[a]

Order	No. of species sampled	Range[b] (°C)
Sphenisciformes (penguins)	6	37.0–38.9
Struthioniformes (ostrich)	1	39.2
Casuariiformes (casuaries and emu)	4	38.8–39.2
Apterygiformes (kiwis)	3	37.8–39.0
Tinamiformes (tinamous)	1	40.5
Gaviiformes (loons)	1	39.0
Podicipediformes (grebes)	4	38.5–40.2
Procellariiformes (albatrosses, shearwaters, petrels, and allies)	13	37.5–41.0
Pelicaniformes (tropic birds, pelicans, frigate-birds, and allies)	9	39.0–41.3
Ciconiiformes (herons, storks, ibises, flamingos, and allies)	12	39.5–42.3
Anseriformes (screamers, swans, geese, and ducks)	28	40.1–43.0
Falconiformes (vultures, hawks, and falcons)	12	39.7–42.8
Galliformes (megapodes, curassows, pheasants, and hoatzins)	22	40.0–42.4
Gruiformes (cranes, rails, and allies)	7	40.1–41.5
Charadriiformes (shorebirds, gulls, auks, and allies)	39	38.3–42.4
Columbiformes (sand-grouse, pigeons, and doves)	5	40.0–43.3
Cuculiformes (cuckoos and plantain eaters)	2	41.9–42.3
Strigiformes (owls)	9	39.2–41.2
Caprimulgiformes (goatsuckers, oilbirds, and allies)	5	37.6–42.4
Apodiformes (swifts and hummingbirds)	25	35.6–44.6
Coraciiformes (kingfishers, motmots, rollers, bee-eaters, and hornbills)	1	40.0
Piciformes (woodpeckers, jacamars, toucans, and barbets)	10	39.0–43.0
Passeriformes (perching birds)	101	39.2–43.8

[a] See Neumann *et al.* (1968) for the species by species compilation on which this table is based.

[b] The values presented are the extremes of the means for the active phase of the daily cycles of the species sampled. Data for species on which only single determinations have been made have been excluded from this summary, although they are included in Neumann *et al.* (1968). These authors made an effort to emphasize values for which adverse thermal conditions or struggling and other vigorous forms of activity were not complicating factors. Inevitably, a few maximum values apparently do reflect activity (e.g., that for the order Passeriformes).

between body temperature and weight. However, smaller members of certain of these orders have body temperatures below 40°C, and large birds of other orders exceed this figure (see McNab, 1966; Neumann *et al.*, 1968). Whatever the explanation of the low body temperatures in the groups mentioned, it is of interest to note that the penguins, ostrich, emu, casuaries, and kiwis are flightless and that dormancy has been observed in goatsuckers, swifts, and hummingbirds (see Section IX).

Diurnal temperature cycles have been recognized in birds for many years (Chossat, 1843; S. Simpson and Galbraith, 1905). The highest levels of body temperature occur during the active phase of the bird's daily activity cycle, whether the particular species is nocturnal or diurnal [cf. data on the nocturnal kiwi (*Apteryx australis*) studied by Farner *et al.* (1956) with those for diurnal species studied by such investigators as Baldwin and Kendeigh (1932), Dawson (1954), Bartholomew and Dawson (1954a, 1958), and Bartholomew and Cade (1957)]. Studies of diurnal species under laboratory conditions, where the transition between the light and dark phases of the cycle is abrupt, illustrate the extent to which the daily

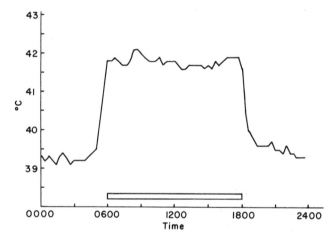

Fig. 1.   Daily cycle of body temperature in Abert's towhees (*Pipilo aberti*) maintained in an undisturbed state at an ambient temperature of 23°C. Photoperiod of 12 hours indicated by horizontal bar. Body temperatures obtained from thermocouples implanted in the pectoral musculature. The curve links mean values for twenty individuals over the course of 24 hours. Data from Dawson (1954).

temperature cycle is keyed to photoperiod (Fig. 1). An extreme example of how seasonal changes in day length influence the temperature cycle is afforded by Veghte's data (1964) (Fig. 2) on a subarctic bird, the gray jay (*Perisoreus canadensis*).

The timing of the diurnal temperature cycles of birds may depend more on endogenous factors than has previously been recognized (see Hudson and Kimzey, 1966; MacMillen and Trost, 1967b). Few experiments have thus far been conducted specifically to test this, but there is some relevant indirect information from laboratory studies of these cycles. This mainly concerns the fact that the rise in body temperature in the morning occurs well in advance of first light in at least some species. A particularly spectacular example of this anticipation, and the capacity for time measurement

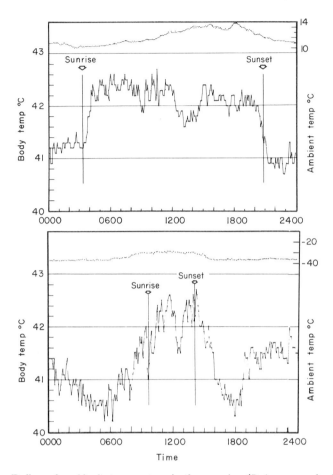

FIG. 2.   Daily cycles of body temperature in the gray jay (*Perisoreus canadensis*) during winter (one bird) and summer (two birds). The animals were maintained in outdoor cages in which the ambient temperature fell between $-30°C$ and $-40°C$ during measurements in winter (bottom) and $+10°C$ and $+15°C$ during the summer (top). These cages were located in the vicinity of Fairbanks, Alaska. Body temperatures were continuously recorded from cloacal thermocouples. Data from Veghte (1964).

which it implies, is afforded by hummingbirds, which tend to emerge from nocturnal torpor before dawn, in nature, and before the time at which the lights are turned on in laboratory experiments (Pearson, 1950; Lasiewski, 1963). It is also of interest that the daily temperature cycle of Inca doves (*Scardafella inca*) persists in complete darkness (MacMillen and Trost, 1967b). Further experimentation of the type recently being applied to study of the rhythmical aspects of activity, metabolism, and photosensitivity in birds (Menaker and Eskin, 1966, 1967; Hudson and Kimzey,

1966; Hamner, 1963, 1964) would appear warranted in connection with avian temperature cycles.

The amplitude of the diurnal cycle varies among the species on which data are available (see Table X in King and Farner, 1961, for a useful compilation), but it is rather difficult to determine whether this reflects differences in the techniques employed or the animals studied. When allowance is made for the differences in procedures used, there appears to be an inverse correlation between amplitude and body size, with the diurnal variation ranging from as much as 8°C in nontorpid hummingbirds (Lasiewski, 1964) to less than 1°C in the ostrich, *Struthio camelus* (Crawford and Schmidt-Nielsen, 1967). For most birds weighing between 30 and 300 gm, the amplitude of the daily temperature cycle is 1°–3°C.

Activity has a marked effect on the body temperatures of birds, and this has created some difficulty in temperature measurements in which handling causes the animal to become excited and to struggle. Brown and Abert's towhees (*Pipilo fuscus* and *P. aberti*) weighing 44 and 47 gm, respectively, became as much as 2°C warmer as a result of bouts of activity when laboratory temperatures approximated 23°C (Dawson, 1954). This elevation of temperature with activity has stimulated the development of techniques for measurement that greatly reduce disturbance of the subject. Indwelling thermocouples have been successfully used (see, for example, Dawson, 1954; Bartholomew and Dawson, 1954a, 1958; Veghte, 1964; Hudson and Kimzey, 1966). More recently, implanted temperature transmitters have been employed (Roy and Hart, 1966; Dawson and Fisher, 1970a).

From the data presented here on temperature cycles and the influence of activity, it is apparent that the thermoregulatory activities of birds serve mainly to restrict body temperature to a range of several degrees rather than to some precise level. Evidently the set point for regulation changes under various conditions (see Section IV). All this affords further evidence that specification of a single body temperature for a bird is of limited utility. This hinders interspecific comparisons, since differences in conditions at the time of measurement can influence the results.

III. Avian Metabolic Levels

A. Methods of Determining Energy Exchange in Birds

Both direct and indirect methods of calorimetry have been used in determining levels of energy metabolism by birds, with the vast preponderance of the data obtained by the latter. Among the indirect methods, some criticism has been expressed concerning the validity of measurements of gas exchange for computing heat production of birds (Henry *et al.,* 1934). This primarily results from uncertainty concerning the proper caloric equivalent to employ in cases where the respiratory quotient falls below 0.71, a frequent situation in normal, fasting birds (see, for example, Mellen and Hill, 1955; King, 1957; Dawson and Tordoff, 1959; Lewies and Dyer, 1969). This criticism is grossly exaggerated in the view of Benedict (1938) and King (1957). As King and Farner (1961) indicate, studies of gas exchange, i.e., respiratory metabolism, form the principal basis of short-term measurements of metabolic rate in birds.

Over the past two decades, in particular, studies of avian respiratory metabolism have been increasingly complemented by studies of energy balance. These latter involve fairly long-term measurements of the caloric content of food ingested and of the excreta. The difference in energy content between the ingested and the egested plus excreted material is equivalent to the *metabolizable energy* obtained by the bird under a particular set of conditions. Kendeigh (1949) subdivides this metabolizable energy into *existence energy,* i.e., the energy expenditure associated with (a) the maintenance of an appropriate level of metabolism for the prevailing temperature conditions; (b) procurement of food and water; and (c) with the specific dynamic action of the foodstuffs ingested, and *productive energy,* i.e., the remainder after existence energy is deducted from metabolizable energy. Although studies of this type have generally involved birds maintained at constant temperatures in confined spaces, they do afford insight concerning the energy budgets of animals, not provided by measurements of respiratory metabolism.

Some concern has been expressed recently (West and Hart, 1966) about apparent discrepancies between metabolic responses of birds to temperature in short-term tests (involving measurements of respiratory metabolism) and in long-term experiments (involving measurements of energy balance). In general, data obtained in the former describe metabolism–temperature curves displaying a zone of thermal neutrality and a relatively steep, negative slope below the lower critical temperature. Metabolism–temperature curves established in long-term experiments, on the other hand, lack a zone of thermal neutrality and have a considerably flatter negative slope than the first type (see, for example, West, 1968). These differences are significant in relation to analysis of avian responses to cold. However, they should not be taken to indicate that one method is necessarily superior to another, for both have their contributions to make to studies of avian energetics and thermoregulation. Short-term studies provide information concerning details of temperature regulation by birds in a particular state of acclimation. Long-term studies of energy balance, on the other hand, afford opportunities for assessing the capacities of these animals for acclimation and the possible extent of their food requirements under various conditions in nature (see Section V,C,3). The relative brevity of severe heat stress each day in nature makes short-term study of respiratory metabolism the method of choice for measurements at very high temperatures.

An additional means of indirect calorimetry has been developed in the past few years, and King and Farner (1961) regard it as most promising for studies of the energetics of free-living wild birds. This method has the following basis according to Lifson *et al.* (1955). The oxygen of respiratory CO_2 is in isotopic equilibrium with the oxygen of the body water (Lifson *et al.,* 1949). Therefore the hydrogen of body water is lost mainly in water, whereas the oxygen is lost in both water and in CO_2. The turnover rate for oxygen in the body water is consequently greater than that for hydrogen, and the difference between the two rates is proportional to CO_2 production. The respective turnover rates are obtainable by labeling the two components of body water with stable isotopes of hydrogen (deuterium) and oxygen (oxygen-18) and then determining the changes in the specific activities of these isotopes in blood or other samples of body water over a specified period of time. This method has been validated on rats and mice under various laboratory conditions by Lifson *et al.* (1955), McClintock and Lifson (1957a,b, 1958a,b), and Lifson and Lee (1961). Some attempts have been made to determine metabolic rates of birds using the $D_2{}^{18}O$ method. Pearson (1964) mentions administration of deuterium and oxygen-18 to tippler pigeons for which he was attempting to determine the metabolic cost of flight, but he reports no results. LeFebvre (1964) compared results obtained by this method with those from gasometric analysis in rock doves (*Columba livia*–the proper common name for this species is used in preference to "pigeon" throughout this review, unless a specific breed is mentioned) and concluded that satisfactory agreement existed. The method of determining CO_2 production by use of deuterium and oxygen-18 therefore appears feasible for use with birds. However, it has thus far been inadequately exploited. The difficulty would appear to be connected with the requirements for a mass spectrometer for the determination of isotopic activity, and for careful distillation of the fluid samples obtained.

B. Metabolism–Weight Relationships in Birds

A comprehensive analysis of the thermoregulatory process requires adequate knowledge of the levels of heat production by the species involved. Attainment of such knowledge for birds is complicated by the fact that their basal metabolic rate varies with a fractional power of body weight, as is the case for the standard metabolism of most animals. The exact value of the exponent and, indeed, the complete equation or equations

for the avian basal metabolism–weight relationship have been the subject
of considerable discussion over the past three or four decades. In 1932,
Brody and Proctor obtained the following equation for the existing data
on basal metabolic rates of birds:

$$M = 89W^{0.64} \tag{1}$$

where M is the basal metabolic rate in kcal/24 hr and W is the body
weight in kg. This expression—in which the exponent (0.64) differs from
those established for mammals (0.73–0.76) by Brody and Proctor (1932),
Kleiber (1932, 1947), Benedict (1938), and Brody (1945)—was generally
accepted until King and Farner (1961) reviewed the situation using more
rigorous criteria for acceptance of basal metabolic values, and more extensive data. They obtained the following equation for birds weighing more
than 0.1 kg:

$$M = 74.3W^{0.74} \tag{2}$$

with the dimensions the same as in Eq. (1). Equation (2) is statistically
indistinguishable from Kleiber's expression (1947) relating basal metabolism
and body weight of mammals. Although King and Farner (1961) found
Eq. (2) superior to that of Brody and Proctor (1932) in predicting the
metabolic rates of birds weighing more than 0.1 kg, they concluded that
it inadequately describes the relationship for smaller birds. They discuss
the possibility that this relationship for these latter animals may be curvilinear rather than linear on a double log grid.

Some of the difficulties in describing the metabolism–weight relation-
ship(s) of birds with a single, comprehensive equation appear to stem
from differences among avian orders in metabolic intensity. This conclusion
results from the fact that virtually all small birds ($<$0.1 kg) for which
metabolic data are available are members of the order Passeriformes,
whereas practically all of the larger species ($>$0.1 kg) are members of
the other orders. On the basis of a preliminary analysis, Dawson and
Lasiewski (see Lasiewski, 1963; Lasiewski *et al.,* 1964) suggested that passerines as a group show the same weight-regression exponent for basal
metabolism as nonpasserines, but have a higher metabolic rate per unit
of weight than comparable members of this other group. An extensive
analysis (Lasiewski and Dawson, 1967) was undertaken after adequate
data had been obtained on very small nonpasserines and large passerines
(a summary of the data used is presented in Table II). This produced
distinct equations for the two groups, as well as a composite expression:

(passerines) $M = 129W^{0.72}$ (3)

(nonpasserines) $M = 78W^{0.72}$ (4)

(all birds) $M = 86W^{0.67}$ (5)

where M is again in kcal/24 hr and W in kg. Equation (5) is statistically indistinguishable from Eq. (1), i.e., the Brody-Proctor (1932) equation, and a corresponding expression for birds generally of King and Farner (1961). The three composite expressions are in a sense artifacts resulting from a failure to recognize inherent differences in metabolic level among representatives of different avian orders. Equation (4) for nonpasserines is also a composite expression, and Lasiewski and Dawson (1967) anticipated that further interordinal differences would be detected in this group. Support for this view has recently been provided by Zar's more detailed analysis (1968a) of the data assembled by Lasiewski and Dawson (see Table II) and by Ligon's finding (1968) that the basal metabolic rates of owls tend to fall significantly below those of other nonpasserines on which data are available.*

The lines described by Eqs. (3) and (4) fit truly basal values for the smallest representatives of the groups to which they pertain. There is no indication of an asymptotic relationship between basal metabolic rate and body weight at the lower limit of size in homeotherms, as suggested by Pearson's studies (1947, 1950) of shrews and hummingbirds. These widely cited investigations deal with small animals that were of necessity not in a truly basal condition (see Lasiewski, 1963; Morrison *et al.*, 1959), unlike the larger animals with which they have been compared.

IV. Control of Thermoregulatory Functions in Birds

Birds have not been subjected adequately to the types of study which have recently given insight concerning the location and nature of the mechanisms controlling thermoregulation in mammals, and thermoregulatory behavior in reptiles (see Benzinger *et al.*, 1963; Hammel *et al.*, 1963a,b, 1967; Jackson and Hammel, 1963; Andersson *et al.*, 1964; Hammel, 1965, 1968; Cabanac *et al.*, 1967). Consequently, knowledge of mechanisms controlling avian thermoregulation is exceedingly limited.

In the limited information thus far available, indications exist that the thermal set point for various activities can change. Domestic chicks (*Gallus gallus*) begin to pant at lower body temperatures than usual following hypothermia (Randall, 1943a).

---

* Equations (1)–(5) were obtained using the method of least squares with logarithmically transformed data. Zar (1968b, 1969) has criticized this procedure and proposed the use of a least squares iterative fit to the untransformed data in its place. With this latter method, he finds that the exponent for the passerine equation falls significantly below that for the nonpasserine one which approximates Eq. (4). This finding is invalidated by the fact that the heteroscedasticity of the data on metabolic rates of passerines necessitates the use of logarithmic transformation (Lasiewski and Dawson, 1969).

TABLE II
BASAL METABOLIC RATES OF BIRDS[a]

Order and species	Weight (kg)	BMR (kcal/24 hr)	Reference
Struthioniformes			
Struthio camelus	100	2350	Crawford and Schmidt-Nielsen (1967)
Casuariiformes			
Casuarius bennetti	17.6	516	Benedict and Fox (1927)
Pelecaniformes			
Pelecanus occidentalis	3.51	264	Benedict and Fox (1927)
Pelecanus conspicillatus	5.09	374	Benedict and Fox (1927)
Ciconiiformes			
Botaurus lentiginosus	0.60	56	Benedict and Fox (1927)
Guara alba	0.94	85	Benedict and Fox (1927)
Ardea herodias	1.87	128	Benedict and Fox (1927)
Mycteria americana	2.5	201	Kahl (1962)
Phoenicopterus antiquorum	3.04	215	Benedict and Fox (1927)
Jabiru mycteria	5.47	272	Benedict and Fox (1927)
Leptoptilos javanicus	5.71	307	Benedict and Fox (1927)
Anseriformes			
Aix sponsa	0.485	65	Herzog (1930)
Branta bernicla			
Summer	1.130	108.5	Irving *et al.* (1955)
Winter	1.168	93.4	Irving *et al.* (1955)
Domestic duck	1.87	157	Giaja and Males (1928)
Chauna chavaria	2.62	142	Benedict and Fox (1927)
Domestic goose	3.3	219	Giaja (1931)
Domestic goose	5.0	280	Benedict and Lee (1937)
Domestic goose	5.89	271	Herzog (1930)
Cygnus buccinator	8.88	418	Benedict and Fox (1927)
Falconiformes			
Falco tinnunculus	0.108	17.0	Giaja and Males (1928)
Geranoaëtus melanoleucus	2.86	106	Benedict and Fox (1927)
Aquila chrysaëtos	3.0	102	Giaja and Males (1928)
Gypaëtus barbatus	5.07	228	Benedict and Fox (1927)
Vultur gryphus	10.32	351	Benedict and Fox (1927)
Galliformes			
Excalfactoria chinensis	0.0427	6.0	Lasiewski and Dawson (1967)
Coturnix coturnix	0.097	23	Giaja and Males (1928)
Lophortyx californicus	0.1371	16.0	Hudson and Brush (1964)
Colinus virginianus	0.194	23.0	Lasiewski and Dawson (1967)
Domestic fowl	2.0	97.5	Benedict (1938)
Domestic fowl ♀ ♀	2.00	137	Barott and Pringle (1941)
Domestic fowl ♀ ♀	2.00	115	Dukes (1937)
Domestic fowl	2.006	130.7	Herzog (1930)
Domestic fowl ♀ ♀	2.430	164.2	Barott and Pringle (1946)
Domestic fowl ♀ ♀	2.71	124	Winchester (1940)
Penelope purpurescens	2.04	112	Benedict and Fox (1927)
Grax alberti	2.80	136	Benedict and Fox (1927)
Domestic turkey	3.7	184	Giaja (1931)

TABLE II (*Continued*)

Order and species	Weight (kg)	BMR (kcal/24 hr)	Reference
Gruiformes			
Grus canadensis	3.89	168	Benedict and Fox (1927)
Anthropoides paradisea	4.03	220	Benedict and Fox (1927)
Charadriiformes			
Catharcta skua	0.97	98	Benedict and Fox (1927)
Gabianus pacificus	1.21	127	Benedict and Fox (1927)
Larus hyperboreus	1.60	304	Scholander *et al.* (1950c)
Columbiformes			
Scardafella inca	0.0405	5.2	Macmillen and Trost (1967a)
Zenaidura macroura	0.0914	13.4	Hudson and Brush (1964)
Zenaidura macroura	0.123	15.2	Riddle *et al.* (1932)
Columba palumbus	0.150	17.0	Benedict (1938)
Streptopelia decaocto	0.152	21.8	Giaja and Males (1928)
Streptopelia decaocto	0.155	18.3	Gelineo (1955)
Rock dove	0.266	33.7	Gelineo (1955)
Rock dove	0.300	30	Benedict (1938)
Rock dove	0.311	32.9	Burckard *et al.* (1933)
Rock dove	0.372	35.5	Herzog (1930)
Strigiformes			
Micrathene whitneyi	0.0377	6.7	Ligon (1968)
Aegolius acadicus	0.1059	16.2	Collins (1963)
Aegolius acadicus	0.0855	14.5	Graber (1962)
Asio otus	0.252	19.7	Graber (1962)
Asio flammeus	0.406	26.6	Graber (1962)
Strix aluco	0.520	43	Herzog (1930)
Bubo virginianus	1.450	108	Benedict and Fox (1927)
Caprimulgiformes			
Phalaenoptilus nuttallii	0.040	3.7	Bartholomew *et al.* (1962)
Nyctidromus albicollis	0.0430	7.7	Scholander *et al.* (1950c)
Chordeiles minor	0.075	9.5	Lasiewski and Dawson (1964)
Apodiformes			
Stellula calliope	0.0030	1.4	Lasiewski (1963)
Calypte costae	0.0032	1.1	Lasiewski (1963)
Archilochus colubris	0.0032	1.6	Lasiewski (1963)
Archilochus alexandri	0.0033	1.3	Lasiewski (1963)
Selasphorus sasin	0.0037	1.6	Lasiewski (1963)
Selasphorus rufus	0.0038	1.5	Lasiewski (1963)
Calypte anna	0.0048	2.2	Lasiewski (1963)
Eugenes fulgens	0.0066	2.4	Lasiewski and Lasiewski (1967)
Lampornis clemenciae	0.0079	2.6	Lasiewski and Lasiewski (1967)
Passeriformes			
Estrilda troglodytes	0.0061	2.8	Lasiewski *et al.* (1964); Cade *et al.* (1965)
Uraeginthus bengalis	0.0081	2.8	Lasiewski *et al.* (1964)
Troglodytes aedon	0.0090	5.3	Kendeigh (1939)
Vidua paradisea	0.0105	4.0	Terroine and Trautmann (1927)
Carduelis flammea	0.0112	5.8	J. Steen (1958)
Taeniopygia castanotis	0.0117	5.0	Cade *et al.* (1965)
Taeniopygia castanotis	0.0117	4.5	Calder (1964)

TABLE II *(Continued)*

Order and species	Weight (kg)	BMR (kcal/24 hr)	Reference
Pipra mentalis	0.012	6.5	Scholander *et al.* (1950c)
Carduelis spinus	0.013	5.8	Gelineo (1955)
Carduelis cannabina	0.0155	7.3	Gelineo (1955)
Spizella arborea	0.0166	6.8	Lasiewski and Dawson (1967)
Junco hyemalis	0.0180	6.1	Lasiewski and Dawson (1967)
Parus major	0.0185	8.4	J. Steen (1958)
Melospiza melodia	0.0186	7.8	Lasiewski and Dawson (1967)
Emberiza hortulana	0.022	8.7	Wallgren (1954)
Passer montanus	0.022	8.5	J. Steen (1958)
Zonotrichia albicollis	0.0225	7.1	Hudson and Kimzey (1964)
Zonotrichia albicollis	0.0236	9.5	Lasiewski and Dawson (1967)
Passer domesticus			
Winter	0.0224	9.5	Fonberg (1932)
Spring	0.0235	11.0	Fonberg (1932)
Passer domesticus	0.0237	10.1	Quiring and Bade (1943)
Passer domesticus	0.0250	6.9	Miller (1939)
Passer domesticus	0.0255	6.9	Hudson and Kimzey (1964)
Passer domesticus	0.0260	9.4	Gelineo (1955)
Passer domesticus	0.0260	7.0	Kendeigh (1944)
Passer domesticus	0.0273	8.5	J. Steen (1958)
Chloris chloris	0.0245	11.1	Gelineo (1955)
Chloris chloris	0.0311	11.2	J. Steen (1958)
Fringilla montifringilla	0.0248	9.5	J. Steen (1958)
Emberiza citrinella	0.0264	9.4	Wallgren (1954)
Zonotrichia leucophrys	0.0286	8.0	King (1964)
Loxia curvirostra	0.0294	10.5	Dawson and Tordoff (1964)
Loxia leucoptera	0.0298	9.6	Dawson and Tordoff (1964)
Passerella iliaca	0.0317	11.3	Lasiewski and Dawson (1967)
Molothrus ater	0.0337	11.0	Lasiewski and Dawson (1967)
Richmondena cardinalis	0.040	12.2	Dawson (1958)
Plectrophenax nivalis	0.0418	11.4	Scholander *et al.* (1950c)
Pipilo fuscus	0.0437	13.7	Dawson (1954)
Pipilo aberti	0.0468	15.0	Dawson (1954)
Hesperiphona vespertina	0.058	16.7	Dawson and Tordoff (1959)
Perisoreus canadensis	0.0645	20	Scholander *et al.* (1950c)
Perisoreus canadensis	0.0712	14.3	Veghte (1964)
Cyanocitta cristata	0.0808	17.6	Misch (1960)
Corvus caurinus			
Summer	0.282	73.2	Irving *et al.* (1955)
Winter	0.306	96.7	Irving *et al.* (1955)
Corvus cryptoleucus	0.640	79.0	Lasiewski and Dawson (1967)
Corvus corax	0.850	92	Scholander *et al.* (1950c)
Corvus corax	0.866	94.9	Lasiewski and Dawson (1967)

[a] This table based on Tables 1 and 2 in Lasiewski and Dawson (1967).

Much of the information on control of avian temperature regulation concerns the extent of the contributions of central and peripheral components. Rogers and Lackey (1923) showed that the destruction of the optic thalamus in rock doves prevented augmentation of heat production when the birds were exposed to cold. Their findings were supplemented by Rogers' observation (1928) that direct cooling of the thalamus induced shivering and a rise of body temperature. Randall's experiments (1943b) in which a cooling tube was placed in the lower bowel of seven-day-old domestic chicks afforded further evidence that central changes in temperature can influence thermogenesis. This treatment induced shivering in these young birds. Despite the fact that this activity commenced before any perceptible change occurred in skin temperature, it appears that peripheral cooling can also produce increased heat production. Randall (1943b) was also able to induce shivering in domestic chicks exposed to a cool environment, before any change occurred in deep body temperature (assuming that the deep body temperature measured was representative of brain temperature).

Observations on the control of physical thermoregulation by birds have thus far dealt largely with panting. Destruction of the thalamus (Rogers and Lackey, 1923) or an area of the midbrain between the optic lobes (Sinha, 1959) abolished panting in the rock dove, just as the production of bilateral lesions in the hypothalamus prevented this activity and normal behavioral responses to heat in the domestic fowl (Feldman *et al.*, 1957). Von Saalfeld (1936) could produce panting in the rock dove by warming the anterodorsal wall of the midbrain. Conversely, his experimental cooling of this region prevented such activity even though the deep body temperature had exceeded the threshold for panting. Åkerman *et al.* (1960) were able to elicit panting by electrical stimulation of the anterior hypothalamus and the preoptic area.

Randall (1943b) has asserted that birds will not pant when their skin is heated, unless a concomitant increase in the temperature of the central thermoregulatory areas occurs. This contrasts with the situation in mammals such as the ram (Waites, 1962) in which peripheral heating alone is sufficient. Randall's assertion has been questioned by Whittow (1965a) because of possible deficiencies in the experiments on which it was based; these experiments employed seven-day-old domestic chicks around whose necks cold water was circulated via a collar, while the surface of the body was heated. Significantly, Howell and Bartholomew (1962a) have reported that young red-tailed tropic birds (*Phaëton rubicauda*) and red-footed boobies (*Sula sula*) commence panting before any detectable elevation of deep body temperature occurs. While there is some disagreement on the role of peripheral heating in the initiation of panting, this thermolytic activity can be terminated by cooling the skin in the domestic chick (Randall and Hiestand, 1939; Randall, 1943a).

Efforts have been made to determine the role of the vagus nerves in both chemical and physical thermoregulation. Bilaterally vagotomized rock doves failed to increase their heat production despite decreased body temperatures (Fazio, 1943; Cascio, 1948). This treatment reduced the panting rate of these birds slightly, but did not abolish it (von Saalfeld, 1936; Sinha, 1959). On the other hand, bilateral vagotomy abolished panting in the domestic fowl (Hiestand and Randall, 1942; Richards, 1969). The basis of this interspecific difference has not been ascertained.

V. Thermoregulatory Responses of Birds to Cold

A. GENERAL CONSIDERATIONS

As noted in the general introduction to this review, most birds are relatively small animals that do not avail themselves of the thermal protection afforded by cavities, burrows, or other shelter, to the extent characteristic of their mammalian counterparts. This probably poses no major difficulties for the majority of species breeding in regions having severe winters because of a more spectacular evasion of cold achieved through large-scale migratory movements. However, species resident in such areas must face challenging problems of existence during winter. Since most regions having severe winters are at high latitudes, these problems are intensified in diurnal birds—which comprise the majority of species—by the shortness of winter days. Restriction of activity to the few daylight hours curtails the period available for foraging at a season when food supplies are likely to be most limited and imposes a very long period of nocturnal fasting. It is of interest in this connection that Seibert (1949) found migratory juncos (*Junco hyemalis*) and white-throated sparrows (*Zonotrichia albicollis*) unable to assimilate sufficient food for their needs at 0°C when maintained on a 10-hour photoperiod approximating that prevailing in their breeding ranges during winter. They were able to do so on a 15-hour photoperiod. Significantly, cardueline finches, which are conspicuously successful in boreal regions (Dawson and Tordoff, 1959, 1964), have unusually large crops and related structures affording extensive capacities for food storage (Butsch, 1957; Fisher and Dater, 1961).

B. MECHANISMS OF HEAT CONSERVATION

1. *Curtailment of Evaporative Heat Loss*

Considerable attention has been devoted to analyzing the role of evaporative cooling in the operation of birds in hot environments. However, the ability of these animals to curtail this activity in cool environments has not received sufficient emphasis, particularly in view of Jackson and Schmidt-Nielsen's demonstration (1964) of the role of countercurrent heat exchange in restricting respiratory water loss in rodents. In most birds, chemical regulation commences at ambient temperatures well above freezing. Since the elevation of heat production associated with declining ambient temperatures requires increased oxygen consumption, it might be assumed a priori that ventilation of the respiratory tract would increase. This and the likelihood that cool air will have a low moisture content should accelerate the rate of evaporative water loss. In actual fact, available data (Kendeigh, 1944; Lasiewski and Dawson, 1964; Lasiewski *et al.*,

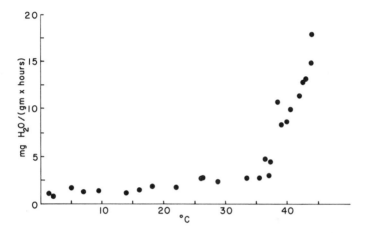

FIG. 3. The relation of evaporative water loss to ambient temperature in postabsorptive common nighthawks (*Chordeiles minor*) resting in the dark. Data from Lasiewski and Dawson (1964).

1966b; Crawford and Schmidt-Nielsen, 1967; Bartholomew and Trost, 1970) indicate that evaporative water loss remains constant or decreases slightly at temperatures below thermal neutrality (Fig. 3).

The decrease of evaporative water loss with falling ambient temperature has the obvious advantage of curtailing evaporative heat loss in cool environments. However, the mechanism by which it is achieved remains to be elucidated. Two explanations that are not mutually exclusive might account for the opposite trends in evaporative water loss and oxygen consumption below thermal neutrality.

1. Air is expired at lower temperatures and therefore with a lower vapor pressure for saturation in the cold. Information concerning temperatures at which air is expired from the avian respiratory tract has only recently been obtained by Schmidt-Nielsen *et al.* (1969b). They find a countercurrent

arrangement analogous to that in rodents (Jackson and Schmidt-Nielsen, 1964), which does indeed result in some cooling and consequent restriction of the moisture-carrying capacity of the air as it is exhaled.

2. Oxygen in the inspired air is utilized to a sufficiently greater extent in cold than in warm environments so that an increased ventilation rate is rendered unnecessary and a reduced ventilation rate is possible despite an increased rate of oxygen consumption. This might work in conjunction with a moderate lowering of the temperature of the expired air. A greater withdrawal of oxygen from each volume of inspired air might well be achieved by a reallocation of the parallel flow of air through the lungs and the air sacs which comprise such a conspicuous and incompletely understood feature of the avian respiratory system (see Salt, 1964; Calder and Schmidt-Nielsen, 1966). Such an arrangement would in effect produce a greater ventilation of the respiratory surfaces without requiring an increase in the ventilation rate of the respiratory system as a whole.

2. *Adjustment of Insulation*

In the model homeotherm discussed by Scholander *et al.* (1950b), heat loss is maintained at the basal level of heat production by a progressive increase of insulation as ambient temperature is lowered through the zone of thermal neutrality. As the lower limit of this zone is reached (the lower critical temperature), insulation reaches a maximum and there is a shift to "chemical regulation," in which thermal balance is maintained despite a further lowering of ambient temperature by augmentation of heat production to the level of heat loss. This model, in which there is an abrupt transition between physical and chemical thermoregulation, adequately describes the situation in some birds (Bartholomew *et al.*, 1962; Hudson and Kimzey, 1966), but not in others (see, for example, Dawson, 1958; Dawson and Tordoff, 1959, 1964; West, 1962; King, 1964; Lasiewski and Dawson, 1964). In these latter animals, the form of the curves relating standard metabolism and ambient temperature (see Fig. 4) indicates a gradual transition over a range of several degrees between physical and chemical regulation, rather than the abrupt change called for in the model. Chemical regulation is considered in more detail in Section V,C. Physical regulation comprises vasomotor, ptilomotor, and behavioral adjustments, and these are discussed in the ensuing paragraphs.

a. Vasomotor and Other Circulatory Adjustments. Little information is available directly concerning the nature and extent of vasomotor adjustments to cold in birds. However, observation of skin temperatures beneath the plumage generally exceeding 30°C and, in a significant proportion of cases, 35°C in cold environments (Kallir, 1930; W. O. Wilson *et al.*,

1952; Bartholomew and Dawson, 1954a; Irving and Krog, 1955; J. Steen and Enger, 1957; Dawson and Tordoff, 1959), suggests that such adjustments are not of major significance at the surfaces covered by feathers. They are, however, of considerable importance in reducing heat loss from the unfeathered surfaces of the legs and feet and, possibly, the bill, by minimizing the thermal difference between the exposed surfaces of these structures and the environment at low ambient temperatures.

Vascular arrangements serving to minimize heat loss in the limbs of aquatic birds must be of considerable importance, owing to the great cooling

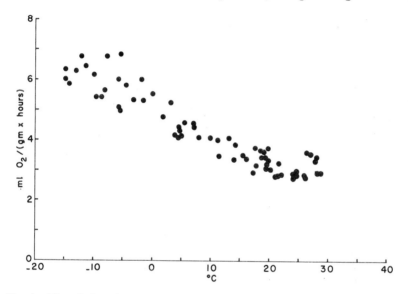

FIG. 4.   The relation of oxygen consumption to ambient temperature in postabsorptive red crossbills (*Loxia curvirostra*) resting at night. Data from Dawson and Tordoff (1964).

power of water. Kallir (1930) noted that the temperature of the feet of *Gallinula chloropus* fell considerably when they were immersed in cold water. In contrast, the temperature of the surfaces covered by feathers fell only slightly over the long period in which the feet were immersed. In the glaucous-winged gull (*Larus glaucescens*), a rapid decline in tissue temperature occurs distally along the tibia, under a thick covering of feathers. This suggests some arrangements for heat exchange that result in the blood flowing into the unfeathered portions of these limbs being quite cool (Irving and Krog, 1955). At an ambient temperature of −16°C, parts of the webbing of the feet of this gull were allowed to cool to near 0°C. Less than 10% of the heat produced by gulls and herons at low ambient temperatures is lost through the legs, according to I. Steen and Steen

(1965). However, all of the heat produced at 35°C may be dissipated through these appendages, if they are immersed in water at this temperature. I. Steen and Steen (1965) found heat loss from the legs to water to exceed that to air by a factor of three to four at all temperatures tested. The rate of heat loss from these appendages was modified within seconds after temperature conditions were altered.

Heat conservation appears to be enhanced in a number of birds by the presence of special vascular arrangements facilitating countercurrent exchange of heat in the legs. Tarsal arteriovenous retia have been noted in wading birds such as cranes, herons, and flamingos, and in some long-legged terrestrial species such as kiwis and ratites (Hyrtl, 1863, 1864). Penguins have brachial arterial retia in the axilla suggestive of a system for heat exchange with the veins, which are fewer in number (Scholander, 1955). Ducks, geese, swans, and gulls lack arteriovenous retia (Hyrtl, 1863), but all may effect some heat exchange in the limbs judging by Irving and Krog's observations (1955) on the glaucous-winged gull.

b. Adjustment of the Plumage. Feathers afford very effective insulation for their weight, and birds resident in northern climates tend to have relatively heavier plumages than their migratory counterparts (Turček, 1966; see also Irving, 1960). The legs and feet of a number of the former group (e.g., ptarmigan, *Lagopus* spp., and various owls) are feathered, whereas the incidence of such protection is considerably lower among representatives of the latter. Penguins from cold regions are better feathered on the head than are those from tropical climates (Stonehouse, 1967). It is of interest that passerines and some small birds of other orders inhabiting cold regions have naked tarsometatarsi and feet.

Birds have an impressive ability to alter the attitude of the contour, or body, feathers, which is nicely shown by illustrations in the papers by Wallgren (1954), Hutchinson (1954), J. Steen (1958), and Veghte and Herreid (1965). Unfortunately, the specific effects of ptilomotor activity on insulation have scarcely been quantified in wild birds. Difficulties in arranging the feathers in a natural manner have prevented the use of hot-plate techniques (Scholander *et al.,* 1950a). Studies of warming or cooling rates of dead animals (Misch, 1960; Prozesky, 1963; Plain and Plain, 1964; Herreid and Kessel, 1967) afford estimates of insulation for only a single arrangement of the plumage and involve unnatural thermal gradients within the body. Probine and Wodzicki's measurement (1955) of the thermal resistance of gannet (*Sula bassana*) feathers by mounting skins of this bird on copper models containing heating elements represents an elaborate attempt to determine insulation, but it, too, affords values pertaining to but a single arrangement of the plumage. Radiometry appears to be a promising technique for use with living birds during exposure to various thermal conditions (see Veghte and Herreid, 1965).

Despite difficulties in assessing the insulative contributions of feathers under physiological conditions, it has been possible to estimate the extent of their importance by comparison of normal and defeathered individuals. Brush (1965) found that defeathered California quail (*Lophortyx californicus*) produced heat 2.4 times as rapidly at 20°C as did normal birds under similar conditions. Dead blue jays (*Cyanocitta cristata*) were found to warm twice as rapidly without their feathers as with them (Misch, 1960). Similarly, freshly killed birds of a variety of species cooled from 1.7 to 3 times more rapidly with the feathers removed than when intact (Herreid and Kessel, 1967).

c. Overall Insulation of Birds. It is possible to determine fairly precisely the overall abilities of birds to curtail nonevaporative losses of heat, despite difficulties in separating the individual contributions of ptilomotor and vasomotor activities, and postural adjustments of the type described in Section V,B,3. Heat loss has been measured directly in the domestic fowl by calorimetry (see Whittow, 1965a,b). However, determinations of capacities for conserving heat are generally based on indirect estimates of thermal conductance (C), or its reciprocal, the insulation index (I). Values for these can be obtained in several ways (see, for example, Veghte and Herreid, 1965; West and Hart, 1966; Lasiewski *et al.*, 1967). They are usually calculated from simultaneous measurements of body temperature (T_B), ambient temperature (T_A), and metabolic rate (M), the relations being

$$C = M(T_B - T_A)^{-1} \tag{6}$$
$$I = (T_B - T_A)M^{-1} \tag{7}$$

These equations neglect correction for evaporative heat loss, unlike the equation provided in Table III, but they still allow a reasonable assessment of the extent to which birds can enhance their conservation of heat in moderate to cool environments over levels seen at higher ambient temperatures. It is apparent from the insulation indices summarized by West (1962) and those presented by West and Hart (1966) and from values for thermal conductance listed in Table III of this review that a variety of birds can increase their overall insulation by a factor of two to at least four (i.e., reduce their thermal conductance to a half or a quarter, or less) during acute exposure to moderate or cool ambient temperatures. This capacity attests to the efficacy of the various types of adjustments considered in Section V,B,2.

Herreid and Kessel (1967) and Lasiewski *et al.* (1967) have obtained equations for the relationship of thermal conductance to body weight in

TABLE III

THERMAL CONDUCTANCES AT VARIOUS TEMPERATURES

Species	Thermal conductance[a] (kcal m⁻² hr⁻¹ °C⁻¹) at ambient temperature (°C)													
	20	20–22	23	25	25–27	28.3	30–31	32.5	35	36–37	40	44–45	48.6	52.8
Ostrich (*Struthio camelus*)[b]	2.9										6.9			
Rock dove (*Columba livia*)[c]		1.8			1.9		2.6			3.7		4.2		
Roadrunner (*Geococcyx californianus*)[d]		1.7			1.8		2.3			3.8		3.8		
Spotted nightjar (*Eurostopodus guttatus*)[e]			1.7			3.3					4.0		4.5	4.9
Common nighthawk (*Chordeiles minor*)[f]	1.8			1.8			2.3		3.3		4.8	6.0		
Yellow bunting (*Emberiza citrinella*)[g]	1.8			2.1			1.9	2.7						
Ortolan bunting (*Emberiza hortulana*)[g]	2.2			2.4			2.1	2.6	4.5					
Gouldian finch (*Poephila gouldiae*)[h]				2.6			3.3		5.3		8.8			

[a] Thermal conductance $= \dfrac{\text{heat production} - \text{evaporative heat loss}}{(\text{surface area})(\text{body temp.} - \text{ambient temp.})}$.

[b] Crawford and Schmidt-Nielsen (1967); body weight of ostrich, 100 kg.
[c] Calder and Schmidt-Nielsen (1966); body weight of rock dove, 315 gm.
[d] Calder and Schmidt-Nielsen (1967); body weight of roadrunner, 285 gm.
[e] Dawson and Fisher (1969); body weight of spotted nightjar, 86 gm.
[f] Lasiewski and Dawson (1964); body weight of common nighthawk, 75 gm.
[g] Wallgren (1954); body weights for yellow and ortolan buntings, 26 and 22 gm, respectively.
[h] Dawson and Tordoff (1970); body weight for Gouldian finch, 13 gm.

birds. The weight regression exponents reported by these authors are similar. However, only the equation of Lasiewski *et al.* (1967), which is based on data for a larger number of species, is presented here, since it deals specifically with minimal values for living birds. This equation is

$$C = 0.848W^{-0.508} \qquad (8)$$

where C is thermal conductance expressed as cm^3 O_2 (gm hr °C)$^{-1}$ and W is body weight in gm. The relatively rapid decline in thermal conductance, i.e., the relatively rapid rise in overall insulation per gm with increasing body weight indicated by Eq. (8), is of particular interest in view of the fact that the weight regression coefficient for metabolic rate/unit of weight approximates only -0.3 on the basis of the various equations referred to in Section III,B. The steeper slope of the conductance–weight curve results in a progressive downward extension of the zone of thermal neutrality with increasing size. However, even the highly cold resistant white-tailed ptarmigan (*Lagopus leucurus*) and the black brant (*Branta nigricans*), weighing approximately 400 and 1100 gm, respectively, show lower critical temperatures exceeding 0°C by several degrees (Irving *et al.*, 1955; Johnson, 1968). Smaller birds, which comprise the vast majority of species, must commence augmenting their heat production under standard conditions at much higher ambient temperatures (see Scholander *et al.*, 1950b; Dawson, 1958; Dawson and Tordoff, 1959, 1964; West, 1962; Lasiewski, 1963; Lasiewski *et al.*, 1964, 1967; Calder, 1964; King, 1964; Kendeigh, 1969). The influence of size on heat exchange of birds is apparent in the application of techniques of thermal modeling to animal systems presented by Birkebak *et al.* (1966).

3. *Behavioral Mechanisms for Heat Conservation*

Birds may reduce their thermoregulatory tasks in cold environments by postural adjustments tending to minimize heat loss, by huddling, and by movement into the most favorable microclimates available. Quantitative information on the result of these activities is, unfortunately, largely unavailable. However, it still seems desirable to consider them briefly.

The most conspicuous postural adjustments that appear thermally significant involve protection of the head and the legs and feet. Penguins from cold climates may sleep with the neck fully retracted and/or the head buried beneath the axilla (Stonehouse, 1967). Veghte and Herreid's radiometric measurements (1965) indicate that the head and bill are indeed sites of rapid heat loss. In chickadees (*Parus atricapillus*) and gray jays, birds weighing approximately 12 and 70 gm, respectively, these sites comprise a relatively high percentage of the total body surface, and they are protected in individuals resting in cold environments by tucking the head beneath the feathers on the back. Some indication of the effectiveness of this adjustment is indicated by Deighton and Hutchinson's observation (1940) that domestic fowl can reduce heat loss by about 12% through tucking the head under a wing. In ptarmigan (*Lagopus leucurus*) and ravens (*Corvus corax*), animals weighing several hundred grams, the bill and the head represent a considerably smaller percentage of the surface than in the chickadee and gray jay, and they do not appear to be protected by any similar postural adjustment (Veghte and Herreid, 1965).

Birds evidently can reduce heat loss through the unfeathered surfaces and the legs and feet by bringing the ventral surface of the body down on them and enclosing them within the ventral portion of the plumage. Domestic fowl were able to reduce heat production by a third through adoption of this "sitting" posture (Deighton and Hutchinson, 1940). It allowed the mourning dove (*Zenaidura macroura*) to maintain its tarso-metatarsi about 5°C warmer than when these segments of the legs were unprotected in a cool (ca. 4°C) environment (Bartholomew and Dawson, 1954a). Obviously, postural adjustments of this type are possible only for birds at rest. Their unavailability to active and, particularly, flying birds may be compensated for by the higher levels of heat production. However, such compensation is complicated by the increased thermal conductance evident during exercise (see Sections V,C and VII).

Some birds are known to reduce heat loss in cool environments by huddling. Such behavior is characteristic of altricial nestlings and of young precocial birds even outside the nest (see, for example, Lehmann, 1941; Bartholomew and Dawson, 1952). Kleiber and Winchester (1933) found that young domestic chicks can reduce their metabolic rates by as much as 15% while huddling. Huddling does not appear so widespread among adult birds. However, gentoo penguins (*Pygoscelis papua*) are reported to congregate on the beaches of South Georgia Island at night, huddling in large numbers (Murphy, 1936). Tree creepers (*Certhia brachydactyla*) gather into tight groups of ten to twenty individuals on cold nights, according to Löhrl (1955). Presumably all of these birds can survive with lower metabolic rates when together than they can singly in the cold.

As noted previously, birds evidently make less use of shelter in cold climates than do their mammalian counterparts (see Irving, 1960). However, many evidently do benefit significantly from occupation of protected situations (see Moore, 1945, for a useful discussion of the thermal characteristics of roosts). Evidence concerning this is fragmentary, and quantitative data are virtually lacking, a situation that is doubtless a reflection of the fact that such occupation occurs mainly at night. According to Irving (1960), willow ptarmigan (*Lagopus lagopus*) make temporary burrows in the snow that run a foot or so beneath the surface and extend 18–24 in. horizontally.

These structures housing the birds overnight have been found in various parts of Alaska, Yukon Territory, and Newfoundland (Wetmore, 1945; Irving, 1960). They must afford somewhat more moderate temperatures than those prevailing on the surface of the snow during winter nights and protection from wind chill and radiational losses of heat to the night sky. Other grouse (e.g., the ruffed grouse, *Bonasa umbellus*) also make use of temporary burrows in the snow (Edminster, 1947). While snow can afford thermal protection to various species, it can also cover food. Therefore, it is of interest that redpolls in Alaska will actually descend into tunnels and crevices in the snow to reach food (Cade, 1953).

Forms of shelter other than snow burrows afford thermal protection to birds (Kendeigh, 1934; Swaine, 1945). Various owls and woodpeckers may occupy cavities in trees during the inactive phase of their daily cycle. The protection from cold thus obtained may well be a by-product of behavior which is mainly significant in protecting these birds from other animals; some species residing in quite equable climates also roost in cavities. Small birds may also roost in cavities, either natural or man-made (Dunsheath and Doncaster, 1941; Kendeigh, 1961). Chickadees (*Parus* spp.) and house sparrows (*Passer domesticus*) utilize nest boxes or holes in trees during cold weather, and the house sparrows and other urban pests such as starlings (*Sturnus vulgaris*) and rock doves undoubtedly obtain considerable protection from winter conditions by use of favorable microclimates about buildings. A considerable portion of the birds living in the Peruvian Andes appear to utilize protected situations for nocturnal roosts and in certain cases for nesting—winter nights are well below freezing and the summers are cool with considerable precipitation in the form of hail, cold rain, and snow. Pearson (1953) found hummingbirds (*Oreotrochilus estella*), a horned owl (*Bubo virginianus*), sparrow hawks (*Falco sparverius*), streaked spinetails (*Leptasthenura andicola*), ground tyrants (*Agriornis montana* and several species of *Muscisaxicola*), a Bolivian goose (*Chloephaga melanoptera*), and a gray-headed finch (*Phrygilus grayi*) in caves or tunnels. He also noted flickers (*Colaptes*), miners (*Geositta*), creepers (*Upucerthia*), cinclodes (*Cinclodes*), cliff swallows (*Petrochelidon*), and ground finches (*Sicalis*) using small holes or crevices. While this behavior may in some cases be related to avoidance of predators, it obviously brings these montane species into more equable temperatures than they would encounter in more exposed situations. In connection with a discussion of species living at high elevations, it is also of interest to note that hummingbirds on Mount Orizaba in Mexico feed at altitudes up to 14,500 ft, but retreat in cloudy weather or at night to lower elevations (Swan, 1952). Details of the nocturnal behavior of birds during cold weather are badly needed. The exact situations in which most species pass the night are unknown and microclimatic information is inadequate to indicate the extent of the thermal protection afforded by these situations.

Most considerations of the effects of solar radiation on avian temperature regulation have been concerned with problems created by heat from this source for individuals in hot environments. However, some attention has recently been given to the potential impact of solar radiation on the heat economies of birds in cool surroundings. Morton (1966) showed that white-crowned sparrows (*Zonotrichia leucophrys*) exposed to radiant heat consumed less food at low ambient temperatures than when not so exposed. The metabolic cost of thermoregulation at an ambient temperature of 10°C was reduced in zebra finches (*Taeniopygia castanotis*) by use of artificial radiation (Hamilton and Hepner, 1967). A similar effect has been demonstrated in cowbirds (*Molothrus ater*), artificial radiation reducing the lower critical temperature by as much as 10°C (Lustick, 1969). In both the zebra finches and cowbirds, the effect was greater in darker colored individuals. The sunbathing observed in various species in nature (see Hauser, 1957) evidently can have a distinctly beneficial effect in cool surroundings.

4. *Long-Term Adjustments of Mechanisms for Heat Conservation*

It is difficult to make a general statement concerning the role of seasonal or experimentally induced "insulative" acclimation in the adjustment of birds to cold. This form of acclimation, which involves vasomotor responses and/or modification of the plumage, does not appear to be significant in northwest crows (*Corvus caurinus*) and black brants, judging from the similarity of metabolism–temperature curves obtained during summer and winter (Irving *et al.*, 1955). A similar situation prevails in house sparrows, starlings, rock doves, and evening grosbeaks (*Hesperiphona vespertina*), judging by metabolic data obtained by Kendeigh (1949), E. A. Davis (1955), and Hart (1962). However, rather fragmentary information suggests that seasonal acclimation of mechanisms for heat conservation does occur in some other species. The metabolism–temperature curves of the yellow bunting (*Emberiza citrinella*) and cardinal (*Richmondena cardinalis*) change from summer to winter in a manner suggestive of the existence of better insulation at the latter season (Wallgren, 1954; Dawson, 1958). Recently, West and Hart (1966) have reported a study of the evening grosbeak, which compares the results of short-term measurements of metabolism at various ambient temperatures with those of long-term measurements, the latter affording time in which the birds could acclimate to the particular thermal conditions under which they were being tested. The difference in results obtained with the two types of measurements suggests that the birds in the long-term tests employed some form of insulative acclimation involving a change in the insulation afforded by the plumage and/or vasomotor responses. This situation contrasts with that noted in short-term metabolic studies of the evening grosbeak by Hart (1962). His data do not indicate the occurrence of any changes in insulation between summer and winter.

C. Mechanisms for Augmenting Heat Production

1. *Muscular vs Nonshivering Thermogenesis*

Both mechanoelectrical and electrophysiological techniques have been employed in attempts to quantify shivering activity in birds. Odum (1941, 1942) was able to record muscle tremors of both nestling and adult birds, using a piezoelectric device. This allowed him to determine the relative intensity of these tremors at various temperatures and to demonstrate that the intensity of shivering can fluctuate over short periods in a cyclical manner. More recent analyses of muscular thermogenesis in birds have depended on registration of electromyograms (EMG's). J. Steen and Enger (1957) recorded EMG's from the pectoral muscles of rock doves and noted an inverse relation between electrical activity and ambient temperature between $+20°C$ and $-24°C$. Hart (1962) provided a more quantitative documentation of this relation over a temperature range extending from $+30°C$ to $-15°C$. West (1965) has extended Hart's technique to the evening grosbeak, common redpoll (*Acanthis flammea*), common grackle (*Quiscalus quiscala*), and the common crow (*Corvus brachyrhynchos*). In both studies (Hart, 1962; West, 1965), intensity of shivering was measured in terms of the average peak-to-peak voltage of the EMG's obtained from electrodes well spaced in the pectoral musculature. Although use of a concentric bipolar electrode and of electronic integration of the EMG's might have given more accurate results, the observations on the rock dove and the four other species are highly informative. Some shivering is evident in even the largest of these, the 350-gm rock dove and the 400-gm common crow, at ambient temperatures as high as 30°C. This temperature is well within the range in which it is commonly assumed that most birds rely exclusively on physical thermoregulation. These electromyographic observations lend further support to the view that the thermal ranges for physical and chemical thermoregulation in birds broadly overlap (see Section V,B,2). Electrical activity associated with shivering appears to increase linearly with decreasing ambient temperatures below 30°C in the evening grosbeak, redpoll, grackle, and crow (West, 1965). In the rock dove, on the other hand, the relation of this activity to temperature appears to be slightly curvilinear (Hart, 1962).

The pronounced thermal dependence of shivering in the five species studied by Hart and West suggests that muscular thermogenesis is the major means of chemical thermoregulation. It does not appear to be supplemented by nonshivering thermogenesis in adult birds, judging by West's observation (1965) that shivering, as measured electromyographically, is linearly related to oxygen consumption. Presumably, the relation between shivering and metabolism would be markedly nonlinear over the range in which chemical thermoregulation is necessary, if the birds employed nonshivering thermogenesis comparable with that described in a variety of mammals (Sellers *et al.,* 1954; Cottle and Carlson, 1956; T. R. A. Davis, 1961; Jánský and Hájek, 1961; Heroux, 1962; Pohl and Hart, 1965). With nonshivering thermogenesis, metabolism would increase, without an increase in shivering, up to some critical level beyond which shivering would increase sharply. Hart (1962) has attempted to examine the question of whether or not adult birds possess a capacity for nonshivering thermogenesis in a more direct manner, by testing the metabolic responses of curarized rock doves to cold and the calorigenic hormone norepinephrine, during winter. The absence of any responses suggests, insofar as the method is valid, that cold-acclimatized rock doves lack nonshivering thermogenesis. This finding contrasts with Kayser's observation (1929) that cold produced a marked elevation of metabolic rate in rock doves prevented from shivering by cervical transection.

   The apparent absence of nonshivering thermogenesis in adult birds contrasts with the situation in young domestic fowl. Propranolol, a β-adrenergic blocking agent, drastically interfered with the thermoregulatory capacities of five-day-old chicks in cool (10°C) environments (Wekstein and Zolman, 1968). This suggests that release of β-activating catecholamines with sympathetic activation during cold stress is involved in the temperature regulation of these birds. The thermoregulatory function of these catecholamines would relate to the control of nonshivering thermogenesis. Wekstein and Zolman (1968) found that five-day-old chicks also underwent some reduction in their capacities for temperature regulation at an ambient temperature of 10°C, when treated with ganglionic blocking agents. However, the agents employed (hexamethonium and mecamylamine) were not as effective as propranolol. This may indicate differences in the effectiveness of blockade at the respective ganglionic and postganglionic sites of action of these drugs. The exact nature of the thermogenic stimulant for the chick has not been identified, but it appears not to be norepinephrine (Freeman, 1967).

   Extensive data persuaded Scholander *et al.* (1950b) that quiescent homeotherms under cold stress can maintain their metabolic rate at a value no higher than three or four times the basal level. A specific example of this is provided by postabsorptive house sparrows. Exposure of these birds to —40°C resulted in a rate 3.3 times the basal level. Evidence cited previously indicates that this augmentation of metabolism must reflect intensive shivering. With this degree of effort, the house sparrows could remain homeothermic for only about 6 hours (Kendeigh, 1944). It is difficult to evaluate Hart's measurements (1962) of maximum rates in relation to basal metabolism, for his experimental animals were studied during the day when metabolism was relatively high, and truly basal rates could not be obtained. The maximal rates he reports for winter-acclimated evening grosbeaks, house sparrows, and rock doves under cold stress exceed the basal values obtained from Lasiewski and Dawson (1967) by factors of 5.6, approximately 9, and 6.6, respectively. These factors surpass the limits defined above, but it is reasonable to ask whether or not it is meaningful to assess metabolic capacity with values drawn from different portions of the daily cycle. Comparison of maximal values in the cold with corresponding minimal values obtained during the day (Hart, 1962) yields factors between 2.8 and 4.7 for winter-acclimated passerines (evening grosbeak, starling, and house sparrow) and 4.8 for winter-acclimated rock doves. The available evidence (J. Steen and Enger, 1957; Hart, 1962; West, 1965) again indicates that the augmentation of heat production was accomplished primarily through shivering. In view of all this information, it appears desirable to provide a slightly modified assessment of avian capacities for augmenting metabolism under acute cold stress: quiescent, postabsorptive birds can, by shivering, maintain metabolic rates in the cold at levels approximating three to five times the minimal level achieved at higher temperatures in the same portion of their daily cycle. This statement has implications beyond evaluation of performance in metabolism chambers. Of more biological importance is the relevance of these capacities to thermoregulatory problems during the inactive phase of the daily cycle and during cold, inclement weather when feeding and movements are restricted.

2. *Contributions of Specific Dynamic Action and Activity to Maintenance of Thermal Balance*

Any attempt to assess the special energetic cost of thermoregulation in the cold is immediately complicated by the contributions of specific dynamic action (SDA) and activity to avian heat production, for heat derived from them might well substitute for that produced in shivering under standard conditions. Heat resulting from the SDA of various foodstuffs, particularly protein, does indeed appear to reduce the need for shivering, and King and Farner (1961) have pointed out the ecological implications of this in relation to the winter food supply of animals and their survival in cold weather. The extent to which the heat derived from activity can substitute for shivering is more difficult to determine, if for no other reason than the paucity of metabolic data on birds in flight. The relatively few experiments on diurnal and nocturnal metabolism of birds suggest that a diurnal metabolic rhythm exists at all temperatures. Dontcheff and Kayser (1934) demonstrated that the diurnal metabolism–temperature curve for the rock dove paralleled, at a higher level, the nocturnal curve. Similarly, metabolic rates of evening grosbeaks resting in the dark at moderate to low ambient temperatures during the day (Hart, 1962) exceeded by a consistent amount the corresponding rates of these birds at night (Dawson and Tordoff, 1959), a relationship subsequently confirmed by West and Hart (1966). Additional indications of metabolic rhythms in birds are afforded by the observations of J. Steen (1958), Hudson and Kimzey (1964), MacMillen and Trost (1967a), Pohl (1969), and Lewies and Dryer (1969). The extra heat production associated with moderate (nonflight) activity and various intrinsic factors tending to elevate metabolic rate during the daytime is evidently offset by a rise in thermal conductance, which prevents any significant reduction in the level of shivering thermogenesis. This situation, which has been analyzed from an insulative standpoint by West and Hart (1966), appears to parallel that described in exercising rodents and rabbits (Hart and Heroux, 1955; Jánský, 1959).

While the low levels of activity possible in metabolic chambers do not provide a basis for significantly reducing shivering, it appears probable that the vigorous activity associated with flight must do so to some extent (see Section VII). Analysis of this presents some challenging technical problems, but recent advances in techniques for studying flight metabolism (Tucker, 1966, 1968) provide some hope of overcoming them.

3. *Metabolic Acclimation to Cold*

Metabolic acclimation to cold (as contrasted with insulative acclimation; see Section V,B,5) occurs in birds, but the exact pattern seems to some extent dependent on the species and on whether the stress is encountered in nature, where fluctuations in temperature and a regular change in photoperiod are the rule, or under experimental conditions, where these physical parameters have generally been held constant. In nature the process of compensation can involve enhancement of capacities for maintaining energy balance and heat production in the cold, and, in certain instances, shifts in overall metabolic level.

a. Seasonal Effects. While results may have been complicated by acclimation in the laboratory, it is evident that house sparrows can maintain energy balance at ambient temperatures as low as $-30°C$ in winter, whereas they fail to do so below $0°C$ in experiments conducted during summer (cf. Kendeigh, 1949; E. A. Davis, 1955). However, tree sparrows (*Spizella arborea*), which are also resident in areas having cold winters, do not seasonally alter their capacities for maintaining energy balance at low ambient temperatures (West, 1960).

Winter-acclimated evening grosbeaks and house sparrows have greater abilities to maintain high metabolic rates under severe cold stress than have their summer counterparts (Hart, 1962). At —65°C to —68°C, evening grosbeaks of the former type (weight, 62 gm) maintained levels of oxygen consumption approximating 800 ml/hr for at least 30 minutes, whereas summer birds (body weight, 58 gm) failed to maintain even somewhat lower levels over this period. The same type of results were obtained for seasonal populations of house sparrows tested for approximately 70 minutes at —39°C to —41°C. West's electromyographic and metabolic analysis (1965) of responses to cold by the evening grosbeak and other passerines suggests that enhancement of metabolic capacity in the cold does not depend on the appearance of nonshivering thermogenesis. The increased resistance to cold apparent in winter-acclimated starlings and rock doves led Hart (1962) to surmise that enhancement of metabolic capacity also occurs in these birds during the colder part of the year, although he was unable to demonstrate it directly. Again, such improvement would not appear to involve nonshivering thermogenesis (Hart, 1962; West, 1965).

Certain birds can undergo seasonal modification of their metabolic rates at various temperatures, and this could indicate a general shift in metabolism. Dontcheff and Kayser (1934) noted seasonal fluctuations in basal metabolic rates of rock doves maintained outdoors throughout the year, but, as Scholander *et al.* (1950c) point out, these fluctuations only amount to ±5%, and they might well be associated with factors other than temperature. Miller (1939) found a pronounced annual metabolic cycle in house sparrows near Iowa City, Iowa. In tests conducted at 28°C [within the zone of thermal neutrality in the nocturnal measurements performed by Hudson and Kimzey (1966) on various populations of house sparrows], birds consumed oxygen at nearly twice the rate per gram of body weight during December, when metabolism was highest, as in April, when it was lowest. Histological observations indicated conspicuously higher thyroid activity in sparrows sampled during the colder part of the year. A. C. Wilson and Farner's histological evidence (1960) indicates the existence of a similar thyroid cycle in the Gambel's white-crowned sparrow (*Zonotrichia leucophrys gambelii*) in eastern Washington. This was interpreted as a response to environmental temperature on the basis of three lines of evidence: (1) thyroid activity was correlated with the mean temperature of the preceding half-month in eastern Washington; (2) the thyroid of white-crowned sparrows from the population under consideration was stimulated by cold under laboratory conditions; (3) populations of the same subspecies that do not encounter a pronounced annual cycle of environmental temperature fail to exhibit a pronounced cycle of thyroid activity (Oakeson and Lilley, 1960). Unlike the house sparrow and white-crowned sparrow from eastern Washington, the majority of passerine birds on which relevant information is available do not augment thyroid activity in cold weather (see the tabulation in A. C. Wilson and Farner, 1960). Perhaps this indicates a wide dependence on insulative acclimation.

Seasonal elevation of metabolic rate has been noted in some other species in addition to those already cited. The basal metabolic rate of a northwest crow was about 20% higher in winter than in summer, during maintenance outdoors at Anchorage, Alaska. A similar but seasonally reversed change was noted in the black brant under the same conditions (Irving *et al.,* 1955). All these findings contrast with the stability of basal metabolic rate in such birds as the yellow bunting, *Emberiza citrinella* (Wallgren, 1954), cardinal (Dawson, 1958), and gray jay (Veghte, 1964). It is difficult to interpret the special significance of an increase in basal metabolic level during winter, in view of the decline evident in the black brant at this season and the stability noted in other species. This emphasizes the existence of alternative pathways among birds for adjustment to winter conditions.

b. Experimental Effects. Experimental exposure of birds to cold routinely produces an elevation in overall metabolic level within 1 to 4 weeks according to Gelineo's studies (1934a,b, 1955). Indeed, Miller (1939) found such an elevation in house sparrows following exposure to $-8°C$ to $-2°C$ for 4 days. The increase in metabolic rate with experimental exposure to cold is apparent below as well as within the zone of thermal neutrality, but its extent can be most conveniently assessed by comparison of basal values for individual birds following adjustment to low ($-14°C$ to $+10°C$), intermediate ($12°C$ to $22°C$), and high ($29°$ to $32°C$) ambient temperatures (Gelineo, 1964). Rates for birds acclimated to low temperatures averaged 38% higher than those adjusted to high temperatures. Comparison of basal values for intermediate and high temperatures revealed nearly as great (32%) a difference. The most spectacular example of compensation among the nine species on which data are summarized by Gelineo (1964) is afforded by the 13-gm siskin [*Chrysomitris (Carduelis) spinus*] which had a basal metabolic rate fully 85% higher when acclimated to $-2°C$ to $+8°C$ than when adjusted to $29°C$ to $32°C$. Increased thermogenic capacity and improved cold resistance are evident in birds experimentally acclimated to low ambient temperatures. The process of acclimation in the laboratory can also produce a modest decline ($<5°C$) in the lower critical temperature (lower boundary of the zone of thermal neutrality), as a result of increased metabolism. More importantly, it typically involves a reduction in insulation, according to Hart (1957). This evidently results from improved peripheral circulation and consequent improved peripheral heating, judging by results for mammals. Such a pattern would afford protection from cold injury in exposed tissues, but it is energetically expensive.

Intensification of heat production during experimental acclimation of adult birds to cold does not appear to involve adrenergic substances, judging by Hart (1962) and Chaffee *et al.*'s demonstrations (1963) of the insensitivity of thermogenesis to noradrenaline in winter-acclimated rock doves and cold-acclimated domestic fowl, respectively. Miller (1939) found that exposure of house sparrows to near-freezing temperatures for 4 days or 2 weeks produced histological indications of increased thyroid activity. Prolonged cold stress (1°C for 7 weeks) resulted in significant enlargement of the heart and kidney in birds of this species (Chaffee *et al.*, 1963). Such stress produced similar results in white-crowned sparrows, which additionally underwent enlargement of the liver (Chaffee *et al.*, 1963). The pectoral muscles in both types of sparrows appeared thicker and darker than those of their respective controls, which had been maintained at moderate ambient temperatures. A subsequent study of the house sparrow (Chaffee *et al.*, 1965) failed to confirm the difference in pectoral mass, but a higher concentration of myoglobin, which would account for the darker color of the muscle, was demonstrated in cold-acclimated individuals. This higher concentration should enhance the capacities of this muscle for remaining aerobic during intensive shivering. It is of interest that cold-acclimated house and white-crowned sparrows, unlike cold-acclimated small mammals, do not show any significant elevation of liver succinoxidase and liver microsomal pyridine nucleotide–cytochrome c reductases (Chaffee *et al.*, 1963). If, despite evidence previously cited, nonshivering thermogenesis occurs in adult birds, it must, in view of these enzymatic observations, have a chemical basis differing from that in mammals.

D. Body Temperatures of Birds in Cold Environments

Reduced availability of food in combination with cold and inclement weather may occasionally jeopardize thermoregulation of birds (Rowan, 1925; McGowan, 1969) or evoke changes involving dormancy (see Section IX). However, winter conditions generally do not produce any pronounced effect on avian body temperature, although J. Steen (1958) noted moderate hypothermia in several small Norwegian passerines that were maintained at fairly low (0° to −10°C) ambient temperatures overnight, and Palmgren (1944) recorded values between 34.6°C and 39.8°C for three Siberian tits (*Parus cinctus*) immediately after they were shot on cold days in

Finland. Udvardy (1955) has questioned the accuracy of Palmgren's measurements, in view of the rapidity of post mortem cooling in small birds
at low ambient temperatures. However, he also occasionally observed low
body temperatures in live parids exposed to low ambient temperatures.
Resting birds of six species were not significantly cooled by prolonged exposure to temperatures as low as −22°C during winter in Anchorage,
Alaska; values obtained for body temperature and the amplitudes of the
daily temperature cycles in these animals were similar to those noted in
various birds observed in more moderate environments (Irving, 1955).
Palmgren's daytime values (1944) for various small Finnish birds during
winter average well in excess of 40°C, except in the case of the Siberian
tit cited previously. Effective temperature regulation proceeds under even
very rigorous conditions. Veghte (1964) found that daytime levels of body
temperature in the gray jay remained essentially unchanged between January, when ambient temperatures lay between −30°C and −40°C, and
July, when they approximated 10°C to 15°C. The minimal body temperatures of gray jays are a few tenths of a degree lower at night during
January than in July (see Fig. 2). However, this appears more related
to the fact that a much longer nocturnal period is available in which
body temperature can decline in winter at Fairbanks, Alaska, than to seasonal difference in ambient temperature.

VI. Thermoregulatory Responses of Birds to Heat

A. General Considerations

As noted in the introduction to this review, most birds face potentially
challenging problems of existence in hot climates, owing to their diurnal
habits and failure to utilize shelter of the type afforded by underground
burrows. These behavioral characteristics reduce opportunities for evasion
of intense heat and force the animals into an extensive reliance on evaporative cooling. Water is often in short supply in the hottest regions of the
earth. Consequently, this reliance on evaporative cooling may create problems relating to maintenance of water balance. This situation has recently
been examined in detail (Dawson and Bartholomew, 1968) and will not
be extensively discussed here. However, its importance to the ensuing consideration of thermoregulation by birds in the heat should be kept in mind.

B. Thermoregulatory Mechanisms

1. *Physiological Factors Influencing Heat Transfer*

Modification of rates of heat transfer can play an important role in
the adjustments of birds to hot environments. Even at 40°C, at least a

fifth of the calories resulting from metabolism are lost by nonevaporative routes in most species (Dawson and Bartholomew, 1968). Losses of this extent are fostered by the moderate hyperthermia that typically develops at high ambient temperatures (see Section VI,D) and increased thermal conductance. A number of activities are known to contribute to the latter: compressing the contour plumage (Dawson, 1954); holding the wings away from the body so that the thinly feathered sides are exposed (Dawson, 1954; Hutchinson, 1954; Bartholomew, 1966; Bartholomew *et al.*, 1968); increasing blood flow to the limbs and feet (Bartholomew and Dawson, 1954a, 1958; Howell and Bartholomew, 1961; I. Steen and Steen, 1965); and, in certain cases, increasing the blood flow to combs or wattles (Yeates *et al.*, 1941). The individual contributions of such activities to heat dissipation largely remain to be quantified. Collectively they can have a significant effect (Table III).

In situations where birds are exposed to intense solar radiation and/or air temperatures exceeding body temperature, it would appear advantageous to reduce thermal conductance as a means of restricting caloric gain from the environment. Such reductions play a significant role in the adjustment of antelope jackrabbits (*Lepus alleni*) to heat (T. Dawson and Schmidt-Nielsen, 1966). However, in the few birds for which detailed information is available, thermal conductance either continues to increase or only falls slightly from maximum levels as ambient temperature exceeds body temperature (Table III). Perhaps the vigorous movements associated with rapid evaporative cooling contribute to this by moving air among the feathers. Some birds evidently can protect themselves from intense solar radiation by ptilomotor activity. For example, the ostrich erects its feathers commencing at 25°C, thereby increasing their thickness from 3 to about 10 cm (Crawford and Schmidt-Nielsen, 1967). Such an action is usually involved in the responses of homeotherms to cold. In this instance, it can serve to retard input of heat from the environment. This response must be very important for a large bird like the ostrich, which should have difficulty obtaining shelter from the sun in nature. Analogous responses have been found in various marine birds. For example, adult masked boobies (*Sula dactylatra*) and sooty terns (*Sterna fuscata*), when exposed to the sun on their tropical nesting grounds, elevate the scapular feathers so that they extend conspicuously above the normal contour of the back. This shades the dorsal integument while permitting movement of relatively cool air (27°–30°C) among the feathers (Howell and Bartholomew, 1962b; Bartholomew, 1966).

2. Evaporative Cooling

Evaporative water loss (EWL) of birds has received considerable attention in recent years (Bartholomew and Dawson, 1953; Dawson, 1958;

Bartholomew *et al.,* 1962; Calder, 1964; Lasiewski, 1964; Lasiewski and Dawson, 1964; Salt, 1964; Cade *et al.,* 1965; Lasiewski *et al.,* 1966a,b, 1967; Calder and Schmidt-Nielsen, 1966, 1967, 1968; Crawford and Schmidt-Nielsen, 1967; Crawford and Lasiewski, 1968). The papers by Lasiewski *et al.* (1966a,b) provide a rigorous treatment of the problems involved in the measurement of this function.

a. Evaporative Water Loss at Moderate Ambient Temperatures. As a prelude to consideration of the evaporative capacities of birds in hot environments, it is useful to review briefly information on the EWL of these animals at moderate (ca. 25°C) ambient temperatures. When expressed on a weight-specific basis, the rates of EWL at such temperatures vary inversely with body weight (Bartholomew and Dawson, 1953). This relation has recently received detailed examination by Crawford and Lasiewski (1968), using data for resting animals ranging in size from hummingbirds to ostriches. The following equations were obtained:

(birds generally) $E = 0.432 W^{0.585}$ (9)

(nonpasserines) $E = 0.351 W^{0.613}$ (10)

where E is EWL in gm/day and W is weight in gm. The fractional exponents (0.585, 0.613) indicate a stronger dependence of weight-specific EWL on body weight than that evident in metabolism–weight relationships [Eqs. (1)–(5)]. Equations (9) and (10) provide convenient yardsticks with which to compare results for individual species in connection with considerations of water economy. Some values predicted for birds of various weights are presented in Table IV.

Crawford and Lasiewski (1968) also provide an equation for the weight dependence of EWL in passerines resting at moderate ambient temperatures:

$$E = 1.563 W^{0.217}$$ (11)

(units as in preceding equations). The data on which this is based span a weight range amounting to only slightly more than one log cycle and are probably not all for animals at a standard level of metabolism. For these reasons, it appears best to reserve judgement as to the functional significance of the conspicuous difference evident between Eqs. (10) and (11).

As the result of the availability of studies in which EWL and metabolic rate of birds have been determined simultaneously, it is possible to express the meaning of the general levels of EWL specified by the preceding equations in terms of their role in heat dissipation at moderate ambient temperatures. It is apparent from the examples presented in Table V that evaporation accounts for between $\frac{1}{3}$ and $\frac{1}{10}$ of the heat loss occurring in most birds resting in environments between 20°C and 30°C. It is somewhat more important than this in the ostrich, the largest contemporary bird. This animal operates at body temperatures somewhat below those characterizing birds in general (Bligh and Hartley, 1965; Crawford and Schmidt-Nielsen, 1967).

b. *Evaporative Cooling in Hot Environments.* Birds respond to heat stress by increasing the evaporation of water from the mucosal surfaces of the mouth and respiratory tract (Fig. 3). Cutaneous loss of water also plays a significant role in the heat defense of these animals, judging by Bernstein's recent (1969) observations on the painted quail (*Excalfactoria chinensis*).

TABLE IV

PREDICTED VALUES OF EVAPORATIVE WATER
LOSS (gm/day) AT 25°C FOR BIRDS OF
DIFFERENT WEIGHTS

Body wt. (gm)	Nonpasserines[a]	All birds[b]
3	0.7	0.8
10	1.4	1.7
100	5.9	6.4
1,000	24.2	24.5
5,000	65.0	63.0
10,000	99.3	94.5
50,000	266.6	242.3
100,000	407.7	363.5

[a] Predicted from Eq. (10)—see text.
[b] Predicted from Eq. (9)—see text.

Cutaneous evaporation in other birds should be studied so that its general significance in avian thermoregulation can be ascertained.

Birds augment EWL in hot environments by panting, a process involving vigorous movements of the thoracic cage at frequencies falling between 40 and 700 cycles/min, depending on the species (Kendeigh, 1944; Calder and Schmidt-Nielsen, 1966, 1967; Lasiewski and Bartholomew, 1966; Schmidt-Nielsen *et al.*, 1969a; Bartholomew *et al.*, 1968). The manner in which panting develops with heat stress varies among the birds that have been studied. In some, breathing rate increases steadily with increasing heat load, and, as body temperature exceeds some characteristic value between 41° and 44°C (King and Farner, 1964), open-mouthed panting commences. This pattern occurs in such birds as the domestic fowl (Hutchinson, 1955), double-crested cormorant, *Phalacrocorax auritus* (Bartholomew *et al.*,

TABLE V
EVAPORATIVE COOLING BY BIRDS

Species	Body wt (gm)	Percent of heat production lost by evaporation at various ambient temperatures (°C)[a]								Reference
		10°	20°	25°	30°	35°	40°	43.5%[b]	44.5%[b]	
Ostrich (*Struthio camelus*)	100,000	<10	10	32	50	65	82		100	Crawford and Schmidt-Nielsen (1967)
Painted quail (*Excalfactoria chinensis*)	43							116		Lasiewski et al. (1966a)
Rock dove (*Columba livia*)	315	8	12	13	16	28	78		118	Calder and Schmidt-Nielsen (1966)
Inca dove (*Scardafella inca*)	42			13	19	30	53	108		Macmillen and Trost (1967a)
Galah (*Kakatoe roseicapilla*)	275			10	13	30	85		148	Dawson and Fisher (1970a)
Roadrunner (*Geococcyx californianus*)	285	10	10	15	21	39	78		137	Calder and Schmidt-Nielsen (1967)
Poor-will (*Phalaenoptilus nuttallii*)	40						36	175		Bartholomew et al. (1962)
Common nighthawk (*Chordeiles minor*)	75	7	14	17	23	35	83	148		Lasiewski and Dawson (1964)
Costa's hummingbird (*Calypte costae*)	3	11				65	66			Lasiewski (1964)
Speckled coly (*Colius striatus*)	44	8	13	18	23	35	99			Bartholomew and Trost (1970)

Species							Reference
Zebra finch (*Taeniopygia castanotis*)	10–13	26	32	72	123[c]		Calder (1964)
		23	29	53	137[d]		Cade et al. (1965)
					94		Lasiewski et al. (1966a)
					96		
Silverbill (*Lonchura malabarica*)					90[c]		Willoughby (1969)
					77[d]		
Gouldian finch (*Poephila gouldiae*)	12–15	17	17	25	58	105	Dawson and Tordoff (1970)
House sparrow (*Passer domesticus*)	25					106	Lasiewski et al. (1966a)
Cardinal (*Richmondena cardinalis*)	40	9	12	17	22	47	Dawson (1958)
House finch (*Carpodacus mexicanus*)	20					130	Lasiewski et al. (1966a)

[a] Relative humidities vary among the various studies. The data included in this table for ambient temperatures of 40°C or higher were for the most part obtained at relative humidities between 10 and 40%. Values for the poor-will and common nighthawk exceed 40% in the vicinity of 44°C, so the performance of these birds is all the more impressive.

[b] ±0.5°C.

[c] Birds provided with water *ad libitum*.

[d] Birds provided with 0.25 ml water/48 hr or only allowed to drink once every 5 to 8 days.

1968), brown pelican, *Pelecanus occidentalis* (Bartholomew *et al.*, 1968), young laughing gull, *Larus atricilla* (Dawson *et al.*, 1970), tawny frogmouth, *Podargus strigoides* (Lasiewski and Bartholomew, 1966), and the house sparrow (Kendeigh, 1944). In the pelican and gull, breathing rate becomes essentially independent of heat load, once heavy panting develops. Direct measurements of tidal volumes accompanying the various rates have been obtained for the domestic fowl (Frankel *et al.*, 1962). In hot environments, breathing of this bird becomes more shallow with increasing respiratory rate, except in extreme hyperthermia. This pattern of response, involving a gradual rise in respiratory activity with increasing body temperature, appears to be the common one in birds like passerines, which do not employ gular fluttering in heat defense (see below). However, it is not confined to them. The double-crested cormorant, for example, not only pants, but has a well-defined gular flutter (Bartholomew *et al.*, 1968).

The ostrich (Schmidt-Nielsen *et al.*, 1969a), barn owl, *Tyto alba* (Bartholomew *et al.*, 1968), rock dove (Calder and Schmidt-Nielsen, 1966) and roadrunner, *Geococcyx californianus* (Calder and Schmidt-Nielsen, 1967), respond to heat stress in another way, abruptly changing from a relatively low breathing rate to a high one characteristic of painting. This pattern is analogous to that of dogs. The panting frequency of these mammals matches the resonant frequency of the entire respiratory system (Crawford, 1962). The amount of muscular work (and heat production) required by panting is thus confined to the value necessary to keep this elastic system oscillating at its natural frequency. However, Schmidt-Nielsen *et al.* (1969a) conclude that the ostrich does not pant at the natural frequency of its thoracic cavity. Since dogs and the birds referred to here use a single frequency for panting, they must adjust evaporative cooling by intermittent operation of the panting mechanism and modulation of tidal volume.

Some birds, e.g., pelicans (Behle, 1944; Bartholomew *et al.*, 1953, 1968), boobies (Howell and Bartholomew, 1962a; Bartholomew, 1966), cormorants (Bartholomew *et al.*, 1968), anhingas (Bartholomew *et al.*, 1968), herons (Bartholomew and Dawson, 1954b; Hudson *et al.*, 1970), ducks and geese (Calder and Schmidt-Nielsen 1968), quail (Brush, 1965; Lasiewski *et al.*, 1966b), domestic fowl (Calder and Schmidt-Nielsen, 1968), cockatoos (Dawson and Fisher, 1970a), owls (Lasiewski *et al.*, 1966b; Ligon, 1968, 1969, Bartholomew *et al.*, 1968), doves and pigeons (Calder and Schmidt-Nielsen, 1966; Lasiewski *et al.*, 1966b; MacMillen and Trost, 1967a; Dawson and Fisher, 1970b), roadrunners (Calder and Schmidt-Nielsen, 1967), caprimulgids (Cowles and Dawson, 1951; Bartholomew *et al.*, 1962, 1968; Lasiewski and Dawson, 1964; Lasiewski and Bartholomew, 1966; Dawson and Fisher, 1969), and colies (Bartholomew *et al.*, 1968; Bartholomew and Trost, 1970) augment panting by rapidly fluttering the gular area. Blood vessels in this area become conspicuously engorged during heat stress. Gular fluttering is driven by flexing of the hyoid apparatus (Bartholomew et al., 1968). The movement not only facilitates evaporative cooling from the moist inner surface of the gular area and upper respiratory tract, but also increases heat loss by forced convection when the external surface of this area is warmer than the air surrounding it. Lasiewski and Snyder's (1969) study of evaporative cooling in young cormorants provides a detailed description of how gular flutter supplements respiratory evaporation.

Rates of gular flutter increase in a few species with increasing heat load, but more generally remain constant (Lasiewski and Dawson, 1964; Calder and Schmidt-Nielsen, 1966, 1967; Lasiewski and Bartholomew, 1966; Lasiewski et al., 1966b; Bartholomew et al., 1968; Ligon, 1968; Bartholomew and Trost, 1970). In the latter case, the contribution of gular fluttering to evaporative cooling is adjusted by intermittent operation (Lasiewski and Dawson, 1964; Lasiewski and Bartholomew, 1966) and by varying the amplitude of the flutter movements and the area affected (Lasiewski and Bartholomew, 1966; Bartholomew et al., 1968). Flutter rates for various birds are indicated in Table VI. In some cases—horned owl, barn owl rock dove, and roadrunner—they match the corresponding breathing rate, panting and gular fluttering evidently proceeding synchronously (Calder and Schmidt-Nielsen, 1966, 1967; Bartholomew et al., 1968). The rate here appears to be determined by the physical properties of the thoracoabdominal structures, because of their relatively great mass in comparison with the gular area (Bartholomew et al., 1968). In other cases—brown pelican, double-crested cormorant, cattle egret (Bubulcus ibis), and caprimulgids— gular fluttering occurs at a distinctly higher rate than panting (Fig. 5), with the two activities proceeding asynchronously (Bartholomew et al., 1968; Hudson et al., 1970). Many species falling in this latter category have relatively enlarged gular areas.

It has been suggested that rates of gular fluttering by birds in which the frequency of this process is independent of breathing rate and heat load match the respective resonant frequencies of their hyoid-gular structures (Dawson and Schmidt-Nielsen, 1964; Lasiewski and Dawson, 1964; Schmidt-Nielsen, 1964; Lasiewski and Bartholomew, 1966; Bartholomew et al., 1968). The relatively light and flexible character of this apparatus undoubtedly allows it to operate at a fundamentally lower metabolic cost than the more rigid and heavier thoracic cage. Utilization of the resonant frequency of the system should minimize the heat production associated with active evaporative cooling, for reasons outlined in connection with the discussion of panting by dogs and certain birds (see above). Less than 20% of the heat dissipated through evaporation at 43°C is required to offset the heat produced by gular fluttering in the poor-will, common night-

TABLE VI

RATES OF BREATHING DURING PANTING AND RATES OF GULAR FLUTTER

Species	Panting rate (cycles/min)	Flutter rate (cycles/min)	Reference
Brown pelican			
(*Pelecanus occidentalis*)	ca. 135[a]	230–290[b]	Bartholomew *et al.* (1968)
Double-crested cormorant			
(*Phalacrocorax auritus*)	20–60	645–730[b]	Bartholomew *et al.* (1968)
Cattle egret			
(*Bubulcus ibis*)	44–100	860–1000[b]	Hudson *et al.* (1970)
Bobwhite			
(*Colinus virginianus*)		360–770	Lasiewski *et al.* (1966b)
California quail			
(*Lophortyx californicus*)		200–750	Lasiewski *et al.* (1966b)
Gambel's quail			
(*Lophortyx gambelii*)		70–700	Lasiewski *et al.* (1966b)
Painted quail			
(*Excalfactoria chinensis*)		600–915	Lasiewski *et al.* (1966b)
Rock dove			
(*Columba livia*)	650(±60)	650(±60)[b]	Calder and Schmidt-Nielsen (1966)
Mourning dove			
(*Zenaidura macroura*)		630–815[b]	Lasiewski *et al.* (1966b)
		680–735[b]	Bartholomew *et al.* (1968)
Roadrunner			
(*Geococcyx californianus*)	356(±58)	356(±58)[b]	Calder and Schmidt-Nielsen (1967)
Barn owl			
(*Tyto alba*)	245–285	245–285	Bartholomew *et al.* (1968)
Whiskered owl			
(*Otus trichopsis*)		220–290	Lasiewski *et al.* (1966b)
Horned owl			
(*Bubo virginianus*)	240–255	210–255[b]	Bartholomew *et al.* (1968)
Elf owl			
(*Micrathene whitneyi*)	135–160	176–523	Ligon (1968)
Poor-will			
(*Phalaenoptilus nuttallii*)		590–690[b]	Lasiewski and Bartholomew (1966)
Common nighthawk			
(*Chordeiles minor*)		500–700[b]	Lasiewski and Dawson (1964); see Lasiewski and Bartholomew (1966)
Speckled coly			
(*Colius striatus*)		510–600[b]	Bartholomew and Trost (1970)

[a] Approximate rate for body temperatures exceeding 41°C. Between 40.2° and 41°C, breathing rate increases from about 9 to 100 cycles/min.

[b] Rate essentially independent of heat load.

hawk, and spotted nightjar (*Eurostopodus guttatus*), birds in which this activity appears to overshadow other means of evaporative cooling. This is reflected in the metabolism–temperature curves for these caprimulgids (Fig. 6), which show little rise at high temperatures. On the other hand, at least 30% of the heat loss is required under similar or more favorable humidity conditions to offset heat resulting from panting in such birds as the zebra finch and cardinal (Dawson and Bartholomew, 1968). In view of these considerations, it is significant that the most effective capacities for evaporative cooling exist in birds with well-developed capacities for gular fluttering (see Table V). Notable among these are the caprimulgids. The large mouths of these animals facilitate evaporation as well as aerial capture

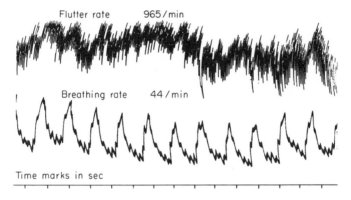

FIG. 5.   Relation of gular flutter to breathing movements in a young egret (*Bubulcus ibis*) subjected to heat stress. Recordings were obtained from impedance pneumographs connected to the base of the gular area and the thoracic cage, respectively. Data from Hudson *et al.* (1970).

of insects. The poor-will and the Australian spotted nightjar with their effortless gular flutter can dissipate heat in excess of three times their caloric production at high ambient temperatures (Lasiewski, 1969; Dawson and Fisher, 1969). This is facilitated in the poor-will by an unusually low level of standard metabolism (Bartholomew *et al.,* 1962).

Estimates of the minimal ventilation of the respiratory tract necessary to produce observed rates of EWL (referred to subsequently as "total ventilation") coupled with direct observations of oxygen consumption, breathing rate, and blood chemistry have enabled Calder and Schmidt-Nielsen (1966) to examine in detail how the rock dove, a bird in which panting and gular fluttering proceed synchronously, responds to heat stress. It appears worthwhile to summarize their findings here as a means of indicating the extent of the capacities for adjustment to heat possessed by some birds.

Their observations were made on intact and unrestrained birds. In contrast, von Saalfeld's widely cited study (1936) of panting by the rock dove was performed on restrained individuals with a tracheal cannula and valves, which Calder and Schmidt-Nielsen's results (1966) suggest may have hindered air flow.

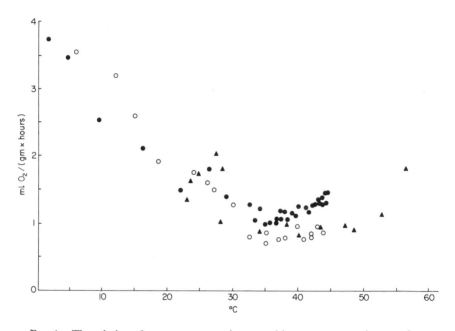

FIG. 6.   The relation of oxygen consumption to ambient temperature in several post-absorptive caprimulgids resting in the dark: poor-will, *Phalaenoptilus nuttallii* (unshaded circles); common nighthawk, *Chordeiles minor* (shaded circles); spotted nightjar, *Eurostopodus guttatus* (triangles). The metabolic values shown all pertain to homeothermic individuals. Note the unusually low basal metabolic rate for the 40-gm poor-will, comparing it with those for the 70-gm nighthawk and the 86-gm nightjar. Data from Bartholomew *et al.* (1962), Lasiewski and Dawson (1964), and Dawson and Fisher (1969).

Rock doves breathe at the rate of 29 cycles/min between 30°C and 40°C. However, total ventilation and, hence, tidal volume are estimated to increase nearly fourfold over this range (from 203 to 777 ml/min and 7 to 26.8 ml, respectively). Between 40°C and 45°C, breathing rate and estimated total ventilation increase from 29 to 650 cycles/min and 777 to 1360 ml/min, respectively. Panting is supplemented by a synchronous gular flutter (also at 650 cycles/min) at the higher temperature. These changes entail a drop in tidal volume from 26.8 to 2.1 ml. Panting and gular fluttering also proceed at 650 cycles/min at 50.9°C. The independence of heat load evident in the rates of these activities suggests that they are occurring at the resonant frequency of the respiratory system, with the advantages this entails (see above). Total ventilation and tidal volume are estimated at 2280 ml/min and 3.5 ml, respectively, at 50.9°C.

Calder and Schmidt-Nielsen (1966) estimate from measurements of blood chemistry and metabolism that pulmonary ventilation (as distinguished from total ventilation) remains constant between 30°C and 40°C. The increase in total ventilation calculated to occur over this range must therefore involve extrapulmonary air spaces, including the air sacs, not the lungs. [See Akester (1960), Salt and Zeuthen (1960), and King and Farner (1964) for details concerning structure and considerations of the function of the avian respiratory system, with its associated air sacs.] The increased total ventilation indicated at 45°C and 50.9°C is accompanied by increased pulmonary ventilation. The latter results in a decreased alveolar P_{co_2} and, consequently, alkalosis. While significant, this condition is apparently not as severe as it might be, since Calder and Schmidt-Nielsen's estimates (1966) indicate that the fraction of the total ventilation involved in pulmonary gas exchange in rock doves actually decreases with temperature. Alkalosis is evidently a widespread problem for birds confronted with heat stress, judging by Calder and Schmidt-Nielsen's results (1968) on a variety of kinds. However, the ostrich did not develop it even after engaging in vigorous evaporative cooling for 8 hours (Schmidt-Nielsen *et al.*, 1969a). The air sac P_{co_2} did fall, suggesting a functional shunt system allowing a regulated by-pass of the lungs.

3. *Behavior Serving to Reduce Heat Stress*

A variety of behavioral activities serve to reduce heat stress imposed on birds. Most species retreat to shaded areas during the middle of very hot days (Madsen, 1930; Dawson, 1954; Bartholomew and Cade, 1957; Howell and Bartholomew, 1962b; Calder, 1968; Ricklefs and Hainsworth, 1968a), thereby reducing radiational heat loads. A notable example of this is afforded by the rock wren (*Salpinctes obsoletus*), which moves deep into crevices among the rocks it frequents during the heat of summer days in North American deserts (Smyth and Bartholomew, 1966). The elf owl (*Micrathene whitneyi*) secures protection from heat in the southwestern United States and Mexico by roosting in cavities in giant cactuses or trees (Ligon, 1968). Conditions within the retreats of most species have not been analyzed in detail. However, Ricklefs and Hainsworth's observations (1968a) of places frequented by cactus wrens (*Campylorhynchus brunneicapillum*) during the heat of the day in the Arizona desert indicate that they afford these birds both protection from the sun and cooler ambient temperatures. Soaring birds evade intense heat in another way, ascending to great heights in some species observed by Madsen (1930) in east Sudan. At these heights air temperature and secondary radiation are likely to be less severe than at the surface.

Certain birds at ground level remain exposed to the sun during the middle of hot days. Some of these spend their time bathing (Dawson, 1954), thereby augmenting evaporative water loss. Others are engaged in sheltering eggs and young from intense solar radiation. Postural adjustments appear to have a significant influence on heat transfer under these conditions. For example, Bartholomew (1966) observed masked boobies to orient themselves randomly with respect to compass direction and azimuth of the sun while incubating or brooding young under cloudy skies in the Galapagos Islands. These animals almost invariably oriented themselves with their backs to the sun when skies were clear and solar radiation intense. Such orientation places the gular area (see Section VI,B,2) and the feet in the shade of the head, neck, and body. A more extreme postural adjustment occurs in juvenal Laysan and black-footed albatrosses (*Diomedia immutabilis* and *D. nigripes*). These birds spend the prefledging period in relatively exposed situations where radiation is intense and air temperatures warm (ca. 27°C). When exposed to the direct rays of the sun, they balance on their heels with the heavily vascularized feet spread and held in the air. The birds almost always orient themselves with their backs to the sun, thus shading the feet. Elevation of the webbed feet in this manner reduces the area across which heat can be gained conductively from the hot substrate, while allowing heat loss by convection and radiation from these structures to the air (Howell and Bartholomew, 1961). Heat dissipation from the legs and feet is augmented in quite a different way in the wood stork (*Mycteria americana*). This bird squirts fluid urine onto them during exposure to heat (Kahl, 1963), thereby producing evaporative cooling.

Exposure of the legs and feet can be important for heat dissipation during and immediately after flight (I. Steen and Steen, 1965). Flying budgerigars (*Melopsittacus undulatus*) extend the unfeathered portions of their limbs into the slipstream while flying at ambient temperatures of 36°–37°C (Tucker, 1968). I. Steen and Steen (1965) note that herons returning from foraging on hot days wade in water at a depth just covering the bare parts of their legs, while panting and fanning themselves with their wings.

Diurnal birds, which comprise the vast majority of species, tend to minimize activity during the middle of hot days (Fig. 7), although remaining active on cooler ones (Dawson, 1954; Calder, 1968; Ricklefs and Hainsworth, 1968a). Such a reduction of activity is of great importance, for exertion can impose severe heat loads on these animals. Even at moderate

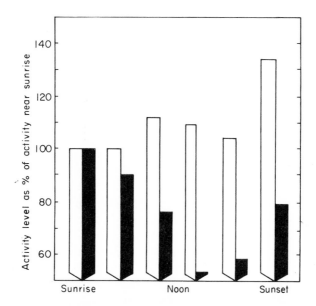

Fɪɢ. 7.   Relation of activity by adult cactus wrens (*Campylorhynchus brunneicapillus*) to temperature. Activity was measured in terms of the frequency of visits by parent birds to their nests in the Arizona desert. Total visits within each of six equal periods between sunrise and sunset are expressed as percentages of number of visits during the first period of the day. Unshaded bars refer to 18 nest-days during which the black bulb temperature remained below 35°C. Shaded bars pertain to 12 nest-days during which the black bulb temperature exceeded 35°C. Data from Ricklefs and Hainsworth (1968a).

ambient temperatures (23°C) birds such as 44-gm brown towhees and 47-gm Abert towhees increase their body temperature by more than 2°C with 3–5 minutes of intensive activity in small cages (Dawson, 1954). Flight imposes particular burdens, as discussed in Section VII.

C. Intraspecific Variation in Tolerance to Heat

It is often difficult to define precisely the level of heat tolerance for a particular species, even after individual variation of the type encountered by Kheireldin and Shaffner (1957) in day-old domestic chicks of a single breed, is taken into account. The difficulty results from: (a) variation of tolerance within a population in response to season or experimental treatment; and/or (b) variation of tolerance among populations of widely distributed birds and among breeds of domesticated species.

1. *Seasonal Variations*

Information concerning the exact nature of seasonal changes in avian heat tolerance is, unfortunately, rather limited. Passerines from temperate regions have significantly fewer contour feathers during the summer when the plumage is worn than in the fall after the completion of the postnuptial molt (Wetmore, 1936). Presumably, feather wear and molting significantly reduce insulation. Such wear might well account for the slightly higher upper critical temperature of the cardinal in late spring and early summer, as compared with winter and early spring (Dawson, 1958). Feather loss during molting appears to improve significantly the heat tolerance of juvenal yellow buntings (Wallgren, 1954). Deterioration of insulation with wear and molt would appear advantageous mainly in environments where ambient temperature remains somewhat below body temperature and protection is available from solar radiation. It might well be disadvantageous in hotter environments where impedance of heat transfer from the environment becomes vital.

Seasonal variation in heat tolerance can depend on things other than variations in plumage insulation. White Leghorn hens responded to hot, humid conditions (40.6°C and 70% RH) with higher maximal breathing rates during summer than in winter. Under these conditions, summer birds became hyperthermic more slowly and survived significantly longer than did winter individuals (Weiss and Borbely, 1957). The higher breathing rates of the former animals presumably reflect a greater capacity for evaporative cooling. Changes in reproductive state can also influence heat tolerance. Nonlaying hens appear to be more tolerant of heat than layers of the same breed. Weiss (1959) associates this with the lower food intake, greater capacity for polypnea during heat stress, and smaller size of the former birds.

It is probable that the main mechanisms for seasonally enhancing avian tolerance of heat remain to be identified. Two obvious means by which such tolerance could be increased involve alteration of the threshold for heat injury and reduction of the general level of metabolism. The former would increase the amount of heat that could safely be stored in hot environments, whereas the latter would reduce the metabolic heat load. The limited evidence available provides no indication that the threshold for heat injury can be modified; White Leghorn hens die at similar body temperatures whether overheated in summer or winter (Weiss and Borbely, 1957). The situation is more complex regarding shifts in metabolic level. Metabolic rate in the zone of thermal neutrality does not change between summer and winter in some birds exposed to outdoor conditions (Wallgren, 1954; Rautenberg, 1957; Dawson, 1958). In cases where the rate does shift seasonally, the change is sometimes very small (Dontcheff and Kayser, 1934) or in the direction of increased heat production during the summer (Irving *et al.*, 1955). Miller's observations (1939) on house sparrows in Iowa do indicate a markedly lower rate of oxygen consumption at 28°C

in summer than during winter. However, the minimal rate at this temperature occurred during April rather than the hottest months of the year.
The decline from winter levels appears to be associated with a reduction
in thyroid level (Miller, 1939). Paradoxically, this reduction, which could
have beneficial effects in hot environments, may well develop with the
disappearance of stimulation resulting from cold, rather than as a direct
response to heat (A. C. Wilson and Farner, 1960).

2. *Experimentally Induced Variations*

Several studies have dealt with acclimation of birds to heat under experimental conditions. In some species, the ambient temperature at which panting commences has been shown to be directly correlated with acclimation
temperature (Gelineo, 1934b, 1936, 1955). Presumably, this results from
the lower levels of metabolism observed in birds adjusted to warmer conditions (Gelineo, 1964). Tolerance of heat by the domestic fowl can be
improved by relatively brief daily exposures to high ambient temperatures
(Hutchinson and Sykes, 1953; Hillerman and Wilson, 1955). Hutchinson
and Sykes' detailed study (1953) merits particular attention. They found
that daily 4-hour exposures to 37.2°C, a vapor pressure of 28 mm Hg,
and air movement at 20 ft/min, significantly improved the heat tolerance
of Brown Leghorns in about 3 weeks. In experiments following this period,
an ambient temperature of 39.1°C (humidity and air movement as specified
previously) was required to produce the same degree of heat stress in
warm-acclimated birds as 37.2°C imposed upon unacclimated individuals.
Further exposure to high ambient temperatures improved the heat resistance
of the acclimated birds. Hens tended to be less heat resistant than cocks
at any stage of acclimation. Hutchinson and Sykes (1953) found that
breathing rates at a standard high rectal temperature rose, and breathing
movements became less labored and more shallow, as the adjustment to
heat proceeded. The latter developments would increase the net effectiveness
of evaporative cooling. The actual rate of evaporation at this high rectal
temperature did not increase with acclimation to heat.

Continued exposure to constant temperatures in the laboratory can significantly influence the general metabolic levels of birds (Dontcheff and
Kayser, 1934; Miller, 1939; Wallgren, 1954; Gelineo, 1955). Most studies
of such temperature conditioning have been concerned with cold acclimation (see Section V,C,3). However, undomesticated birds have been acclimated to warm ambient temperatures between 29°C and 32.5°C in some
experiments. This produces a lowering of metabolic rate (Gelineo, 1955),
a finding consistent with the reduction of basal metabolism observed in
young domestic fowl growing in a warm environment (Hoffman and Shaffner, 1949). While an overall lowering of the level of metabolism could

be beneficial in contending with heat, it is by no means certain that such a shift represents a specific response to warm ambient temperatures. It may in fact come about in the absence of thyroid stimulation associated with lower temperatures, as suggested previously in connection with Miller's observations (1939) on seasonal changes of metabolic rate in house sparrows. The reduction in heat production that develops with continued exposure of the domestic fowl to warm ambient temperatures has been attributed to a decrease in thyroid activity (Hoffman and Shaffner, 1950; Huston *et al.,* 1962).

The relevance to natural situations of capacities of birds for acclimation to constant temperatures in the laboratory is not presently clear. Wallgren (1954) found that the basal metabolic rate of yellow buntings did not vary seasonally in birds maintained on a natural thermal regimen. However, birds of this species and ortolan buntings (*Emberiza hortulana*) exhibited a decline in basal metabolic rate with acclimation to 27.5°C and 32.5°C, respectively. This decline did not occur in individuals that were treated similarly, except for being exposed to 10°–14°C for 8 hours each day. Evidently, fluctuating temperatures suppress the process of acclimation to warm temperatures. These observations suggest a need for additional experimental studies in which temperature, and other factors such as photoperiod can be varied in an appropriate manner.

3. *Differences among Populations within Wild Species*

The extent to which populations of widely distributed species of birds differ in their thermal tolerances has not been widely investigated, despite the evolutionary implications of such differences. Hudson and Kimzey (1966) found that the heat resistance of house sparrows varies geographically. Birds from Houston, Texas, survived higher ambient temperatures than did those from Ann Arbor, Michigan, or Boulder, Colorado. This appears correlated with the fact that the Houston birds have a lower metabolism and greater insulation than have those from cooler climates. These characteristics were unaltered in captivity when the birds were maintained under identical conditions. Hudson and Kimzey (1966) therefore concluded that the differences in physiological performance have a genetic basis. This conclusion is of special interest in view of the fact that the house sparrow is a recent arrival in North America, having been introduced along the Atlantic seaboard in the middle of the nineteenth century. Since that time it has spread widely and undergone some significant modifications of morphological characters, which Johnston and Selander (1964) interpret as representing evolutionary changes. Hudson and Kimzey's observations (1966) indicate that physiological changes have also occurred in the house sparrow within approximately a century.

4. *Differences among Breeds within Domesticated Species*

Assessment of the tolerance of domesticated species to heat must take into account basic differences among breeds, as well as the effects of acclimation. Such differences appear responsible for the superior heat tolerance of Indian domestic fowl over warm-acclimated representatives of breeds from the cooler parts of North America (Hutchinson and Sykes, 1953) and for the lower mortality rate of Single Comb White Leghorns in comparison with Rhode Island Reds and Barred Plymouth Rocks during an unusually severe heat wave in Ithaca, New York (Hutt, 1938). Differences among breeds in tolerance to heat have also been documented in some experimental studies of the domestic fowl. White Leghorns surpassed Australorps and Rhode Island Reds in restricting hyperthermia during comparable exposures to stress involving an ambient temperature of 40.6°C and a relative humidity of 25%. Brown Leghorns were the least able to avoid overheating under these hot, dry conditions. However, they were found to be the most tolerant of hot, humid conditions (40.6°C and 75% RH), surpassing White Leghorns, Minorcas, Australorps, and Rhode Island Reds, in that general order (Lee *et al.,* 1945). W. O. Wilson (1949) observed that White Leghorns displayed more effective control of body temperature than did Rhode Island Reds at ambient temperatures of 32.2°C and 37.8°C. Maintenance at warm ambient temperatures curtailed egg production less in White Leghorns than in New Hampshires or White Plymouth Rocks (Huston *et al.,* 1957). Single Comb White Leghorns were judged to perform better when exposed to heat stress than New Hampshires or Delawares (Ahmad *et al.,* 1967).

The factors responsible for the differences among breeds of domestic fowl in tolerance of heat are probably complex. Differences in plumage color appear to be involved in instances where solar radiation is a factor, the plumage of white breeds reflecting a greater portion of the energy in the visible part of the spectrum than that of dark ones (Okamoto *et al.,* 1958). Such an advantage was not evident in studies conducted indoors, where radiant heating is less significant (Fox, 1951). Size also appears to influence heat tolerance, for breeds that are lighter in weight often appear less susceptible to heat stroke than do heavier ones (Hutchinson, 1954). The superiority of White Plymouth Rocks over Single Comb White Leghorns during exposure, without drinking water, to a high ambient temperature (42.4°C) and fairly high humidities (30–50% RH) constitutes an exception to this (Fox, 1951). However, birds of the latter breed surpassed both White Plymouth Rocks and Rhode Island Reds under the ambient conditions just specified, when water was provided (Fox, 1951). The general superiority of White Leghorn fowl over other breeds in performance at high temperatures with water available depends on a number of things. It was originally attributed to the tendency of birds of this breed to splash water over their bodies while drinking (Lee *et al.*, 1945). Fox (1951) related it to the greater persistence with which White Leghorns drink under heat stress, in comparison with other breeds. Ingestion of large amounts of water would probably contribute directly to the prevention of overheating, as well as supporting rapid evaporative cooling. White Leghorns are known to lose more heat per unit of weight than either Rhode Island Reds or New Hampshire–Cornish cross birds. It therefore appears that this first breed has unusually good capacities for evaporative cooling (Ota and McNally, 1961). Detailed studies of the thermoregulatory capacities of various tropical domestic fowl would afford a useful perspective concerning the extent of fundamental differences in heat tolerance among breeds of this species. Such studies would be particularly valuable in view of the paucity of information concerning temperature regulation of birds in hot, humid environments (King and Farner, 1964).

D. Body Temperatures of Birds in Hot Environments

Birds inhabiting areas having extremely hot summers do not differ significantly from their counterparts in more equable climates regarding body temperatures maintained in the absence of excitement, activity, and thermal stress (Dawson and Schmidt-Nielsen, 1964). Upper lethal temperatures for these animals also appear similar. No birds appear to tolerate body temperatures above 47°C, and survival between 46°C and 47°C is of very limited duration (Calder, 1964). Temperature thresholds for heat injury may be lower for birds maintaining relatively low body temperatures in the absence of thermal stress, e.g., ratites (Table I), although quantitative information is lacking. The comparisons of related species existing under markedly different temperature regimes suggest that avian body temperatures are fundamentally nonadaptive to climate, a view previously advanced by Scholander *et al.* (1950c) on the basis of studies of arctic and tropical homeotherms. Hudson and Kimzey's observations (1966) on heat resistance of house sparrows from divergent climates in the United States provide additional documentation for this interpretation at the intraspecific level.

The ostrich possesses an impressive capacity for temperature regulation in hot environments, maintaining body temperature essentially unchanged at 39.3°C in ambient temperatures between 25°C and 51°C (Crawford and Schmidt-Nielsen, 1967). This performance is in marked contrast to the significant rise in body temperature that most other birds undergo when subjected to heat stress, even during inactivity at low humidities (W. O. Wilson, 1948; Dawson, 1954; Bartholomew and Dawson, 1958; Bartholomew *et al.,* 1962; Calder, 1964; Lasiewski and Dawson, 1964; Calder and Schmidt-Nielsen, 1966, 1967; Lasiewski *et al.,* 1966a). The evaporative cooling of these animals appears to function in limiting rather than preventing the storage of calories. Since birds readily tolerate elevations of body temperature on the order of 4°C (Bartholomew and Dawson, 1958), moderate hyperthermia conveys distinct advantages in connection with temperature regulation and water economy. A higher body temperature permits some loss of heat by nonevaporative means at ambient temperatures approximating the thermal level maintained by the bird in the absence of heat stress. Hyperthermia will also reduce the tendency of the animal to gain heat from the environment. Such a reduction lowers requirements for evaporative cooling and, consequently, for rapid water loss in the heat. The fact that the heat stored is probably dissipated by nonevaporative means during the cooler part of the day, also makes a modest contribution to conservation of body water. These things taken together make controlled hyperthermia a cornerstone of avian adjustment to dry heat in particular (King and Farner, 1961; Dawson and Schmidt-Nielsen, 1964; Dawson and Bartholomew, 1968).

The precise levels of body temperature maintained by birds subjected to heat stress will be influenced by a variety of factors, e.g., ambient temperature, air movement, absolute humidity, intensity of radiation, and activity. Under standardized conditions (ambient temperature, 44°–46°C; air movement, 4 km/hr; vapor pressure of water, approximately 8 mm Hg; low radiational flux; inactivity), Lasiewski *et al.* (1966a) found that the extent of hyperthermia differed among the species tested (Table VII). Body temperatures of small passerines (<50 gm) often closely approached ambient temperature, in line with the capacities of these animals for dissipating, through evaporation, all of the heat they produce, but little more (Table V). Larger birds (>100 gm), including two white-necked ravens (*Corvus cryptoleucus*), generally remained 1°–3°C cooler than the environment during exposures of 1–4 hours to 44°–46°C. Several of these larger birds employ gular fluttering as well as panting in their evaporative cooling. However, the white-necked raven, like other passerines, only pants. Lasiewski *et al.* (1966a) suggest that the generally high body temperatures of small passerines at 44°–46°C may result from a combination of factors: (1) a relatively large surface:weight ratio; (2) a higher level of body temperature in the absence of activity and thermal stress than is found in larger species; and (3) a relatively high weight-specific level of standard metabolism in comparison with nonpasserine species of comparable weight (see Section III,B).

The maximum capacities of the more heat resistant birds for coping with thermal stress have not been fully explored. However, certain species

TABLE VII

Body Temperatures of Birds Maintained at High
Ambient Temperatures and Low Humidities[a]

Species	Body wt (gm)	Total time (min)	Mean ambient temp (°C)	Mean body temp (°C)	Water vapor (mm Hg)	Rel. humidity (%)
Sparrow hawk						
(*Falco sparverius*)		60	45.0	43.0	7.4	10
Bobwhite						
(*Colinus virginianus*)[b]	164	100	44.4	44.1	7.5	11
	167	100	45.1	43.1	7.5	10
Gambel's quail						
(*Lophortyx gambelii*)[b]	165	100	44.4	43.4	8.4	12
	167	100	45.1	44.0	7.5	10
Mourning dove						
(*Zenaidura macroura*)[b]	91	120	45.4	43.6	8.9	12
	104	120	45.4	43.4	8.9	12
	117	120	45.4	43.3	8.9	12
White-necked raven						
(*Corvus cryptoleucus*)	583	240	45.8	42.9	7.2	10
	445	60	45.9	43.6	7.2	10
Zebra finch						
(*Taeniopygia castanotis*)	11	60	45.3	44.0	7.5	10
House sparrow						
(*Passer domesticus*)						
	25	60	44.1	44.0	9.6	14
	22	60	45.2	44.4	7.7	11
	25	60	45.2	44.7	7.7	11
	25	60	44.0	44.0	8.3	12
House finch						
(*Carpodacus mexicanus*)	21	60	44.2	44.0	7.2	10
	19	60	44.0	44.5	7.8	11
Brown towhee						
(*Pipilo fuscus*)	42	60	44.2	44.1	7.2	10
	41	60	44.1	44.3	9.6	14

[a] Based on Table 2 in Lasiewski *et al.* (1966a).
[b] Utilize gular fluttering in addition to panting.

have been observed to prevent overheating during exposure to ambient temperatures in excess of 50°C at low humidities. As noted previously, the ostrich (100 kg) maintained a body temperature below 40°C throughout a 7.5-hour exposure to 51°C (Crawford and Schmidt-Nielsen, 1967). Rock doves (315 gm) had body temperatures averaging 43.1°C after resting for several hours at an ambient temperature approximating 51°C. A few individuals became active during the tests and this caused body temperature to rise explosively (Calder and Schmidt-Nielsen, 1966). With their extensive capacities for evaporative cooling (Table V), caprimulgids should be able to rival these performances, despite their smaller size. It is therefore of interest that the spotted nightjar (86 gm) was observed to have a body temperature of 43.1°C following exposure for about 2 hours to 52.8°C (Dawson and Fisher, 1969). These observations indicate that some birds, particularly large ones or those with a well-developed gular flutter, can prevent overheating during exposure to ambient temperatures 4°C or more in excess of upper lethal body temperatures.

VII. Thermoregulation during Flight

Avian flight generally is a vigorous activity that produces hyperthermia even in the absence of heat stress. Elevations of body temperature averaging 2.6°C and 1.9°C were noted in the fairy prion (*Pachyptila turtur*) and the red-tailed tropic bird, respectively, at the completion of flights (Farner, 1956; Howell and Bartholomew, 1962a). In rock doves fitted with a telemetry device, body temperature tended to stabilize at about 44.5°C after 1.5–2 minutes of flight, a value 1.5°–2.0°C above the level for resting birds (Hart and Roy, 1967). In view of these developments in the absence of high ambient temperatures, it is not surprising that budgerigars became overheated within 20 minutes of flight in a wind tunnel at 36°–37°C (Tucker, 1968).

Until recently, the principal basis for detailed consideration of the thermoregulation of flying birds depended largely on indirect estimates of flight metabolism and evaporative cooling. Zeuthen's treatment of the rock dove in this manner has been widely quoted (Zeuthen, 1942; see also Salt and Zeuthen, 1960). He estimated that birds of this species, flying at 70 km/hr would have metabolic rates nearly 27 times the resting level. Since it was expected that the plumage would prevent a high rate of cutaneous heat loss, nearly 60% of the heat production associated with this flight speed was estimated to be dissipated by respiratory evaporation. This would entail the output of water at the rate of approximately 66 gm/hr in these doves, which weigh approximately 300–350 gm.

Direct measurements of a few species have made it possible in recent years to undertake an evaluation of Zeuthen's flight estimates (1942). Pearson (1950) and Lasiewski (1963) found metabolic rates during hovering flight to fall between 31 and 147 ml O_2 (gm hr)$^{-1}$ in several hummingbirds (*Selasphorus sasin, S. rufus, Calypte anna, C. costae, Stellula calliope*) weighing between 2.3 and 4.5 gm. The latter author followed the oxygen consumption of an immature male Costa's hummingbird as it hovered continuously for 50 minutes in a metabolism chamber (ambient temperature, 24°C). The average value obtained, 42.4 ml O_2 $(gm\ hr)^{-1}$, is seven times the standard rate at 24°C and fourteen times the basal rate. Presumably, level flight would produce additional lift that would reduce these values. LeFebvre (1964) determined the metabolism and water loss of free-flying rock doves, utilizing the $D_2^{18}O$ method referred to in Section III,A, and measurements of body composition. These birds had an average metabolic rate of 22 kcal/hr at a mean flight speed of 58 km/hr. This exceeds the resting level by a factor of 8.2 and the basal metabolic rate determined for this bird by Calder and Schmidt-Nielsen (1967) by a factor of 14.7. LeFebvre (1964) determined that the average rate of water loss by rock doves flying at 58 km/hr was 3.8 gm/hr. This represents no more than 13% of the heat production associated with flight (assuming that rock doves are able to convert chemical energy to external work with an efficiency of 25%). These results are distinctly lower than the estimates by Zeuthen (1942) for this dove, which were in part predicated on the assumption that evaporative cooling must necessarily dissipate a major fraction of heat production during flight, owing to the barrier to heat flow represented by the feathers. He predicted that a bird flying at 60 km/hr would have a metabolic rate of 39.5 kcal/hr and a requirement for dissipating heat at the rate of 30.2 kcal/hr. He expected that half of this would be met by evaporation. Consequently, evaporative water loss would have to proceed at the rate of 52 gm/hr.

Since rock doves normally dissipate such a small fraction of their heat production by evaporation, caloric losses by heat transfer must be relatively high. These losses have been estimated with heat-flow disks implanted subcutaneously over the pectoral muscles (Hart and Roy, 1967). Telemetry of information from these disks in birds exposed to ambient temperatures between 6°C and 17.5°C indicated that the rate of heat flow during flight averaged 5.3 to 6.8 times that during rest. Values observed in flying birds appeared independent of external temperature over the interval of 11.5°C, in which measurements were performed. The rate of heat flow reached a maximum within 60 seconds after flight began and showed irregular variations thereafter, frequently with a tendency to fall.

Rock doves studied by Hart and Roy (1966) were fitted with a face mask containing a sensitive transducer capable of registering the pressure changes associated with air flow during breathing. Information telemetered from this transducer allowed determination of both tidal volume and breathing rate while the birds were in flight. This in turn permitted computation of ventilation rates. Tidal volume was found to increase only slightly from the resting level during flight, the twentyfold rise noted in ventilation resulting mainly from an increased breathing rate (rate for resting birds, 26 breaths/min; that for flying birds, 487 breaths/min). This rise in ventilation is conspicuously greater than the eightfold difference between the metabolic rates of resting and flying rock doves found by LeFebvre (1964). Ventilation during flight, therefore, would be considerably in excess of the minimal respiratory requirements if Hart and Roy's birds (1966) were metabolizing at the same level during their short flights as were LeFebvre's birds (1964) during more extended movements. Presumably the excess ventilation would be required for evaporative cooling.

Hart and Roy (1966) observed the tidal volume of rock doves to more than double immediately after landing. Ventilation remained at the flight level owing to a commensurate decline in breathing rate. After repeated flights under certain conditions, some of Hart and Roy's birds evidently became overheated. This produced vigorous evaporative cooling which involved a reduction in tidal volume to about a third of the value for birds resting at moderate ambient temperatures (1.5 vs 4.6 ml). Breathing rates of these overheated birds were only slightly below flight levels (437 vs 487 breaths/min).

It is of interest that the estimates of tidal volume and ventilation for resting rock doves thermoregulating at an ambient temperature of 50.9°C (Calder and Schmidt-Nielsen, 1966), approximate values determined for these birds in flight (Hart and Roy, 1966)—3.5 ml (50.9°C) vs 5.0 ml and 2280 ml/min (50.9°C) vs 2452 ml/min. Although the resultant evaporative water loss can dissipate sufficient calories to exceed the heat production of the birds resting at this high ambient temperature, it accounts for only about 13% of that by the flying individuals (LeFebvre, 1964). Resting rock doves become alkalotic with prolonged exposure to heat stress (Calder and Schmidt-Nielsen, 1966). This should not be a problem during flight, owing to the much higher rate of CO_2 production. Presumably the rock dove could therefore utilize rates of ventilation well in excess of 2500 ml/min if it has the mechanical capacity. Such rates would be of great importance in augmenting the contribution of evaporative cooling during flight in hot environments. Unfortunately, relevant data are lacking for the rock dove under these conditions.

Although studies of rock doves flying in hot environments remain to be performed, some insight concerning the problem of flight and heat stress is possible, as a result of Tucker's detailed study (1968) of metabolism and evaporative water loss of flying budgerigars. His measurements were carried out as these birds were forced to fly against an air stream in a wind tunnel. Their metabolic rate during level flight at 35 km/hr remained at 3.7 kcal/hr between 20° and 37°C. This is 12.8 times the basal metabolic rate for a nonpasserine the size of these 35-gm budgerigars (Lasiewski and Dawson, 1967). Radiative, convective, and conductive losses of heat during flight at 20°C and 30°C accounted for 85 and 82%, respectively, of the heat produced, evaporative cooling taking care of the remainder. However, nonevaporative heat loss only accounted for 40% of the heat production at 37°C. At this ambient temperature, evaporative cooling accounted for 47% and some heat was stored. The thermal conductance of budgerigars flying at 37°C reached 5 cal (gm hr °C)$^{-1}$, a value that is approximately five times the maximum observed in resting birds and mammals. This is consistent with Hart and Roy's findings (1967) for flying rock doves (see above).

Much remains to be done to obtain a comprehensive understanding of the thermoregulatory problems associated with flight, but certain things have been clarified with the data at hand. The contention that the heat production of flying birds is dissipated primarily by evaporative means under all conditions (Zeuthen, 1942; Salt and Zeuthen, 1960) is not borne out by the facts. Clearly, convective and radiative heat transfer account for a major share of heat dissipation at moderate ambient temperatures (Le-Febvre, 1964; Tucker, 1968). Only at high ambient temperatures does evaporative cooling become of paramount importance. The thermoregulatory performance of birds flying in warm environments merits detailed consideration. They appear to be confronted with some challenging problems in view of Tucker's previously cited finding (1968) that overheating occurs within 20 minutes in budgerigars during flight at 37°C.

The more restricted role currently allocated to evaporative cooling in birds flying under many conditions is of considerable interest in view of the fact that migratory birds must in certain cases move long distances without drinking. It has been assumed that these animals face severe problems of dehydration (Yapp, 1956, 1962). Some perspective concerning this situation is provided by Tucker's construction (1968) of a water budget for flying budgerigars. Metabolic production of water by one of these animals during level flight at 35 km/hr in a wind tunnel was computed to be 13 mg (gm hr)$^{-1}$, on the assumption that 25% of the energy for flight is derived from carbohydrate and the remainder from fat. Water was found to be evaporated at the rate of 20 mg (gm hr)$^{-1}$. Water loss via the excrement amounted to 4 mg (gm hr)$^{-1}$. On the basis of these figures the budgerigar would have a net water loss of 11 mg (gm hr)$^{-1}$, i.e., 24 minus 13. This corresponds to a loss of 1.1% of body weight/hr. If the budgerigar can tolerate a loss of water equivalent to 15% of body weight, it should be able to fly for about 14 hours, covering a distance of 490 km in the process. Tucker (1968) regards this as an adequate range for most migratory species, but recognizes that some birds are estimated to fly at least 50 hours without drinking (Moreau, 1961; Nisbet *et al.*, 1963). Perhaps these birds lose water more slowly than budgerigars during flight. Studies of additional species with Tucker's methods (1968) would be valuable in resolving this, particularly in species which do not appear to become significantly dehydrated during migration (Nisbet *et al.,* 1963).

VIII. Ontogeny of Thermoregulation in Birds

A. ONTOGENETIC PATTERNS

It has long been appreciated that birds differ conspicuously in their thermoregulatory capacities at hatching, in a manner correlated with their overall stage of development at this time (Edwards, 1839; Pembrey, 1895; Pembrey *et al.,* 1895). Altricial birds (e.g., members of the orders Passeriformes and Columbiformes), which are essentially naked and in a generally immature state on emerging from the egg, possess little or no capacity for temperature regulation at ambient temperatures below 35°–40°C. The transition from this essentially poikilothermic state to a homeothermic one can be remarkably rapid in certain species (Fig. 8). On the other hand, precocial birds (e.g., members of the orders Anseriformes, Galliformes, and Charadriiformes), which are hatched with a downy coating and well-developed nervous and muscular function, possess moderately effective control of body temperature at this point in their lives, even at fairly low ambient temperatures (Fig. 9). Some indications exist that certain precocial birds— domestic fowl (Romanoff, 1941) and gulls (Bartholomew and Dawson, 1952; Dawson *et al.,* 1970)—actually attain a degree of homeothermy before hatching. Much of the pertinent literature on the ontogeny of temperature regulation in birds has been reviewed by King and Farner (1961) and will not be considered in detail here.

It should be emphasized that some birds, e.g., shearwaters (Farner and Serventy, 1959) and common nighthawks (Howell, 1959), are intermediate between altricial and precocial species in their thermoregulatory capacities at hatching. For that matter, it is now apparent that differences in thermoregulatory capacities at hatching can exist among species of precocial birds within the same group; day-old ducks vary significantly in their cold-hardiness in a manner directly correlated with size and insulation at hatching (Koskimies and Lahti, 1964). All these ducklings appear to surpass the precocial chicks of gallinaceous birds in thermoregulatory capacities in cool environments. Whatever the capacities of embryos or young may be, they appear universally complemented by behavioral activities (brooding, shading, etc.) of the parents, so even altricial birds spend much of the prehatching and nestling periods at essentially homeothermic levels of temperature (Irving and Krog, 1956). The importance of this interaction between physiology and behavior is emphasized by comparison of the response of different

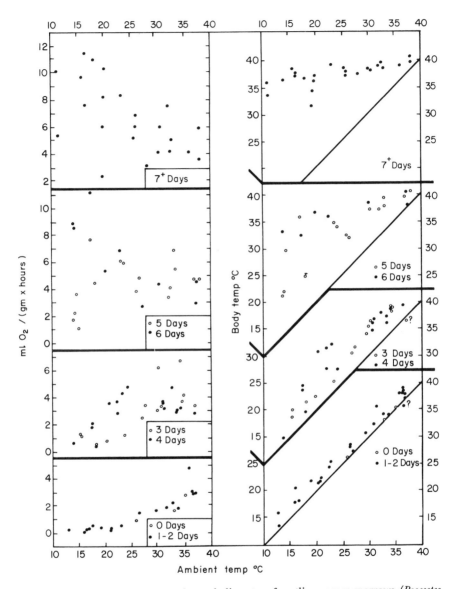

Fig. 8. Body temperatures and metabolic rates of nestling vesper sparrows (*Pooecetes gramineus*) at the end of 2-hour exposures to various ambient temperatures. The diagonal lines on the right-hand side of the figure indicate equivalence between body and ambient temperatures. Data on this altricial bird from Dawson and Evans (1960).

kinds of birds to the same environmental stress. Young aquatic birds of three species—western gulls (*Larus occidentalis*), great blue herons (*Ardea herodias*), and brown pelicans—are hatched near one another in exposed situations on a hot desert island in the Gulf of California, Mexico (Bartholomew and Dawson, 1954b), despite marked differences in thermoregulatory capacities. The gulls are fully covered with down at hatching and are

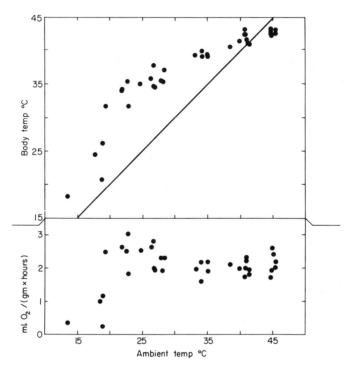

Fig. 9.   Body temperatures and metabolic rates of young laughing gulls (*Larus atricilla*) at the end of 2-hour exposures to various ambient temperatures. All of these precocial birds were studied within 24 hours of hatching. The diagonal line in the upper part of the figure indicates equivalence between deep body temperature and ambient temperature. Data from Dawson *et al.* (1970).

able to move about and obtain shelter from the sun and wind within a short time of emerging from the egg. They are generally attended by their parents only when being fed. Pelicans are hatched in a naked and helpless condition and lack any significant capacities for temperature regulation for the first few days of nestling life. They are prevented from becoming overheated in this period only by the extreme attentiveness of the adults, which closely brood or shade them. The young herons are intermediate between the other two species in thermoregulatory capacities at hatching, and their parents are also intermediate in attentiveness.

The diversity of attentive patterns of birds toward their young is revealed by Kendeigh's detailed review (1952) of the subject. While these patterns go a long way toward guaranteeing that the young develop under essentially homeothermic conditions, circumstances inevitably develop in which the possibilities of chilling or overheating arise for some species. The embryos and chicks of a number of species have been shown to be quite tolerant of low body temperatures (Baldwin and Kendeigh, 1932; Böni, 1942; Randall, 1943b; Koskimies, 1950; Barth, 1951; Ryser and Morrison, 1954; Westerkov, 1956; Dawson and Evans, 1957, 1960; Hudson *et al.,* 1970). This tolerance generally diminishes as the young attain full capacities for temperature regulation. The actions of the parents can be crucial in protection of both altricial and precocial young from solar radiation in hot environments (Bartholomew and Dawson, 1954b; Howell, 1959). However, overheating could still develop if ambient temperatures were at levels frequently seen during the middle of the day in parts of the tropics and subtropics. This threat is countered in at least some species—e.g., wrens (Kendeigh, 1939; Ricklefs and Hainsworth, 1968b), gulls (Dawson *et al.,* 1970), and cattle egrets (Hudson *et al.,* 1970)—by the establishment of effective evaporative cooling soon after hatching. The early development of this activity in altricial birds such as the wrens and cattle egret has not been widely appreciated. Nestling cactus wrens of all ages show open-mouthed breathing and increased respiratory rates at high ambient temperatures. Consequently, even very young birds can maintain their body temperatures below an ambient temperature of 44°C (Ricklefs and Hainsworth, 1968b). Gular fluttering is present in nestling cattle egrets on the day of hatching when they can barely hold their heads up (Hudson *et al.,* 1970; a record of gular fluttering by a nestling is shown in Fig. 5).

B. Events in the Development of Homeothermy in Altricial Birds

The pattern of development in altricial birds affords excellent opportunities for examining the ontogenetic events specifically involved in the attainment of complete homeothermy. Attention has been directed toward the three obvious categories: (1) development of mechanisms of nervous and endocrine control; (2) restriction of thermolysis; and (3) improvement of thermogenic capacities. These have been considered in some detail by Dawson and Evans (1957, 1960) in connection with their studies of the development of temperature regulation in nestling sparrows (data on the vesper sparrow, *Pooecetes gramineus,* are presented in Fig. 8). The development of control mechanisms cannot presently be directly evaluated, owing to the lack of suitable information. Changes in the relation of metabolism to ambient temperature in the sparrows and some other passerines indicate that neural mechanisms controlling thermogenesis are functional to some degree a few days before really effective regulation of body temperature is apparent (Kendeigh, 1939; Dawson and Evans, 1957, 1960). The active heat defense by at least some very young altricial birds (Ricklefs and Hainsworth, 1968b; Hudson *et al.,* 1970) indicates that thermostatic control is in fact present very early in the nestling period. The lack of neurophysiological information on nestlings is largely paralleled by the situation regarding endocrine function. However, Dawson and Allen (1960) have reported some histological observations on the thyroid glands of young and adult vesper sparrows. Their findings suggest that thyroid activity of the young birds throughout the nestling period matches or exceeds that of adults, a condition regarded as permissive to the establishment of effective regulation of body temperature. Thus, functional developments in both the nervous and endocrine systems appear to anticipate rather than delay the establishment of fully effective temperature control. The precise timing of the onset of homeothermy therefore appears most directly linked with the development of effector systems relating to thermogenesis and thermolysis.

Newly hatched nestlings have little ability to conserve heat, owing to their small size and naked condition. In the field sparrow (*Spizella pusilla*), chipping sparrow (*S. passerina*), and vesper sparrow, the ratio of body surface to volume declines by 50% between hatching and the appearance of reasonably effective temperature control on about the sixth day of the nestling period (Dawson and Evans, 1957, 1960). Such an improvement in the relation between surface and the amount of metabolically active tissue is of obvious importance in the establishment of such control. The development of feathers is also of importance to the restriction and control of heat loss. However, these structures appear more important for the perfection of temperature regulation than for its initiation—the sparrows studied by Dawson and Evans (1957, 1960) all displayed fairly effective control of body temperature at moderate and low temperatures before the eruption of the contour feathers from their sheaths. A similar condition has been noted in the rock dove (Pembrey, 1895; Ginglinger and Kayser, 1929) and house wren, *Troglodytes aedon* (Baldwin and Kendeigh, 1932; Kendeigh, 1939).

The growth producing a more favorable ratio between surface and volume in nestling altricial birds involves tissues that play predominant roles in the thermogenesis of the adult. The increase in skeletal muscle and the concurrent improvement of motor ability are particularly conspicuous. Within five days, these and related developments transform nestling sparrows from passive creatures capable of little more than ingestion, digestion, and egestion into active young birds that can stand, move about, and attempt to fly (Dawson and Evans, 1957, 1960). Over the same period, the liver and heart grow at relatively more rapid rates than does the body as a whole (Dawson and Evans, 1960). These changes are accompanied by an increase in the intensity of metabolism (Dawson and Evans, 1957); the development of the musculature and motor capacity also contribute to the establishment of effective shivering (Kendeigh, 1939; Odum, 1942; Hudson *et al.,* 1970).

The speed with which altricial birds develop effective temperature control at moderate ambient temperatures (20°–25°C) varies from species to species. Field, chipping, and vesper sparrows (Fig. 8) do not possess such control until approximately 6–7 days after hatching. This compares with 9–12 days for wrens (Baldwin and Kendeigh, 1932; Kendeigh, 1939; Ricklefs and Hainsworth, 1968b); 10 days for the red-backed shrike, *Lanius collurio,* 11 days for the wryneck, *Jynx torquilla,* 10 days for the budgerigar (Böni, 1942); 11 days for the rock dove (Ginglinger and Kayser, 1929); 6–7 days for the snow bunting, *Plectrophenax nivalis,* and Lapland longspur, *Calcarius lapponicus* (Maher, 1964); and 6–7 days for the cattle egret (Hudson *et al.,* 1970). Ricklefs and Hainsworth's (1968b) comparison of their data on nestling cactus wrens with those of Dawson and Evans (1960) on vesper sparrows indicates that various regulatory capacities develop at an earlier stage of growth in the latter species, which has a significantly shorter nestling period. The establishment of effective thermogenesis, in particular, seems to bear an evolutionarily flexible relation to growth.

C. The Significance of the Altricial Condition

The rudimentary capacities for thermoregulation evident in altricial forms at hatching make it tempting to equate their pattern of development with primitiveness, despite the fact that no contemporary bird is especially close in a phylogenetic sense to the stem of its class. The altricial condition actually appears to be a highly adaptive arrangement permitting rapid development at a low energetic cost. The immature state of newly hatched young and the relatively short period between fertilization and hatching characteristic of altricial species allow a relatively small egg with a lower energy content than is generally found in precocial forms of comparable size (Huxley, 1927). Witschi (1956) suggests that the adequacy of a smaller egg for animals of the former type was actually a key factor in the evolution of very small size, with all its challenging bioenergetic problems, in birds. Its importance is suggested by the fact that precocial shore birds lay eggs nearly twice as heavy as those produced by altricial birds of comparable size (Heinroth, 1922). Altricial young do not leave the shelter of the nest until they approach mature size. This, coupled with extensive brooding by the parents in the early part of the nestling period, would favor conversion of a relatively greater portion of their food into avian protoplasm than if they were less protected from the environment and compelled to expend more heat in temperature regulation.

The changes in metabolic rate per unit of weight that occur over the nestling period in birds of the order Passeriformes, in which the majority of species are small, also appear highly adaptive from an energetic standpoint. Among the few representatives of this order on which appropriate measurements have been performed (Kendeigh, 1939; Dawson and Evans, 1957, 1960), a weight-relative metabolism lower than, or only slightly exceeding, the basal rates of their parents is employed by young birds during the nestling period. The utilization of such relatively low metabolic rates during much of post-hatching development appears to favor conversion by the nestlings of a large portion of the food ingested into protoplasm, owing to low maintenance costs. The gross efficiency of this conversion during the first couple of days of the nestling period of the vesper sparrow (Dawson and Evans, 1960) seems to compare very favorably with the energetic efficiency estimated for precocial birds just prior to hatching (Brody, 1945). However, it should be noted that altricial nestlings convert food directly into protoplasm, rather than having it first converted to egg nutrients by the female parent, as in these precocial individuals. This in effect moves one link from the food chain, with a corresponding rise in the overall efficiency of energy conversion. Such a rise would tend to have a beneficial effect on the energetics of altricial species at the population level. For the individual, the various considerations outlined here undoubtedly contribute to achieving the growth rates exceeding 40% per day which have been documented in various sparrows and buntings for the first days after hatching (Dawson and Evans, 1957, 1960; Banks, 1959; Maher, 1964). Far from being merely a condition of transient unreadiness, the altricial mode of development has indeed afforded advantages for coping with the energetic problems of small size.

IX. Dormancy in Adult Birds

A. General Distribution among Birds

Adult birds of several orders can undergo moderate hypothermia or allow body temperature to drop sufficiently to induce torpor and later spontaneously arouse (see Table VIII; Bartholomew et al., 1957; Pearson, 1960). It remains to be determined whether moderate hypothermia and torpidity

William R. Dawson and Jack W. Hudson

TABLE VIII

Torpor and Hypothermia in Birds

Order, family, and species	Body wt (gm)	Minimal body temp observed[a] (°C)	Threshold for active arousal[a] (°C)	Observations and comments
Falconiformes, Cathartidae				
Turkey vulture (*Cathartes aura*)	2230	34.0		Moderate hypothermia induced by darkness. Bird shivering on arousal.[b]
Columbiformes, Columbidae				
Inca dove (*Scardafella inca*)	42	22	28.5	Hypothermia associated with inanition. Body temperature (T_B) more closely correlated with weight deficit than with ambient temperature (T_A). Arousal not observed with weight deficits greater than 15%. Authors question whether response strictly comparable to torpor of other birds.[c]
Cuculiformes, Cuculidae				
Smooth-billed ani (*Crotophaga ani*)	113	32.6		Hypothermia associated with inanition. No shivering detected on arousal. Rate of arousal, 0.01°C/min.[d]
Caprimulgiformes, Caprimulgidae				
Nightjar (*Caprimulgus europaeus*)	69	7.0	20	Torpidity on daily basis, associated with inanition. Rate of arousal 0.13° to 0.8°C/min, depending on initial T_B.[e]
Spotted nightjar (*Eurostopodus guttatus*)	86	29.6		Torpidity associated with 13% loss of wt T_A 23.7 during both torpor and arousal.[f]
Poor-will (*Phalaenoptilus nuttallii*)	39[g]	6.0		Torpor extends over 0.5 to 4 days; associated with severe inanition. Arousal occurred only after passive heating to higher T_B.[g]
Poor-will (*Phalaenoptilus nuttallii*)	32, 43.5	4.8–5.9	15	Torpidity associated with inanition and low T_A. Arousal rate, 0.30°–0.36°C/min. Arousal involves vigorous shivering.[h,i]
Common nighthawk (*Chordeiles minor*)	75	18		Torpidity associated with 28–34% loss of wt.[i]
Lesser nighthawk (*C. acutipennis*)		18.6–19.2		Large fat reserves apparent in torpid individuals.[g]
Apodiformes, Apodidae				
White-throated swift (*Aëronautes saxatilis*)	31	20	20	Torpidity associated with inanition.[h]
Common swift (*Apus* [*Micropus*] *apus*)	42	27[k]		Torpor associated with inanition. Occurs on daily basis in both fasting young and adults. Survival time without food, approximately 5 days.[k]
Apodiformes, Trochilidae				
Black-chinned hummingbird (*Archilochus alexandri*)	3	ca. 15		Torpid during restraint in flannel jacket in dark without food. T_B within 1.2° of T_A during torpor. Rate of arousal 1.0°–1.5°C/min.[k,l]
Anna hummingbird (*Calypte anna*)	4	8.8[g]	ca. 13[k,l]	Torpor associated with inanition. T_B within 1.2°C of T_A during torpor. Arousal rate of 1.0°–1.5°C/min at T_A of 21°–23°C.[g,l]
Costa's hummingbird (*Calypte costae*)	3	ca. 8	ca. 13	Torpor associated with conditions noted for *A. alexandri*. T_B within 1.2°C of T_A. Arousal rate 1.0°–1.5°C/min.[l,m]
Rufous hummingbird (*Selasphorus rufus*)	4	19		Torpor associated with conditions specified for *A. alexandri*.[m]

TABLE VIII *(Continued)*

Order, family, and species	Body wt (gm)	Minimal body temp observed[a] (°C)	Threshold for active arousal[a] (°C)	Observations and comments
Allen hummingbird (*Selasphorus sasin*)	3			Torpid at T_A of 22°C.[n]
Rivoli's hummingbird (*Eugenes fulgens*)	8	22.5		T_B obtained at T_A of 20°C. Torpor noted at T_A's of 15°–28°C. Estimated rate of arousal, 1.2°C/min.[o]
Blue-throated hummingbird (*Lampornis clemenciae*)	8	22.5		T_B obtained at T_A of 20°C. Torpor found at T_A's of approximately 15°–26°C. Rate of arousal at T_A of 20°C, estimated at 0.7°C/min.[o]
Chlorestes notatus	3	31		Fall of T_B to level noted occurred at night. Arousal occurred at rate of 0.4°C/min.[p] Lasiewski (1964) questions if birds truly torpid.
Hylocharis cyanus	3	31[p]		See above.
Amazilia leucogaster	4	32[p]		See above.
Giant hummingbird (*Patagona gigas*)	19	21.4[q]		See text.
Oreotrochilus chimborato				Observed torpid at T_A's of 3.5°–5°C.[r]
Eulampis jugularis	8	18[s]		See text.
Coliiformes, Coliidae				
Speckled coly (*Colius striatus*)		24.0		T_B obtained from bird in dark at T_A of 22°C.[t]
Speckled coly (*Colius striatus*)	42.5–45	22.8		Torpor associated with 10–15% loss of body weight produced by reduction of food ration. T_B obtained from bird in dark at T_A of 20°C.[t]
Passeriformes[u] Hirundinidae				
Violet-green swallow (*Tachycineta thalassina*)				Bird found torpid in nature at cool T_A's. Aroused with handling.[v]

[a] Minimal body temperature observed refers to lowest values that were not injurious. Threshold for active arousal refers to lowest body temperature at which spontaneous arousal can be initiated.

[b] Heath (1962).

[c] MacMillen and Trost (1967b).

[d] Warren (1960).

[e] Peiponen (1966).

[f] Dawson and Fisher (1969).

[g] Marshall (1955). Marshall's birds had been heavier than shown. The 39-gm wt is average of lowest values for three birds at which torpor did *not* occur. Jaeger (1949) found a 52-gm poor-will torpid in nature at T_B of ca 18°C.

[h] Bartholomew *et al.* (1957). White-throated swifts have been reported to be torpid in nature.

[i] Howell and Bartholomew (1959).

[j] Lasiewski and Dawson (1964).

[k] Koskimies (1948, 1950). The T_B of 27°C is for an adult at T_A of 19°C. T_B's approaching 20°C were noted in young birds.

[l] Lasiewski (1963).

[m] Lasiewski (1964).

[n] Pearson (1950). A female bird used in this study was found torpid in nature.

[o] Lasiewski and Lasiewski (1967).

[p] Morrison (1962).

[q] Lasiewski *et al.* (1967).

[r] French and Hodges (1959).

[s] Hainsworth and Wolf (1969).

[t] Bartholomew and Trost (1970).

[u] J. Steen (1958) observed T_B's of newly captured individuals of families Paridae, Ploceidae, and Fringillidae to drop between 30° and 38°C at night at low T_A's. Detailed data on the individual species are lacking.

[v] Lasiewski and Thompson (1966).

share any functional basis. Emphasis here will be on the latter condition on which a fair amount of data are available. Torpor usually lasts but a few hours in truly heterothermic birds. In nature, it would presumably be confined to the inactive phase of their respective daily cycles or to other periods in which food is temporarily unavailable. Although seasonal dormancy has been found in representatives of some mammalian orders, indications of its existence in birds are thus far confined to a single family, the Caprimulgidae (goatsuckers). It is to be anticipated from field observations that the list of species observed to become torpid under natural or laboratory conditions (Table VIII) will continue to grow. McAtee (1947) was led by certain of these observations to suggest that several species (chimney swifts, *Chaetura pelagica;* swallows; and, possibly, ptarmigan) become dormant on occasion. He also cites accounts indicating that the now extinct Carolina parakeet (*Conuropsis carolinensis*) possessed a capacity for dormancy.

Most birds that can enter torpor and spontaneously arouse feed on insects or nectar, both of which may become temporarily unavailable. It therefore appears significant that most instances of torpor in these species have been associated with reduction of energy reserves. This suggests that the initiation of dormancy is primarily an emergency measure serving to husband remaining reserves. The natural incidence of torpor has been difficult to judge from laboratory observations, for problems of establishing proper diets for the birds in captivity may in some instances have resulted in their being in negative energy balance throughout studies. The best example of this is provided by hummingbirds, a few representatives of which have actually been observed in a torpid state in nature (Huxley *et al.,* 1939; Pearson, 1950, 1953; French and Hodges, 1959), unlike many of the heterothermic species included in Table VIII. Pearson (1950) suggested that torpor occurred nightly in adult hummingbirds, as a consequence of the energetic problems associated with small size and the inability of these animals to feed in the dark. However, young Anna hummingbirds (*Calypte anna*) did not become torpid (Pearson, 1950) and an incubating female of this species remained continuously homeothermic (Howell and Dawson, 1954). Subsequently, Lasiewski (1963) demonstrated that several species of hummingbirds (Costa's hummingbird, *Calypte costae;* Anna hummingbird; rufous hummingbird, *Selasphorus rufus;* and black-chinned hummingbird, *Archilochus alexandri*) resorted to torpor only when their energy reserves were curtailed. On a proper diet, these animals could pass the night in a homeothermic condition even at low ambient temperatures.

Despite numerous studies concerned with the documentation of the existence of torpidity in various species (Table VIII), relatively little information is available concerning the actual mechanisms utilized by birds while entering or arousing from this state. Perhaps this is in part a tacit recognition of the difficulties involved in capturing and maintaining the appropriate species.

B. ENTRANCE INTO TORPOR

Much of the information on physiological processes of birds entering torpor results from the studies of Lasiewski and associates on hummingbirds restrained in cloth jackets (Lasiewski, 1963, 1964; Lasiewski and Lasiewski, 1967; Lasiewski *et al.,* 1967). Although such restraint can induce hypothermia in mammals (Lipp and Folk, 1960), the ability of hummingbirds to arouse swiftly in response to disturbance by light or sound suggests that restraint did not seriously modify their pattern of torpor.

During the entry of the giant hummingbird (*Patagona gigas*) into torpor, little or no electromyographic activity is evident (Lasiewski *et al.,* 1967). Shivering activity is also greatly reduced in the poor-will at this time (Bartholomew *et al.,* 1962). Therefore, muscular thermogenesis may not significantly modulate the rate of cooling. Further insight concerning the cooling process of heterothermic birds is provided by information on several hummingbirds (black-chinned hummingbird; Rivoli's hummingbird, *Eugenes fulgens;* blue-throated hummingbird, *Lampornis clemenciae;* and the giant hummingbird) weighing between 4 and 21 gm, and on the 40-gm poor-will (Lasiewski and Lasiewski, 1967; Lasiewski *et al.,* 1967). The decline of body temperature as these birds enter torpor follows a Newtonian cooling curve (i.e., it yields a straight line when the logarithms of the difference between body and ambient temperatures are plotted against time). Lasiewski and Lasiewski (1967) have taken this to suggest that the entry into torpor is largely a passive affair, the rate of which is primarily determined by purely physical considerations such as body weight, effective surface area, and thermal conductance. Such an interpretation is not inconsistent with the previously noted reduction of electromyographic activity in the giant hummingbird and poor-will. It would be of interest to test this interpretation by comparing the cooling curves of live and dead birds of the same species under similar environmental conditions.

The actual rates of entry of the hummingbirds and poor-will into torpor have been found to be inversely related to body weight (Lasiewski and Lasiewski, 1967; Lasiewski *et al.,* 1967). In this connection, it should be kept in mind that thermal conductance (cal gm^{-1} hr^{-1} $°C^{-1}$) and surface area/gm are both inversely correlated with body weight (Lasiewski and Lasiewski, 1967). The relation determined for cooling and body weight is of such a nature that approximately 65 minutes are required at an ambient temperature of 20°C for a 4-gm bird to cool from 35°–40°C to within a few degrees of its surroundings, whereas over four hours are needed in the case of a 40-gm individual (Lasiewski and Lasiewski, 1967).

The claim that entry into torpor is largely a passive affair raises some questions concerning the nature of the transition of various physiological processes from one level to another with cooling. This transition appears to be a smooth one judging from data on the oxygen consumption of the Anna hummingbird and poor-will (Bartholomew *et al.,* 1957; Howell and Bartholomew, 1959). Whether the rates of physiological processes decline in a manner determined by their individual sensitivities to temperature, or in partial response to nervous or hormonal modulation as well, remains to be determined. In this determination, it would be useful to have information on rate processes under the following conditions: (a) during entry into torpor of normal individuals and ones subjected to appropriate blockade of the autonomic nervous system, and (b) during *in vitro* study of various organs and tissues at various temperatures. It is of interest that the decline in heart rate of the giant hummingbird with declining body temperature appears to be essentially exponential. When Lasiewski *et al.*'s data (1967) on a 21-gm bird of this species are plotted on a semilogarithmic grid, a straight line with a slope corresponding to a Q_{10} of 2.6 can be fitted to the points.

C. The Torpid State in Birds

The metabolic rates of torpid birds may fall to less than $\frac{1}{50}$ of basal levels, depending on the actual body temperature reached after cooling (Lasiewski, 1963; Lasiewski and Lasiewski, 1967). The Q_{10} for the metabolism of hummingbirds in this state is 4.1. The level of oxygen consumption for these birds in the vicinity of 20°C approximated that of torpid little brown bats, *Myotis lucifugus* (Lasiewski, 1963). Reductions in metabolism are paralleled by the changes in heart rates and in the frequency and pattern of breathing. Heart rates of torpid hummingbirds ranged from 48 beats/min at an ambient temperature of 7°C to 180 beats/min at 29.6°C (Lasiewski, 1964). Body temperature approximated ambient temperature during the measurements. The rates obtained amount to $\frac{1}{50}$ to $\frac{1}{3}$ the heart rates noted in homeothermic individuals within the zone of thermal neutrality. During entry into torpor at an ambient temperature of 5°C, the heart rate of a poor-will declined from about 500 beats/min to less than 10 beats/min. The minimal rate is less than $\frac{1}{20}$ of that noted in homeothermic poor-wills within the zone of thermal neutrality (Bartholomew *et al.,* 1962). Atrioventricular dissociation was detected electrocardiographically in a Costa's and in a black-chinned hummingbird at body temperatures of 11.5°C and 7°C, respectively. Both birds ultimately died at these temperatures (Lasiewski, 1964). Torpid hummingbirds breathed irregularly at slow rates, with long periods of apnea (Bartholomew *et al.*, 1957; Lasiewski, 1964). Their rates of water loss are significantly reduced, ranging from $\frac{1}{3}$ to approximately $\frac{1}{10}$ of values for homeothermic individuals (Lasiewski, 1964; Lasiewski and Lasiewski, 1967). Torpidity therefore allows conservation of water as well as energy.

The poor-will can endure body temperatures of 5°–8°C for many hours without ill effect (Bartholomew *et al.*, 1957; Howell and Bartholomew, 1959), and the nightjar (*Caprimulgus europaeus*) appears endowed with similar tolerance (Peiponen, 1966). On the other hand, body temperatures below 8°C appear lethal for hummingbirds, although Lasiewski (1963) has not excluded the possibility that some form of acclimation might increase the resistance of these animals to chilling. As noted previously, body temperatures at which atrioventricular dissociation was detected in the black-chinned and Costa's hummingbirds are close to 8°C (Lasiewski, 1964). In connection with these observations of goatsuckers and hummingbirds, it should be emphasized that body temperatures of 5°–8°C are well below those at which spontaneous arousal has generally been found to be possible (see Section IX,D).

Most available studies of the physiology of birds in deep torpor contribute to a basis for estimating the conservation of energy and water possible at low body temperatures. However, they do not permit an adequate evaluation of the state of various thermoregulatory processes during dormancy. Body temperature generally remains within a degree or so of ambient temperature once entry into torpor has been completed in poor-wills and hummingbirds. This agreement persists in the poor-wills even when the environment is cooled to slightly below 5°C (Bartholomew *et al.*, 1957; Howell and Bartholomew, 1959); the lowering of body temperature to potentially dangerous levels does not produce arousal as it does in certain hibernating mammals. This unresponsiveness is linked with the fact that birds generally must be at a body temperature exceeding at least 13°C before they can actively arouse from a torpid state (see Section IX,D). The close conformance of body temperature to ambient temperature in birds in deep torpor indicates a lack of effectiveness of the various processes involved in control of body temperature, but it should not be taken to mean that all regulatory activity is suppressed. Indeed, electromyographic measurements indicate that a torpid poor-will shivered weakly in response to a 0.5°C drop in body temperature accompanying an abrupt decrease of ambient temperature from 6°C to 4°C. The particular bird was one in which active arousal was not initiated until body temperature had passively increased to 15°C (Bartholomew *et al.*, 1962). In most torpid hummingbirds, body temperature approximates ambient temperature. The tropical species *Eulampis jugularis* appears to represent a notable exception. Temperatures of torpid *E. jugularis* do fall near those of the environment between 18° and 30°C, metabolism varying directly with temperature in this interval. However, an inverse relation exists between the metabolic rates of these torpid individuals and ambient temperature below 18°C, and this serves to stabilize body temperature at 18°–20°C (Hainsworth and Wolf, 1969).

D. Arousal from Torpor

As noted in the preceding section, torpid birds usually must be at moderately warm body temperatures before they can actively initiate arousal. Lasiewski (1963) found that this process did not begin in hummingbirds at ambient temperatures below 12°C. This would place the minimal body temperature for arousal in the vicinity of 13°C (Lasiewski, 1964). It is interesting to speculate whether or not this figure applies to representatives of *Oreotrochilus chimborato* found torpid at ambient temperatures of 3.5°C to 5°C in the Andes (French and Hodges, 1959). Spontaneous arousal did not commence in the poor-will at body temperatures below 15°C in the studies of Howell and Bartholomew (1959) and Bartholomew *et al.* (1962). Successful arousal occurred at body temperatures as low as 18°C or 19°C in the lesser nighthawk and common nighthawk, *Chordeiles minor* (Marshall, 1955; Lasiewski and Dawson, 1964). The threshold for this process approximated 20°C in the white-throated swift, *Aëronautes saxatilis,* and nightjar (Bartholomew *et al.,* 1957; Peiponen, 1966). Thus far, the best indication of the existence of a lower temperature threshold for arousal is provided by Ligon's observations (1967) on a poor-will during late fall. This captive individual repeatedly initiated successful arousals at body temperatures in the vicinity of 6°C. Why it differed from the other poor-wills on which information is available is unknown.

The process of spontaneous arousal from torpor involves a dramatic rise in oxygen consumption, which appears to depend primarily on vigorous shivering (Bartholomew *et al.,* 1962). This is evidently accompanied by greatly increased circulatory activity. The best available indication of this concerns the changes of heart rate in an arousing giant hummingbird (Lasiewski *et al.,* 1967). As the body temperature of this bird rose from 21°C to 26°C, the heart rate increased from about 150 to 570 beats/min. The rate increased from 570 to over 1000 beats/min between 26°C and 36°C, but at a relatively slow pace ($Q_{10} < 2$). All the rates observed during arousal are more than double the ones noted at the corresponding body temperatures during entry into torpor (see Section IX,B). This attests to the vigor of the arousal process and suggests that extensive stimulation of the heart by the sympathetic nervous system occurs. Such stimulation has also been implicated in the arousal of the Beechey ground squirrel (*Citellus beecheyi*) from torpor (Strumwasser, 1960).

The rate of warming by birds actively arousing from torpor appears inversely related to body weight (Lasiewski and Lasiewski, 1967; Lasiewski *et al.*, 1967). The relation is such that at an ambient temperature of 20°C, a 4-gm black-chinned hummingbird required approximately 10 minutes to raise its body temperature from the environmental level to above 35°C, whereas a 40-gm poor-will needed about 35 minutes to accomplish this (Lasiewski and Lasiewski, 1967). This inverse relation parallels that between cooling rates of birds entering torpor, and body weight. Consequently, the overall time required for an animal to cool to, and rewarm from, a particular body temperature rises conspicuously with increasing size, the 4-gm and 40-gm birds requiring approximately 75 and 285 minutes, respectively. On the basis of their analysis, Lasiewski and Lasiewski (1967) estimate that a bird weighing 80 to 100 gm would require about 12 hours merely to cool to near an ambient temperature of 20°C and then actively return to a homeothermic level of body temperature. A period of this or longer duration would make daily reliance on deep torpidity impractical. The active phase of the daily cycle would be greatly restricted and the caloric savings achieved by a larger bird during a necessarily brief period in deep torpor would probably be overshadowed by the amount of energy required for arousal.

E. Some Questions Regarding Dormancy in Birds

The studies of torpid birds cited in the preceding sections comprise a promising beginning for the analysis of the physiological basis of dormancy in birds. However, it is apparent that such an analysis has been hindered by: (1) the paucity of quantitative observations on torpid birds in nature; (2) the difficulty of obtaining appropriate subjects for experimentation; and (3) the restriction of the vast majority of the physiological measurements performed thus far to body temperature and the most easily measured rate processes of heterothermic birds. Several aspects of avian dormancy have received insufficient attention and it appears worthwhile to direct attention toward the more important of these in the remainder of this section.

Obviously, one major problem meriting study is that concerning determination of whether or not the moderate reductions in body temperature noted (see Table VIII) in birds such as the turkey vulture (*Cathartes aura*) and smooth-billed ani (*Crotophaga ani*) have the same functional basis as the much more profound reductions associated with deep torpor. The fact that the minimal levels of body temperature observed in the turkey vulture and the smooth-billed ani exceed 30°C cannot a priori be taken as an indication that these birds differ fundamentally from those that enter deep torpor, e.g., hummingbirds and goatsuckers. In the case of the vulture, the fact that body temperature did not fall below 34°C in an environment at 15°C may reflect a very low rate of cooling associated with large body size (see Table VIII). In this connection, it is appropriate to mention again the inverse relation between cooling rate and body weight found by Lasiewski and Lasiewski (1967) and Lasiewski *et al.* (1967). The apparent restriction of the minimal body temperature of the smooth-billed ani to a relatively high level (see Table VIII) may have been entirely adventitious. The two birds of this species studied by Warren (1960) were both maintained at ambient temperatures in excess of 30°C, which would not permit a large drop in body temperature. The major indication that the response of the smooth-billed ani may in fact differ qualitatively from that characterizing a truly heterothermic bird is its apparent lack of shivering and slow rate of warming during arousal (Warren, 1960). More detailed physiological observations are certainly warranted on this largely tropical species.

Another major problem that requires extensive investigation concerns the nature of the stimulus or stimuli capable of inducing birds to become torpid in nature. In most experimental studies performed thus far, entry into torpor has been associated with moderate to severe depletion of energy reserves (see Table VIII). However, the dormant poor-will observed in nature by Jaeger (1949) was quite heavy (52 gm), a fact suggesting a good nutritional state. Marshall's discovery (1955) of significant fat reserves in captive lesser nighthawks following their entry into torpidity also implies adequate energy reserves. In view of these findings, it appears reasonable to ask whether or not inanition is the only factor involved in the induction of dormancy in goatsuckers and other truly heterothermic species. Other stimuli may well exist in nature, which could either act independently or increase the sensitivity of the birds to reduction of energy reserves. Perhaps the propensity of birds for becoming dormant changes seasonally in a manner correlated with photoperiod, ambient temperature, or other environmental factors, as the observations of Huxley *et al.* (1939) suggest. Studies of endocrinological activity would appear useful in contributing to an understanding of the nature of any seasonal changes; thus far endocrine studies of heterothermic birds are confined to Shellabarger *et al.*'s observations (1961) of thyroid activity in homeothermic and torpid hummingbirds. It would also appear useful to determine the extent to which purely endogenous factors influence the incidence of dormancy in birds.

A final line of physiological investigation that should be mentioned concerns full characterization of the temperature sensitivities of heterothermic birds and their constituent organs and tissues. Can the threshold for spontaneous arousal be reduced from 13°–20°C, the range most commonly observed in the laboratory, as Ligon's observations (1967) on the poor-will suggest? Can the tolerance of heterothermic birds to chilling be improved by some form of thermal acclimation? How do the thermal characteristics of intact heterothermic and persistently homeothermic birds and of their respective organs and tissues compare?

Obviously, a full evaluation of the biological significance of avian dormancy requires a better understanding of the frequency and timing of its occurrence in nature. Where representatives of a heterothermic species have not been found in a dormant state under natural conditions, the possibility always exists that torpidity observed in the laboratory may be merely a response to unnatural and highly stressful conditions. Unfortunately, an immense amount of field work by persons interested in birds has to date yielded meager results in terms of location and observation of dormant individuals.

X. Some Evolutionary Considerations

Attempts to trace the evolution of homeothermy in birds are fraught with difficulties. First of all, current concepts of the origin and early deployment of birds are largely a matter of inference, owing to a very incomplete fossil record. The structure of the earliest known bird, *Archeopteryx lithographica,* from the upper Jurassic of Bavaria, places the origin of the class among the thecodont reptiles (Swinton, 1960). Birds appear to have arisen from a single line that appeared with the radiation of this reptilian group in the Triassic. The stage in the evolution of this line at which homeothermy was definitively established is unknown.

A second reason for the difficulty in treating the evolution of homeothermy in birds concerns the restricted utility in this context of physiological observations on contemporary species. Potentially, comparative studies of "primitive" and "advanced" species might provide information contributing to a reconstruction of the historical development of physiological temperature regulation. Unfortunately, no living bird is especially primitive, all contemporary members of the class appearing highly modified for their respective niches. This was recognized many decades ago by Beddard (1898), who concluded: "the few specially reptilian features in the organisation of birds have, so to speak been distributed with such exceeding fairness through the class that no type has any great advantage over its fellows." Mammals, on the other hand, include both fairly primitive and highly advanced types. Among the former, the monotremes, though specialized in some respects, have many features of therapsid reptiles (G. G. Simpson, 1959).

It is always possible that indications of steps in the evolution of physiological temperature regulation might be obtained by study of the ontogeny of this process. However, great caution must be exercised in interpretation of data for young birds. Altricial species, those in which the development of homeothermy can most easily be traced, develop according to patterns that must have been the subject of rigorous selection (see Section VIII). In this instance, ontogeny probably only recapitulates phylogeny when expedient. However, it is of interest that fairly effective temperature control at moderate ambient temperatures coincides with the development of thermogenic capacities and precedes the appearance of an insulating plumage (Dawson and Evans, 1957, 1960).

A desire to understand steps in the evolution of homeothermy might lead one to turn entirely to studies of contemporary reptiles, in view of the problems just enumerated. None of these animals is very close in a phylogenetic sense to any line of direct importance in the evolution of birds, but their study does provide some estimate of the thermoregulatory capacities possible within a reptilian grade of organization. The abilities of many reptiles to maintain their body temperatures at characteristic levels by behavioral means during activity are well known (Dawson, 1967). These abilities are of particular interest because of the capacities for thermal perception which they imply (see Heath, 1968). The nature of this perception has recently been examined in the blue-tongued skink (*Tiliqua scincoides*) through analysis of the effects of altering temperature of the brain on thermoregulatory behavior (Hammel *et al.*, 1967) and through study of thermally sensitive neurons in this organ (Cabanac *et al.*, 1967; see also Chapter 5).

Mechanisms for physiological as well as behavioral regulation of body temperature exist in reptiles (see Chapter 5). Possibly the most spectacular example of the former is the muscular thermogenesis found in a brooding female Indian python, *Python molurus bivittatus* (Hutchison *et al.*, 1966). This results from spasmodic contractions of the body musculature at frequencies inversely related to ambient temperature between 25°C and 33°C. Muscular thermogenesis gave the brooding snake a metabolism–temperature curve similar in form to those of true homeotherms. This permitted the animal to remain about 5°C warmer than the environment with ambient temperature at approximately 25°C, and so maintain its eggs under relatively warm conditions. Another brooding python was earlier found to remain as much as 7.3°C warmer than the environment with an ambient temperature of about 25°C.

Other forms of physiological temperature regulation are known in reptiles.

The collared lizard (*Crotaphytus collaris*), for example, conspicuously aug-
ments its evaporative water loss at body temperatures above 40°C. This
affords it a modest capacity for remaining cooler than the environment
at ambient temperatures approaching injurious levels (Dawson and Templeton, 1963). Other lizards can modulate their rates of cooling and heating
by changes in thermal conductance (Bartholomew and Tucker, 1963, 1964;
Bartholomew *et al.*, 1965; Bartholomew and Lasiewski, 1965). The Galapagos marine iguana (*Amblyrhynchus cristatus*) is the most spectacular
in this regard, heating approximately twice as fast as it cools under standardized conditions in both air and water (Bartholomew and Lasiewski,
1965). The changes in thermal conductance demonstrated in lizards appear
to be effected by vasomotor activity.

Observations of the type just cited concerning the thermoregulatory
capacities of reptiles certainly do not permit the tracing of the historical
events leading to the establishment of homeothermy in birds. However,
they do suggest that some thermally significant physiological and behavioral
abilities were present in the antecedants of the avian class. The actual
establishment of homeothermy in this group would therefore appear to
have involved the enhancement of existing capacities as much as the development of qualitatively new ones.

Dawson (1962) has suggested, from a review of information on the
physiology of contemporary reptiles and young birds, that the crucial steps
in the transition from poikilothermy to homeothermy were probably metabolic, involving: (1) an overall intensification of levels of heat production
with its far reaching demands on various organ systems, and then (2)
the development of chemical regulation with its underlying control mechanisms. Certain components of physical regulation (active evaporative cooling
and vasomotor activity) were probably already present in the avian evolutionary line as legacies from its reptilian antecedants. Other components
probably developed only after the intensification of metabolism occurred.
The full development of insulation must have been influenced not only
by thermal considerations, but also by requirements of birds for gliding
and, ultimately, flight.

Bartholomew and Tucker (1963) provide an essentially parallel interpretation to that just outlined, from their studies of modulation of rates
of heating and cooling in an agamid lizard, *Amphibolurus barbatus*. They
suggest that the variable conductance allowing control of rates of temperature change in this animal would be appropriate for a form evolving toward
homeothermy, but still dependent on solar radiation for attaining the body
temperature associated with activity. For such a form, even a slight increase
in endogenous heat production would allow greater precision of control
of rate of change of body temperature. Bartholomew and Tucker (1963)

further assume that natural selection for increased metabolic rate could ultimately lead to the persistently high level of metabolism found in homeotherms. Fur or feathers would appear maladaptive in an animal dependent on exogenous heat, for they would retard the absorption of solar radiation. Only after an intensification of metabolism, which would decrease dependence of the nascent homeotherm on solar heating, would the insulation afforded by pelage or plumage become advantageous.

Although reconstruction of the exact steps leading to the appearance of homeothermy in the avian line cannot be made with certainty, it is possible with the information at hand to outline the character of certain subsequent evolutionary developments pertaining to thermal adaptation. Adaptation of any bird to a new set of temperature conditions might involve evolutionary modification of any or all of the following: (1) body temperature, (2) metabolic level, and (3) abilities to control the dissipation of heat. Body temperature appears essentially nonadaptive to climate, despite the temporary hypothermia or hyperthermia evident in some species under adverse conditions. Temporary hypothermia leading to dormancy is restricted to relatively few species and may be only of an emergency nature in the majority of these (see Section IX). Temporary hyperthermia, which plays such an important role in the adjustment of most birds to heat, capitalizes on a general avian tolerance of elevated body temperatures (see Section VI; Bartholomew and Dawson, 1958). In general, comparable species from markedly different climates tend to have similar body temperatures when tested under similar conditions (Scholander *et al.,* 1950c; Scholander, 1955; Dawson and Schmidt-Nielsen, 1964).

Metabolic level generally appears more closely correlated with body weight and taxonomic position of birds (see Section III,B) than with climatic characteristics of the regions in which they reside, if the influence of differences in thermal acclimation are excluded. It appears that evolutionary shifts in this level have not been significantly involved in the process of adaptation to cold in birds (Scholander *et al.,* 1950c; Scholander, 1955). Such a conclusion may not be so generally applicable to birds that must contend with severe heat. Hudson and Kimzey (1966) concluded that house sparrows occupying the hot, humid climate of Houston, Texas, benefit in their heat tolerance from a persistently lower metabolic level than that found in more northern populations of this species. There can be little doubt that the unusually low level of heat production by the poor-will contributes significantly to its impressive heat resistance (Bartholomew *et al.,* 1962). Perhaps this actually represents a case of preadaptation to thermal stress, for goatsuckers generally tend to have fairly low basal metabolic rates for birds of their size (Lasiewski and Dawson, 1967). A relatively low metabolic level not only offers the advantage of a low caloric burden in hot environments, it also restricts the amount of water that must be expended in evaporative cooling. Attention should be directed to determination of just how prevalent evolutionary modification of metabolic level has been in the process of adaptation to heat by birds.

Scholander *et al.* (1950c) and Scholander (1955) have stressed the importance of improving mechanisms for controlling heat loss in the evolutionary adjustment of homeotherms to cold. Larger arctic mammals, in particular, possess effective insulation that allows them to maintain thermal balance with no more than a basal level of heat production in even subfreezing environments. Enhancement of mechanisms for conservation of heat has also figured in the evolutionary adaptation of birds to cold (see Section V), but the relatively small size of the majority of the species resident in cold climates and the constraints apparently placed upon plumage development by aerodynamic requirements of flight have tended to restrict its role. Consequently, a basal level of heat production will not allow most of these animals to maintain thermal balance in very cold environments. This must have created selective pressure related to the development of effective muscular thermogenesis and, in at least some instances, establishment of capacities for seasonally enhancing capabilities for heat production (see Section V).

Relatively few options would exist in the process of adaptation to heat. Behavior serving to reduce heat stress, hyperthermia, and, in certain cases, reduced metabolic levels, each make an important contribution (see Section VI), but they cannot exempt a bird from extensive evaporative cooling in very hot environments. However, it should not be inferred from this that selective demands of hot environments were entirely responsible for the evolution of effective mechanisms for evaporative water loss. Requirements for rapid dissipation of heat loads accumulated during vigorous flight (see Section VII) may well have constituted a selective pressure favoring establishment of the capacities for markedly augmenting evaporation now characterizing birds generally (Calder and Schmidt-Nielsen, 1967). In certain notable instances, the development of these capacities appears to have depended in part on exploitation of structures functioning primarily in procurement or handling of food. Among species with gular fluttering, the large mouth and extensive oral surface facilitating aerial capture of insects by goatsuckers, and the pouches of pelicans and cormorants are clearly of this sort.

Any consideration of the evolutionary aspects of thermoregulation inevitably leads to some mention of the so-called climatic rules of Bergmann and Allen. The controversy surrounding these rules and their possible significance from the standpoint of temperature adaptation have been thoughtfully evaluated by King and Farner (1961), and the arguments will not be rehearsed here. It does appear useful to point out that the latitudinal clines in body size with which Bergmann's rule is concerned may not have been considered from a sufficiently broad perspective. Changes in the ratio of surface to body weight have traditionally been regarded as the potentially adaptive feature of these clines, a reduced ratio favoring heat conservation and an increased one, heat dissipation. The small extent of the changes in this ratio typically observed in species in which the appropriate clines occur led Scholander (1955) to question their thermal significance. However, the fact that the amount of insulation carried by small homeotherms tends to vary directly with body weight has been insufficiently emphasized. This could reinforce the effects relating to the ratio of surface to weight, as Herreid and Kessel (1967), Brown (1968), and Brown and Lee (1969) have suggested from studies of birds and rodents, respectively. Thus a definitive evaluation of the functional significance of size clines conforming to Bergmann's Rule should involve insulative as well as geometric considerations. The types of analyses of avian energetics recently employed by Kendeigh (1969) and Porter and Gates (1969) should facilitate such an evaluation.

ACKNOWLEDGMENTS

Preparation of this review was supported in part by grants from the National Science Foundation (GB-1455 and GB-6269) and from the National Institutes of Health (GM-11368-04 and GM-15889-01). Our original research was supported in part by grants from the National Science Foundation (W. R. D.) and the National Institutes of Health (J. W. H.).

REFERENCES

Ahmad, M. M., Moreng, R. E., and Muller, H. D. (1967). *Poultry Sci.* **46**, 6.
Åkerman, B., Andersson, B., Fabricius, E., and Svensson, L. (1960). *Acta Physiol. Scand.* **50**, 328.
Akester, A. R. (1960). *J. Anat.* **94**, 488.
Andersson, B., Gale, C. C., and Hökfelt, B. (1964). *In* "Major Problems in Neuroendocrinology" (E. Bajusz and G. Jasmin, eds.), pp. 42–61. Williams & Wilkins, Baltimore, Maryland.
Baldwin, S. P., and Kendeigh, S. C. (1932). *Sci. Publ. Cleveland Museum Nat. Hist.* **3**, 1.
Banks, R. C. (1959). *Condor* **61**, 96.
Barott, H. G., and Pringle, E. M. (1941). *J. Nutr.* **22**, 273.
Barott, H. G., and Pringle, E. M. (1946). *J. Nutr.* **31**, 35.
Barth, E. K. (1951). *Nyt Mag. Naturv.* **88**, 213.
Bartholomew, G. A. (1966). *Condor* **68**, 523.
Bartholomew, G. A., and Cade, T. J. (1957). *Wilson Bull.* **69**, 149.
Bartholomew, G. A., and Cade, T. J. (1963). *Auk* **80**, 504.
Bartholomew, G. A., and Dawson, W. R. (1952). *Condor* **54**, 58.

Bartholomew, G. A., and Dawson, W. R. (1953). *Physiol. Zool.* **26,** 162.
Bartholomew, G. A., and Dawson, W. R. (1954a). *Ecology* **35,** 181.
Bartholomew, G. A., and Dawson, W. R. (1954b). *Ecology* **35,** 466.
Bartholomew, G. A., and Dawson, W. R. (1958). *Auk* **75,** 150.
Bartholomew, G. A., and Lasiewski, R. C. (1965). *Comp. Biochem. Physiol.* **16,** 573.
Bartholomew, G. A., and Trost, C. H. (1970). *Condor* (in press).
Bartholomew, G. A., and Tucker, V. A. (1963). *Physiol. Zool.* **36,** 199.
Bartholomew, G. A., and Tucker, V. A. (1964). *Physiol. Zool.* **37,** 341.
Bartholomew, G. A., Dawson, W. R., and O'Neill, E. J. (1953). *Ecology* **34,** 554.
Bartholomew, G. A., Howell, T. R., and Cade, T. J. (1957). *Condor* **59,** 145.
Bartholomew, G. A., Hudson, J. W., and Howell, T. R. (1962). *Condor* **64,** 117.
Bartholomew, G. A., Tucker, V. A., and Lee, A. K. (1965). *Copeia* p. 169.
Bartholomew, G. A., Lasiewski, R. C., and Crawford, E. C., Jr. (1968). *Condor* **70,** 31,
Beddard, F. E. (1898). "The Structure and Classification of Birds." Longmans, Green. New York.
Behle, W. H. (1944). *Condor* **46,** 128.
Benedict, F. G. (1938). *Carnegie Inst. Wash. Publ.* **503.**
Benedict, F. G., and Fox, E. L. (1927). *Proc. Am. Phil. Soc.* **66,** 511.
Benedict, F. G., and Lee, R. C. (1937). *Carnegie Inst. Wash. Publ.* **489.**
Benzinger, T. H., Kitzinger, C., and Pratt, A. W. (1963). *In* "Temperature—Its Measurement and Control in Science and Industry," Part 3 (J. D. Hardy, ed.), pp. 637–665. Reinhold, New York.
Bernstein, M. H. (1969). *Am. Zoologist* **9,** 1099.
Birkebak, R. C., Cremers, C. J., and LeFebvre, E. A. (1966) *J. Heat Transfer* **88,** 125.
Bligh, J., and Hartley, T. C. (1965). *Ibis* **107,** 104.
Böni, A. (1942). *Schweiz. Arch. Ornithol.* **2,** 1.
Brody, S. (1945). "Bioenergetics and Growth." Reinhold, New York.
Brody, S., and Proctor, R. C. (1932). *Missouri, Univ., Agr. Expt. Sta., Res. Bull.* **166,** 89.
Brown, J. H. (1968). *Misc. Publ. Museum Zool., Univ. Mich.* No. 135, 1–48.
Brown, J. H., and Lee, A. K. (1969). *Evolution* **23,** 329.
Brush, A. H. (1965). *Comp. Biochem. Physiol.* **15,** 399.
Burckard, E., Dontcheff, L., and Kayser, C. (1933). *Ann. Physiol. Physicochim. Biol.* **9,** 303.
Butsch, R. S. (1957). *Jack Pine Warbler* **35,** 14.
Cabanac, M., Hammel, H. T., and Hardy, J. D. (1967). *Physiologist* **10,** 137.
Cade, T. J. (1953). *Condor* **55,** 43.
Cade, T. J., Tobin, C. A., and Gold, A. (1965). *Physiol. Zool.* **38,** 9.
Calder, W. A. (1964). *Physiol. Zool.* **37,** 400.
Calder, W. A. (1968). *Condor* **70,** 84.
Calder, W. A., and Schmidt-Nielsen, K. (1966). *Proc. Natl. Acad. Sci. U.S.* **55,** 750.
Calder, W. A., and Schmidt-Nielsen, K. (1967). *Am. J. Physiol.* **213,** 883.
Calder, W. A., and Schmidt-Nielsen, K. (1968). *Am. J. Physiol.* **215,** 477.
Cascio, G. (1948). *Boll. Soc. Ital. Biol. Sper.* **24,** 565.
Chaffee, R. R. J., Mayhew, W. W., Drebin, M., and Cassuto, Y. (1963). *Can. J. Biochem. Physiol.* **41,** 2215.
Chaffee, R. R. J., Cassuto, Y., and Horvath, S. M. (1965). *Can. J. Physiol. Pharmacol.* **43,** 1021.
Chossat, C. (1843). *Ann. Sci. Nat. Zool.* [2] **20,** 54.
Collins, C. T. (1963). *Condor* **65,** 528.
Cottle, W. H., and Carlson, L. D. (1956). *Proc. Soc. Exptl. Biol. Med.* **92,** 845.
Cowles, R. B., and Dawson, W. R. (1951). *Condor* **53,** 19.
Crawford, E. C., Jr. (1962). *J. Appl. Physiol.* **17,** 249.

Crawford, E. C., Jr., and Lasiewski, R. C. (1968). *Condor* **70**, 333.

Crawford, E. C., Jr., and Schmidt-Nielsen, K. (1967). *Am. J. Physiol.* **212**, 347.

Davis, E. A., Jr. (1955). *Auk* **72**, 385.

Davis, T. R. A. (1961). *J. Appl. Physiol.* **16**, 1011.

Dawson, T., and Schmidt-Nielsen, K. (1966). *J. Cell Physiol.* **67**, 463.

Dawson, W. R. (1954). *Univ. Calif. (Berkeley) Publ. Zool.* **59**, 81.

Dawson, W. R. (1958). *Physiol. Zool.* **31**, 37.

Dawson, W. R. (1962). *In* "Comparative Physiology of Temperature Regulation" (J. P. Hannon and E. Viereck, eds.), pp. 45–71. Arctic Aeromed. Lab., Fort Wainwright, Alaska.

Dawson, W. R. (1967). *In* "Lizard Ecology: A Symposium" (W. W. Milstead, ed.), pp. 230–257. Univ. of Missouri Press, Columbia, Missouri.

Dawson, W. R., and Allen, J. M. (1960). *Condor* **62**, 403.

Dawson, W. R., and Bartholomew, G. A. (1968). *In* "Desert Biology" (G. W. Brown, ed.), Vol. 1, pp. 357–394. Academic Press, New York.

Dawson, W. R., and Evans, F. C. (1957). *Physiol. Zool.* **30**, 315.

Dawson, W. R., and Evans, F. C. (1960). *Condor* **62**, 329.

Dawson, W. R., and Fisher, C. D. (1969). *Condor* **71**, 49.

Dawson, W. R., and Fisher, C. D. (1970a). Temperature regulation and water economy of the galah (*Kakatöe roseicapilla*). MS.

Dawson, W. R., and Fisher, C. D. (1970b). Temperature regulation and water balance of the crested pigeon. MS.

Dawson, W. R., and Schmidt-Nielsen, K. (1964). *In* "Handbook of Physiology" (Am. Physiol. Soc., J. Field, ed.), Sect. 4, pp. 481–492. Williams & Wilkins, Baltimore, Maryland.

Dawson, W. R., and Templeton, J. R. (1963). *Physiol. Zool.* **36**, 219.

Dawson, W. R., and Tordoff, H. B. (1959). *Condor* **61**, 388.

Dawson, W. R., and Tordoff, H. B. (1964). *Auk* **81**, 26.

Dawson, W. R., and Tordoff, H. B. (1970). Temperature regulation and water economy of the Gouldian finch. MS.

Dawson, W. R., Hudson, J. W., and Hill, R. W. (1970). Thermoregulatory capacities of newly hatched laughing gulls. MS.

Deighton, T., and Hutchinson, J. C. D. (1940). *J. Agr. Sci.* **30**, 141.

Dontcheff, L., and Kayser, C. (1934). *Ann. Physiol. Physicochim. Biol.* **10**, 285.

Dukes, H. H. (1937). *J. Nutr.* **14**, 341.

Dunsheath, M. H., and Doncaster, C. C. (1941). *Brit. Birds* **25**, 138.

Edminster, F. C. (1947). "The Ruffed Grouse." Macmillan, New York.

Edwards, W. F. (1839). *In* "Todd's Cyclopedia of Anatomy and Physiology," Vol. 2, pp. 648–684.

Eisentraut, M. (1961). *Bull. Museum Comp. Zool. Harvard Coll.* **124**, 31.

Farner, D. S. (1956). *J. Appl. Physiol.* **8**, 546.

Farner, D. S., and Serventy, D. L. (1959). *Condor* **61**, 426.

Farner, D. S., Chivers, N., and Riney, T. (1956). *Emu* **56**, 199.

Fazio, F. (1943). *Arch. Fisiol.* **43**, 326.

Feldman, S. E., Larsson, S., Dimick, M. K., and Lepkovsky, S. (1957). *Am. J. Physiol.* **191**, 259.

Fisher, H. I., and Dater, E. E. (1961). *Auk* **78**, 528.

Fonberg, A. (1932). *Sprawozdania Posiedzen Towarz. Nauk. Warszaw. Wydzial IV, Nauk Biol.* **25**, 59.

Fox, T. W. (1951). *Poultry Sci.* **30**, 477.

Frankel, H., Hollands, K. G., and Weiss, H. S. (1962). *Arch. Intern. Physiol. Biochim.* **70**, 555.

Freeman, B. M. (1967). *Comp. Biochem. Physiol.* **20,** 179.

French, N. R., and Hodges, R. W. (1959). *Condor* **61,** 223.

Gelineo, S. (1934a). *Compt. Rend. Soc. Biol.* **116,** 672.

Gelineo, S. (1934b). *Compt. Rend. Soc. Biol.* **117,** 40.

Gelineo, S. (1936). *Compt. Rend. Soc. Biol.* **122,** 337.

Gelineo, S. (1955). *Arch. Sci. Physiol.* **9,** 225.

Gelineo, S. (1964). *In* "Handbook of Physiology" (Am. Physiol. Soc., J. Field, ed.), Sect. 4, pp. 259–282. Williams & Wilkins, Baltimore, Maryland.

Giaja, J. (1931). *Ann. Phvsiol. Physicochim. Biol.* **7,** 12.

Giaja, J., and Males, B. (1928). *Ann. Physiol. Physicochim. Biol.* **4,** 875.

Ginglinger, A., and Kayser, C. (1929). *Ann. Physiol. Physicochim. Biol.* **5,** 710.

Graber, R. R. (1962). *Condor* **64,** 473.

Grinnell, J., and Miller, A. H. (1944). *Pacific Coast Avifauna* No. 27.

Hainsworth, F. R., and Wolf, L. L. (1969). *Am. Zoologist* **9,** 1100.

Hamilton, W., and Hepner, F. (1967). *Science* **155,** 196.

Hammel, H. T. (1965). *In* "Physiological Controls and Regulations" (W. S. Yamamoto and J. R. Brobeck, eds.), pp. 71–97. Saunders, Philadelphia, Pennsylvania.

Hammel, H. T. (1968). *Ann. Rev. Physiol.* **30,** 641.

Hammel, H. T., Jackson, D. C., Stolwijk, J. A. J., Hardy, J. D., and Strømme, S. B. (1963a). *J. Appl. Physiol.* **18,** 1146.

Hammel, H. T., Strømme, S., and Cornew, R. W. (1963b). *Life Sci.* **2,** 933.

Hammel, H. T., Caldwell, F. T., Jr., and Abrams, R. M. (1967). *Science* **156,** 1260.

Hamner, W. M. (1963). *Science* **142,** 1294.

Hamner, W. M. (1964). *Nature* **203,** 1400.

Hart, J. S. (1957). *Rev. Can. Biol.* **16,** 133.

Hart, J. S. (1961). *Brit. Med. Bull.* **17,** 19.

Hart, J. S. (1962). *Physiol. Zool.* **35,** 224.

Hart, J. S. (1964). *Symb. Soc. Exptl. Biol.* **18,** 31.

Hart, J. S., and Heroux, O. (1955). *Can. J. Biochem. Physiol.* **33,** 428.

Hart, J. S., and Roy, O. Z. (1966). *Physiol. Zool.* **39,** 291.

Hart, J. S., and Roy, O. Z. (1967). *Am. J. Phvsiol.* **213,** 1311.

Hauser, D. C., (1957). *Wilson Bull.* **69,** 78.

Heath, J. E. (1962). *Condor* **64,** 234.

Heath, J. E. (1968). *In* "Evolution and Environment" (E. Drake, ed.), pp. 259–278. Yale Univ. Press, New Haven, Connecticut.

Heinroth, O. (1922). *J. Ornithol.* **70,** 172.

Henry, K. M., Magee, H. E., and Reid, E. (1934). *J. Exptl. Biol.* **11,** 58.

Heroux, O. (1962). *Can. J. Biochem. Physiol.* **40,** 537.

Herreid, C. F., II, and Kessel, B. (1967). *Comp. Biochem. Physiol.* **21,** 405.

Herzog, D. (1930). *Wiss. Arch. Landwirtsch. Abt. B. Tierenäehr. Tierzucht* **3,** 610.

Hiestand, W. A., and Randall, W. C. (1942). *Am. J. Physiol.* **138,** 12.

Hillerman, J. P., and Wilson, W. O. (1955). *Am. J. Physiol.* **180,** 591.

Hoffman, E., and Shaffner, C. S. (1949). *Poultry Sci.* **28,** 768.

Hoffman, E., and Shaffner, C. S. (1950). *Poultry Sci.* **29,** 365.

Howell, T. R. (1959). *Wilson Bull.* **71,** 19.

Howell, T. R., and Bartholomew, G. A. (1959). *Condor* **61,** 180.

Howell, T. R., and Bartholomew, G. A. (1961). *Condor* **63,** 185.

Howell, T. R., and Bartholomew, G. A. (1962a). *Condor* **64,** 6.

Howell, T. R., and Bartholomew, G. A. (1962b). *Ibis* **104,** 98.

Howell, T. R., and Dawson, W. R. (1954). *Condor* **56,** 93.

Hudson, J. W., and Brush, A. H. (1964). *Comp. Biochem. Physiol.* **12,** 157.

Hudson, J. W., and Kimzey, S. L. (1964). *Am. Zoologist* **4,** 294.

Hudson, J. W., and Kimzey, S. L. (1966). *Comp. Biochem. Physiol.* **17**, 203.

Hudson, J. W., Dawson, W. R., and Hill, R. W. (1970). Development of temperature regulation in nestling cattle egrets. MS.

Huston, T. M., Joiner, W. P., and Carmon, J. L. (1957). *Poultry Sci.* **36**, 1247.

Huston, T. M., Edwards, H. M., Jr., and Williams, J. J. (1962). *Poultry Sci.* **41**, 640.

Hutchinson, J. C. D. (1954). *In* "Progress in the Physiology of Farm Animals" (J. Hammond, ed.), Vol. I, pp. 299–362. Butterworth, London and Washington, D.C.

Hutchinson, J. C. D. (1955). *J. Agr. Sci.* **45**, 48.

Hutchinson, J. C. D., and Sykes, A. H. (1953). *J. Agr. Sci.* **43**, 294.

Hutchison, V. H., Dowling, H. G., and Vinegar, A. (1966). *Science* **151**, 694.

Hutt, F. B. (1938). *Poultry Sci.* **17**, 454.

Huxley, J. S. (1927). *J. Linnean Soc. London, Zoology* **36**, 457.

Huxley, J. S., Webb, C. S., and Best, A. T. (1939). *Nature* **143**, 683.

Hyrtl, J. (1863). *Sitzber. Akad. Wiss. Wien., Math.-Naturu. Kl. Abt. III* **48**, 6 (quoted in King and Farner, 1961).

Hyrtl, J. (1864). *Denkschr. Akad. Wiss. Wien.* **22**, 113 (quoted in King and Farner, 1961).

Irving, L. (1955). *Condor* **57**, 362.

Irving, L. (1960). *U.S. Natl. Museum, Bull.* **217**, 1.

Irving, L. (1962). *In* "Comparative Physiology of Temperature Regulation" (J. P. Hannon and E. Viereck, eds.), pp. 133–174. Arctic Aeromed. Lab., Fort Wainwright, Alaska.

Irving, L., and Krog, J. (1955). *J. Appl. Physiol.* **7**, 355.

Irving, L., and Krog, J. (1956). *Physiol. Zool.* **29**, 195.

Irving, L., Krog, H., and Monson, M. (1955). *Physiol. Zool.* **28**, 173.

Jackson, D. C., and Hammel, H. T. (1963). *Life Sci.* **2**, 554.

Jackson, D. C., and Schmidt-Nielsen, K. (1964). *Proc. Natl. Acad. Sci. U.S.* **51**, 1192.

Jaeger, E. C. (1949). *Condor* **51**, 105.

Jánský, L. (1959). *Physiol. Bohemoslov.* **8**, 472.

Jánský, L., and Hájek, I. (1961). *Physiol. Bohemoslov.* **10**, 283.

Johnson, R. E. (1968). *Comp. Biochem. Physiol.* **24**, 1003.

Johnston, R. F., and Selander, R. K. (1964). *Science* **144**, 548.

Kahl, M. P., Jr. (1962). *Condor* **64**, 169.

Kahl, M. P., Jr. (1963). *Physiol. Zool.* **26**, 141.

Kallir, E. (1930). *Z. Vergleich. Physiol.* **13**, 231.

Kayser, C. (1929). *Ann. Physiol. Physicochim. Biol.* **5**, 131.

Kendeigh, S. C. (1934). *Ecol. Monographs* **4**, 299.

Kendeigh, S. C. (1939). *J. Exptl. Zool.* **82**, 419.

Kendeigh, S. C. (1944). *J. Exptl. Zool.* **96**, 1.

Kendeigh, S. C. (1949). *Auk* **66**, 113.

Kendeigh, S. C. (1952). *Illinois Biol. Monographs* **22**, 1.

Kendeigh, S. C. (1961). *Wilson Bull.* **73**, 140.

Kendeigh, S. C. (1969). *Auk* **86**, 13.

Kheireldin, M. A., and Shaffner, C. S. (1957). *Poultry Sci.* **36**, 1334.

King, J. R. (1957). *Northwest Sci.* **31**, 155.

King, J. R. (1964). *Comp. Biochem. Physiol.* **12**, 13.

King, J. R., and Farner, D. S. (1961). *In* "Biology and Comparative Physiology of Birds" (A. J. Marshall, ed.), Vol. 2, pp. 215–288. Academic Press, New York.

King, J. R., and Farner, D. S. (1964). *In* "Handbook of Physiology" (Am. Physiol. Soc., J. Field, ed.), Sect. 4, pp. 603–624. Williams & Wilkins, Baltimore, Maryland.

Kleiber, M. (1932). *Hilgardia* **6**, 315.

Kleiber, M. (1947). *Physiol. Rev.* **27**, 511.

Kleiber, M., and Winchester, C. F. (1933). *Proc. Soc. Exptl. Biol. Med.* **31**, 158.

Koskimies, J. (1948). *Experientia* **7**, 274.

Koskimies, J. (1950). *Ann. Acad. Sci. Fennicae: Ser. A IV* **15**, 1.

Koskimies, J., and Lahti, L. (1964). *Auk* **81**, 281.

Lasiewski, R. C. (1963). *Physiol. Zool.* **36**, 122.

Lasiewski, R. C. (1964). *Physiol. Zool.* **37**, 212.

Lasiewski, R. C. (1969). *Am. J. Physiol.* **217**, 1504.

Lasiewski, R. C., and Bartholomew, G. A. (1966). *Condor* **68**, 253.

Lasiewski, R. C., and Dawson, W. R. (1964). *Condor* **66**, 477.

Lasiewski, R. C., and Dawson, W. R. (1967). *Condor* **69**, 13.

Lasiewski, R. C., and Dawson, W. R. (1969). *Condor* **71**, 335.

Lasiewski, R. C., and Lasiewski, R. J. (1967). *Auk* **84**, 34.

Lasiewski, R. C., and Snyder, G. K. (1969). *Auk* **86**, 529.

Lasiewski, R. C., and Thompson, H. J. (1966). *Condor* **68**, 102.

Lasiewski, R. C., Hubbard, S. H., and Moberly, W. R. (1964). *Condor* **66**, 212.

Lasiewski, R. C., Acosta, A. L., and Bernstein, M. H. (1966a). *Comp. Biochem. Physiol.* **19**, 445.

Lasiewski, R. C., Acosta, A. L., and Bernstein, M. H. (1966b). *Comp. Biochem. Physiol.* **19**, 459.

Lasiewski, R. C., Weathers, W. W., and Bernstein, M. H. (1967). *Comp. Biochem. Physiol.* **23**, 797.

Lee, D. H. K., Robinson, K. W., Yeates, N. T. M., and Scott, M. I. R. (1945). *Poultry Sci.* **24**, 195.

LeFebvre, E. A. (1964). *Auk* **81**, 403.

Lehmann, V. W. (1941). *North Am. Fauna* **57**, 1.

Lewies, R. W., and Dyer, M. I. (1969). *Condor* **71**, 291.

Lifson, N., and Lee, J. S. (1961). *Am. J. Physiol.* **200**, 85.

Lifson, N., Gordon, G. B., Visscher, M. B., and Nier, A. O. (1949). *J. Biol. Chem.* **180**, 803.

Lifson, N., Gordon, G. B., and McClintock, R. (1955). *J. Appl. Physiol.* **7**, 704.

Ligon, J. D. (1967). Personal communication.

Ligon, J. D. (1968). *Misc. Publ. Museum Zool., Univ. Mich.* No. 136, 1–70 pp.

Ligon, J. D. (1969). *Auk* **86**, 458.

Lipp, J. A., and Folk, G. E., Jr. (1960). *Ecology* **41**, 377.

Löhrl, H. (1955). *Vogelwarte* **18**, 71.

Lustick, S. (1969). *Science* **163**, 387.

McAtee, W. L. (1947). *Am. Midland Naturalist* **38**, 191.

McClintock, R., and Lifson, N. (1957a). *J. Biol. Chem.* **226**, 153.

McClintock, R., and Lifson, N. (1957b). *Am. J. Physiol.* **189**, 463.

McClintock, R., and Lifson, N. (1958a). *Am. J. Physiol.* **192**, 76.

McClintock, R., and Lifson, N. (1958b). *Am. J. Physiol.* **195**, 721.

McGowan, J. D. (1969). *Auk* **86**, 142.

MacMillen, R. E., and Trost, C. H. (1967a). *Comp. Biochem. Physiol.* **20**, 263.

MacMillen, R. E., and Trost, C. H. (1967b). *Comp. Biochem. Physiol.* **23**, 243.

McNab, B. K. (1966). *Condor* **68**, 47.

Madsen, H. (1930). *Videnskab. Medd. Dansk Naturh. Foren. Kbh.* **8**, 301.

Maher, W. J. (1964). *Ecology* **45**, 520.

Marshall, J. T., Jr. (1955). *Condor* **57**, 129.

Mellen, W. J., and Hill, F. W. (1955). *Poultry Sci.* **34**, 1085.

Menaker, M., and Eskin, A. (1966). *Science* **154**, 1579.

Menaker, M., and Eskin, A. (1967). *Science* **157**, 1182.

Miller, D. S. (1939). *J. Exptl. Zool.* **80**, 259.

Misch, M. S. (1960). *Physiol. Zool.* **33**, 252.

Moore, A. D. (1945). *Wilson Bull.* **57**, 253.

Moreau, R. E. (1961). *Ibis* **103a**, 373.

Morrison, P. (1962). *Condor* **64**, 315.

Morrison, P., Ryser, F. A., and Dawe, A. R. (1959). *Physiol. Zool.* **32**, 256.

Morton, M. L. (1966). *Ecology* **48**, 690.

Murphy, R. C. (1936). "Oceanic Birds of South America," Vol. I. Macmillan, New York.

Neumann, R. Hudson, J. W., and Hock, R. J. (1968). *In* "Metabolism" (P. L. Altman, ed.), pp. 335–343. Fed. Am. Soc. Exptl. Biol., Bethesda, Maryland.

Nisbet, I. C. T., Drury, W. H., Jr., and Baird, J. (1963). *Bird Banding* **34**, 107.

Oakeson, B. B., and Lilley, B. R. (1960). *Anat. Record* **136**, 41.

Odum, E. P. (1941). *Ecol. Monographs* **11**, 299.

Odum, E. P. (1942). *Am. J. Physiol.* **136**, 618.

Okamoto, S., Otsubo, T., Ogawa, K., and Masamitsu, S. (1958). *World's Poultry Sci. J.* **14**, 57.

Ota, H., and McNally, E. H. (1961). *U.S. Dept. Agr., ARS* **ARS 42–43**, 34 pp.

Palmgren, P. (1944). *Ornis Fennica* **21**, 99.

Pearson, O. P. (1947). *Ecology* **28**, 127.

Pearson, O. P. (1950). *Condor* **52**, 145.

Pearson, O. P. (1953). *Condor* **55**, 17.

Pearson, O. P. (1960). *Bull. Museum Comp. Zool. Harvard Coll.* **124**, 93.

Pearson, O. P. (1964). *Condor* **66**, 182.

Peiponen, V. A. (1966). *Ann. Acad. Sci. Fennicae: Ser. A IV* **101**, 1.

Pembrey, M. S. (1895). *J. Physiol.* (London) **18**, 363.

Pembrey, M. S., Gordon, M. H., and Warren, R. (1895). *J. Physiol.* (London) **17**, 331.

Plain, G. J., and Plain, M. E. (1964). *Nature* **201**, 635.

Pohl, H. (1969). *Federation Proc.* **28**, 1059.

Pohl, H., and Hart, J. S. (1965). *J. Appl. Physiol.* **20**, 398.

Porter, W. P., and Gates, D. M. (1969). *Ecol. Monographs* **39**, 227.

Probine, M. C., and Wodzicki, K. A. (1955). *New Zealand J. Sci. Technol.* **B57**, 158.

Prozesky, O. P. M. (1963). *Nature* **197**, 401.

Quiring, D. P., and Bade, P. H. (1943). *Growth* **7**, 309.

Randall, W. C. (1943a). *Proc. Soc. Exptl. Biol. Med.* **52**, 240.

Randall, W. C. (1943b). *Am. J. Physiol.* **139**, 46.

Randall, W. C., and Hiestand, W. A. (1939). *Am. J. Physiol.* **127**, 761.

Rautenberg, W. (1957). *J. Ornithol.* **98**, 36.

Richards, S. A. (1969). *Comp. Biochem. Physiol.* **29**, 955.

Ricklefs, R. E., and Hainsworth, F. R. (1968a). *Ecology* **49**, 227.

Ricklefs, R. E., and Hainsworth, F. R. (1968b). *Condor* **70**, 121.

Riddle, O., Smith, G. C., and Benedict, F. G. (1932). *Am. J. Physiol.* **101**, 260.

Rogers, F. T. (1928). *Am. J. Physiol.* **86**, 639.

Rogers, F. T., and Lackey, R. W. (1923). *Am. J. Physiol.* **66**, 453.

Romanoff, A. L. (1941). *Science* **94**, 218.

Rowan, W. (1925). *Brit. Birds* **18**, 296.

Roy, O. Z., and Hart, J. S. (1966). *Med. Biol. Eng.* **4**, 457.

Ryser, F. A., and Morrison, P. R. (1954). *Auk* **71**, 253.

Salt, G. W. (1964). *Biol. Rev. Cambridge Phil. Soc.* **39**, 113.

Salt, G. W., and Zeuthen, E. (1960). *In* "Biology and Comparative Physiology of Birds" (A. J. Marshall, ed.), Vol. 1, pp. 363–409. Academic Press, New York.

Schmidt-Nielsen, K. (1964). "Desert Animals." Oxford Univ. Press, London and New York.

Schmidt-Nielsen, K., Kanwisher, J., Lasiewski, R. C., Cohn, J. E., and Bretz, W. L. (1969a). *Condor* **71**, 341.

Schmidt-Nielsen, K., Hainsworth, F. R., and Murrish, D. E. (1969b). *Federation Proc.* **28**, 459.

Scholander, P. F. (1955). *Evolution* **9**, 15.

Scholander, P. F., Walters, V., Hock, R., and Irving, L. (1950a). *Biol. Bull.* **99**, 225.

Scholander, P. F., Hock, R., Walters, V., Johnson, F., and Irving, L. (1950b). *Biol. Bull.* **99**, 237.

Scholander, P. F., Hock, R., Walters, V., and Irving, L. (1950c). *Biol. Bull.* **99**, 259.

Seibert, H. C. (1949). *Auk* **66**, 128.

Sellers, E. A., Scott, J. W., and Thomas, N. (1954). *Am. J. Physiol.* **177**, 372.

Shellabarger, C. J., Lasiewski, R. C., and Hyncik, G. E. (1961). *Nature* **191**, 1318.

Simpson, G. G. (1959). *Evolution* **13**, 405.

Simpson, S., and Galbraith, J. (1905). *J. Physiol. (London)* **33**, 225.

Sinha, M. P. (1959). *Abstr. Commun., 21st Intern. Congr. Physiol. Sci., Buenos Aires, 1959*, p. 254. Intern. Union Physiol. Sci., Naples, Italy.

Smyth, M., and Bartholomew, G. A. (1966). *Condor* **68**, 447.

Steen, I., and Steen, J. B. (1965). *Acta Physiol. Scand.* **63**, 285.

Steen, J. (1958). *Ecology* **39**, 625.

Steen, J., and Enger, P. S. (1957). *Am. J. Physiol.* **190**, 157.

Stonehouse, B. (1967). *Advan. Ecol. Res.* **4**, 131.

Strumwasser, F. (1960). *Bull. Museum Comp. Zool. Harvard Coll.* **124**, 285.

Sturkie, P. D. (1954). "Avian Physiology." Cornell Univ. Press (Comstock), Ithaca, New York.

Swaine, C. M. (1945). *Brit. Birds* **28**, 329.

Swan, L. W. (1952). *Ecology* **33**, 109.

Swinton, W. E. (1960). *In* "Biology and Comparative Physiology of Birds" (A. J. Marshall, ed.), Vol. 1, pp. 1–14. Academic Press, New York.

Terroine, E. F., and Trautmann, S. (1927). *Ann. Physiol. Physicochim. Biol.* **3**, 422.

Tucker, V. A. (1966). *Science* **154**, 150.

Tucker, V. A. (1968). *J. Exptl. Biol.* **48**, 67.

Turček, F. J. (1966). *Ekol. Polska* **A14**, 617.

Udvardy, M. D. F. (1955). *Ornis Fennica* **32**, 101.

Veghte, J. H. (1964). *Physiol. Zool.* **37**, 316.

Veghte, J. H., and Herreid, C. F. (1965). *Physiol. Zool.* **38**, 267.

von Saalfeld, E. (1936). *Z. Vergleich. Physiol.* **23**, 727.

Waites, G. M. H. (1962). *Quart. J. Exptl. Physiol.* **47**, 314.

Wallgren, H. (1954). *Acta Zool. Fennica* **84**, 1.

Warren, J. W. (1960). *Condor* **62**, 293.

Weiss, H. S. (1959). *Poultry Sci.* **38**, 430.

Weiss, H. S., and Borbely, E. (1957). *Poultry Sci.* **36**, 1383.

Wekstein, D. R., and Zolman, J. F. (1968). *Am. J. Physiol.* **214**, 908.

West, G. C. (1960). *Auk* **77**, 306.

West, G. C. (1962). *In* "Comparative Physiology of Temperature Regulation" (J. P. Hannon and E. Viereck, eds.), pp. 291–333. Arctic Aeromed. Lab., Fort Wainwright, Alaska.

West, G. C. (1965). *Physiol. Zool.* **38**, 111.

West, G. C. (1968). *Ecology* **49**, 1035.

West, G. C., and Hart, J. S. (1966). *Physiol. Zool.* **39**, 171.

Westerkov, K. (1956). *Emu* **56**, 405.

Wetmore, A. (1936). *Auk* **53**, 159.

Wetmore, A. (1945). *Auk* **62**, 638.

Whittow, G. C. (1965a). *In* "Avian Physiology" (P. D. Sturkie, ed.), 2nd ed., pp. 186–238. Cornell Univ. Press (Comstock), Ithaca, New York.

Whittow, G. C. (1965b). *In* "Avian Physiology" (P. D. Sturkie, ed.), 2nd ed., pp. 239–271. Cornell Univ. Press (Comstock), Ithaca, New York.

Willoughby, E. J. (1969). *Comp. Biochem. Physiol.* **28,** 655.

Wilson, A. C., and Farner, D. S. (1960). *Condor* **62,** 414.

Wilson, W. O. (1948). *Poultry Sci.* **27,** 813.

Wilson, W. O. (1949). *Poultry Sci.* **28,** 581.

Wilson, W. O., Hillerman, J. P., and Edwards, W. H. (1952). *Poultry Sci.* **31,** 843.

Winchester, C. F. (1940). *Missouri, Univ., Agr. Expt. Sta., Res. Bull.* **315,** 56 pp.

Witschi, E. (1956). "Development of Vertebrates." Saunders, Philadelphia, Pennsylvania.

Yapp, W. B. (1956). *Wilson Bull.* **68,** 312.

Yapp, W. B. (1962). *Ibis* **104,** 86.

Yeates, N. T. M., Lee, D. H. K., and Hines, H. J. G. (1941). *Proc. Roy. Soc. Queensland* **53,** 105.

Zar, J. H. (1968a). *Condor* **70,** 278.

Zar, J. H. (1968b). *Bioscience* **18,** 1118.

Zar, J. H. (1969). *Comp. Biochem. Physiol.* **29,** 227.

Zeuthen, E. (1942). *Kgl. Danske Videnskab. Selskab, Biol. Medd.* **17,** 1.

AUTHOR INDEX

Numbers in italics refer to the pages on which the complete references are listed.

311

Fox, T. W., 273, 274, *304*
Foxon, G. E. H., 199, *219*
Fraenkel, G., 27, 30, *72*
Fraenkel, G. S., 17, 18, 22, 36, 58, 59, *73*
Frankel, H., 262, *304*
Franklin, D. L., 101, *132*
Franz, H., 28, *73*
Free, J. B., 37, 40, 57, 64, 67, *73*
Freed, J., 121, 124, *131*
Freed, J. M., 108, 112, 116, *131*
Freeman, B. M., 250, *305*
Freeman, J. A., 86, *131*
French, N. R., 289, 290, 294, *305*
Fromm, P. O., 137, 149, 156, 157, *163*
Fry, F. E. J., 83, 84, 86, 87, 90, 91, 99, 100, *131, 132,* 142, 150, *163,* 193, *219*

G

Gahery, Y., 29, *70*
Galbraith, J., 227, *309*
Gale, C. C., 233, *302*
Garrett-Jones, C., 34, 37, *73*
Garside, E. T., 92, 94, *132, 133*
Gasdorf, E., 216, *219*
Gates, D. M., 302, *308*
Gebhardt, H., 23, *73*
Geijskes, D. C., 41, *76*
Geist, R. M., 22, *73*
Gelineo, A., 186, 189, *219*
Gelineo, S., 55, 57, *73,* 186, 189, *219,* 235, 236, 254, 271, *305*
Gevers, W., 114, *133*
Giaja, J., 234, 235, *305*
Giese, A. C., 12, *13*
Gillett, J. D., 19, *77*
Ginglinger, A., 285, 286, *305*
Glaser, R., 214, *219*
Glass, H. B., 191, *220*
Goin, C. J., 135, 136, *163*
Goin, O. B., 136, *163*
Gold, A., 235, 258, 261, *303*
Goldschmidt, R., 66, *73*
Gomazkov, O. A., 99, *132*
Gonzales, M. D., 64, *72*
Gordon, G. B., 231, *307*
Gordon, M. H., 281, *308*
Gordon, M. S., 117, 120, *132*

Gorman, J., 142, *163*
Gosner, K. L., 143, *163*
Graber, R. R., 235, *305*
Grant, C., 176, *219*
Grant, G. R. M., 23, *73*
Grant, W. C., 26, 54, *73*
Gray, F. J., 41, *73*
Green, G. W., 27, *73*
Greenfield, L. J., 199, *219*
Grewal, M. S., 142, *163*
Griffith, J., 199, *219*
Griffiths, J. F., 24, 27, *76*
Grigg, G. C., 100, *132*
Grinnell, J., 225, *305*
Grossman, L. I., 127, *134*
Grozdonovíc, J., 58, *70*
Guimond, R. W., 156, *163*
Gunn, D. L., 10, *13,* 17, 18, 21, 22, 34, 36, 37, *73,* 169, *219*
Guthrie, F. E., 37, *73*

H

Hadfield, S., 137, 142, *163*
Hafez, M., 17, 22, 43, 61, *73*
Hainsworth, F. R., 239, 267, 268, 269, 284, 285, 286, 289, 294, *304, 308, 309*
Hájek, I., 250, *306*
Hall, F. G., 158, *163*
Halperin, A., 212, *218*
Hamilton, W., 248, *305*
Hammel, H. T., 216, 217, *219,* 225, 233, 298, *303, 305, 306*
Hammel, T., 217, *218*
Hamner, W. M., 229, *305*
Hardy, J. D., 215, 217, *218, 219,* 233, 298, *303, 305*
Hart, J. S., 82, 84, 86, 101, *131, 132,* 225, 229, 248, 249, 250, 251, 252, 253, 255, 277, 278, 279, 280, *305, 308*
Hartley, T. C., 259, *303*
Hartmann-Goldstein, I., 67, *73*
Harwood, R. F., 22, 67, *70, 73, 74*
Haschemeyer, A. E. V., 124, *132*
Hastings, E., 27, 30, *75*
Hau Fe, W. O., 31, *73*
Hauser, D. C., 248, *305*
Hayes, F. R., 124, *132*
Hazelhoff, E. H., 28, *73*

SUBJECT INDEX

A

Acanthis flammea, 249
Acantholepis frauenfeldi, 29
Acclimation
  in amphibia, 147
  in aquatic invertebrates, 5
  in fish, 120
  in terrestrial invertebrates, 53
    in Annelids and Molluscs, 55
    in Arthropods
      to heat, 57
      to cold, 59
Acris, 158
Acris crepitans, 142, 154
Acrolita naevana, 48, 68
Active metabolism in reptiles, 191
Activity temperatures in amphibians, 138
Adesmia antiqua, 21
Admixture of oxygenated and deoxy-
    genated blood in reptiles, 199
Aedes, 19
Aedes aegypti, 19, 20, 22
Aedes communis, 30
Aedes elutella, 65
Aegolius acadicus, 235
Aequipecten irradians, 11
Aëronautes saxatilis, 288, 294
Agriolimax reticulatus, 26, 55
Agriornis montana, 247
Agriotes, 18, 21, 34, 49
Aiolopus thalaninus, 43
Aix sponsa, 234
Alligator mississippiansis, 202
Allolobophora longa, 44
Allolobophora terrestris, 34, 55

Altricial birds, thermoregulation in,
    284–287
Amazilia leucogaster, 289
Amblyrhynchus, 196, 204
Amblyrhynchus cristatus, 180, 196, 299
Ambystoma, 139, 144
Ambystoma jeffersonianum, 139
Ambystoma macrodactylum, 139
Ambystoma opacum, 139
Ambystoma tigrinum, 139, 140, 143, 155
Ambystomidae, 140
Ameiurus natalis, 92
Amphibolurus, 172, 186, 188, 193, 194,
    196, 197, 203–205
Amphibolurus barbatus, 180, 186, 209,
    299
Amphibolurus barbatus barbatus, 170
Amphibolurus barbatus minimus, 170,
    187
Amphibolurus barbatus minor, 170
Amphibolurus caudicinctus, 170
Amphibolurus inermis, 170
Amphibolurus ornatus, 170
Amphibolurus reticularis, 170, 209
Anagosta (Ephestia) *kühniella,* 47–49,
    62
Aneides, 154
Anniella, 177
Anolis, 172, 210
Anolis allogus, 178
Anolis carolinesis, 191
Anolis lucius, 178
Anopheles maculipennis, 34
Anopheles quadrimaculatus, 34
Anseriformes, 226, 234, 281
Antenna of insects, 22

Antheraea polyphemus, 49
Anthropoides paradisea, 235
Anura, 141
Aortic arches, function of in reptiles, 200
Apis indica, 67
Apis mellifera, 42, 43, 67
Apoda, 140
Apodidae, 288
Apodiformes, 225, 226, 235, 288
Aptenodytes foresteri, 225
Apterygiformes, 225, 226
Apteryx australis, 227
Apus (Micropus) *apus,* 288
Aquatic reptiles, 175
Aquila chrysaëtos, 234
Archeopteryx lithographica, 297
Archilochus alexandri, 235, 288, 290
Archilochus colubris, 235
Ardea herodias, 234, 283
Arion ater, 10, 33, 34
Arion circumscriptus, 55, 56
Arior hortensis, 55
Armadillidium vulgare, 34, 35, 57, 63
Ascaphidae, 140
Ascaphus, 141
Ascia monuste, 64
Asio flammeus, 235
Asio otus, 235
Auchmeromyia luteola (larva), 34
Austroicetes cruciata, 45
A–V O₂ difference in reptiles, 197

B

Behavioral thermoregulation
  in amphibia, 153
  in aquatic invertebrates, 12
  in birds, 245, 267
  in fish, 92
  in reptiles, 175
  in terrestrial invertebrates, 16, 27, 29
Bembex, 43
Blaniulus guttulatus, 17
Blastophagus piniperda, 21, 61
Blatella germanica, 18, 60, 61
Blatta orientalis, 18, 21, 34, 36, 37, 59
Blood pressure in reptiles, 202
Blood-sucking Arthropods, 19
Body temperature
  of aquatic invertebrates, 9
  of birds, 225, 226

  in cold, 255
  in heat, 274, 276
  of reptiles, 168
Bolitoglossa, 151
Bolitoglossa striatulata, 151
Bombina bombina, 144
Bombyx mori, 65
Bonasa umbellus, 247
Boophilus microplus, 20
Botaurus lentiginosus, 234
Bracon cephi, 46, 47
Branta bernicla, 234
Branta nigricans, 245
Bubo virginianus, 235, 247, 264
Bubulcus ibis, 263, 264, 265
Bufo alvarius, 152
Bufo boreas, 148, 150, 152, 153
Bufo bufo, 144, 157
Bufo californicus, 144
Bufo canorus, 136
Bufo debilis, 152
Bufo exsul, 153
Bufo fowleri, 152
Bufo marinus, 141, 152
Bufo mazatlanensis, 141
Bufo melanostictus, 149
Bufo nelsoni, 153
Bufo terrestris, 144, 150
Bufo valliceps, 141
Bufo viridis, 157
Bufonidae, 140
Burrowing
  in Annelids, 25
  in Arthropods, 26
  in Molluscs, 25
  in reptiles, 177
Buthotus minax, 43

C

Calcarius lapponicus, 286
Calliphora erythrocephala, 59
Calliphora stygia, 18
Calypte anna, 235, 277, 288, 290
Calypte costae, 235, 260, 277, 288, 290
Camponotus pennsilvanicus, 48
Campylorhynchus brunneicapillum, 267, 269
Capacity adjustment in fish, 83
Caprimulgidae, 288, 290
Caprimulgiformes, 225, 226, 235, 288

Richmondena cardinalis, 236, 248, 261
Rothschildia jacobae, 39
Rutilus rutilus, 102

S

Salamanders, 138
Salamandra salamandra, 149
Salamandridae, 140
Salmo gairdneri, 103, 106
Salmo salar, 89
Salpinctes obsoletus, 267
Salvelinus fontinalis, 90, 93
Samia cecropia, 38
Saturnia pyri, 46
Sauromalus, 179, 196, 197, 200, 202,
   213
Sauromalus obesus, 186, 203
Scardafella inca, 228, 235, 260, 288
Sceloporus, 172, 196, 209, 211, 214
Sceloporus graciosus, 172
Sceloporus occidentalis, 172–174, 186,
   187, 190
Scheloporus orcutti, 180
Sceloporus undulatus, 213
Schistocerca gregaria, 24, 27, 30, 36, 37,
   39
Scolopendra, 26
Seasonal acclimatization in insects, 63
Seasonal changes, activity of, in insects,
   32
Selasphorus rufus, 235, 277, 288, 290
Selasphorus sasin, 235, 277, 289
Semiaquatic reptiles, 176
Sensillae
   in bees, 24
   in beetles, 23
Sensory physiology of insects, 21
Shivering, *see also* Cold tolerance
   in birds, 249
Sicalis, 247
Skin blood flow in reptiles, 202
Smilisca baudini, 142
Social insects, *see also* Behavioral
      thermoregulation
   behavioral thermoregulation in, 28
Sphaenodon punetatum, 178
Sphenisciformes, 225, 226
Sphenodon, 214
Sphenomorphus sabanus, 178
Spheroides maculatus, 83

Sphinogonotus carinatus, 43
Spizella arborea, 236, 252
Spizella passerina, 285
Spizella pusilla, 285
Standard metabolism, *see also* Metabo-
      lism, Heat production
   in reptiles, 184
Stellula calliope, 235, 277
Sterna fuscata, 257
Sternotherus odoratus, 173, 176
Stomoxys, 17
Streptopelia decaocto, 235
Strigiformes, 226, 235
Strix aluco, 235
Stroke volume in reptiles, 197
Strongylocentrotus purpuratus, 12
Struthio camelus, 229, 234, 244, 260
Struthioniformes, 225, 226, 234
Sturnus vulgaris, 247
Sula bassana, 242
Sula dactylatra, 257
Sula sula, 237
Supercooling, *see also* Cold tolerance
   in insects, 46
Symbranchus, 118, 119
Syritta, 31

T

Tachycineta thalasinna, 289
Taeniopygia castanotis, 235, 248, 261,
   276
Talorchesfia megalopthalma, 63
Tarentola, 172
Taricha, 139, 144
Taricha granulosa, 139, 154
Taricha rivularis, 140
Taricha torosa, 139, 150
Temperature compensation in fish, 81
Temperature control mechanism, *see also*
      Temperature regulation center
   in birds, 233
   in reptiles, 215
Temperature orientation in insects, 16
Temperature preferences
   in amphibians, 138
   in insects, 16
   in reptiles, 171
Temperature regulation center, site of
   in reptiles, 216
Temperature regulation in fish, 90